COLÁISTE DE LACY
BOOK RENTAL

GW00857609

Geography Now!

New Junior Cycle

Liam Ashe and Kieran McCarthy

The Educational Company of Ireland

colaistedelacy
3 9100 000015644

First published 2018

The Educational Company of Ireland

Ballymount Road

Walkinstown

Dublin 12

www.edco.ie

A member of the Smurfit Kappa Group plc

© Liam Ashe and Kieran McCarthy, 2018

All rights reserved. No part of this publication may be reproduced, stored in a retrieval system, or transmitted in any form or by any means, electronic, mechanical, photocopying, recording or otherwise, without either the prior permission of the Publisher or a licence permitting restricted copying in Ireland issued by the Irish Copyright Licensing Agency, 63 Patrick Street, Dún Laoghaire, Co Dublin.

ISBN: 978-1-84536-781-7

The paper used in this book comes from Managed Forests in Northern Europe For every tree felled, at least one new tree is planted

Editor:	Sally Vince
Design:	EMC
Layout:	Outburst Design
Proofreader:	Neil Burkey
Cover Design:	EMC
Cover Photography:	Shutterstock

Ordnance Survey maps and aerial photographs
Ordnance Survey Ireland Permit No. 9140 EDCO
© Ordnance Survey Ireland/Government of Ireland

National Mapping Agency - www.osi.ie

The authors wish to acknowledge the support of Frances Ashe, Rose McCarthy, Shane McCarthy, Margaret Guerin, Shauna Kenneally, Lucy Taylor, Sally Vince, Deirdre O'Neill.

While every care has been taken to trace and acknowledge copyright, the publishers tender their apologies for any accidental infringement where copyright has proved untraceable. They would be pleased to come to a suitable arrangement with the rightful owner in each case.

Web references in this book are intended as a guide only. At the time of going to press, all web addresses were active and contained information relevant to the topics in this book. However, The Educational Company of Ireland and the authors do not accept responsibility for the views or information contained on these websites. Content and addresses may change beyond our control and pupils should be supervised when investigating websites.

05M20

Foreword

The Educational Company of Ireland is proud to present *Geography Now!* This textbook is designed to meet the needs of the new Junior Cycle Geography course. *Geography Now!* has been written by two highly experienced teachers.

The book offers a well-structured and thorough coverage of the new specification. Each of the learning outcomes is comprehensively covered.

Geoliteracy, the development of students' ability to develop far-reaching decisions through geographic thinking and reasoning, is actively fostered through the text. The components of geoliteracy – interaction, interconnections and implications – are examined throughout the three strands that make up the Junior Cycle Geography specification.

The sustainable use of resources in our fragile planet is treated through numerous case studies. The life chances for young people in countries at different stages of development are examined.

Great care has been taken to ensure that the language level is appropriate to Junior Cycle Geography students. Age-appropriate literacy and numeracy skills are developed. Bullet points and bold typeface highlight key terms and concepts.

A wide range of visual stimuli including photographs, charts, graphs and maps are an important learning instrument in every chapter. Learning activities, individual, paired and in larger groups, provide students with opportunities for independent thought and interaction with their peers through discussions and debates.

There is a comprehensive range of Ordnance Survey maps along with aerial photographs and satellite images.

Each chapter begins with learning intentions and definitions and there is wide use of geo facts throughout each chapter. End-of-chapter reflections will help students to assess their learning. Linkages between topics are used to help students to learn in a non-linear way.

Geography Now! is part of a package of textbook, student activity book, e-book, students' graphic organiser, teacher's resource book and online digital resources. The Educational Company of Ireland is very confident that this package provides a full and comprehensive treatment of the syllabus.

Acknowledgements

The authors and publisher wish to thank the following for permission to reproduce photos and other material:
Smit/Shutterstock p1, Shutterstock p2, NASA p3, Darren J Bradley/Shutterstock p10, Kieran McCarthy p10, Pierre Leclerc/Shutterstock p11, Daniel Prudek/Shutterstock p12, Poppicnic/Shutterstock p14, Juergen HasenkopfAlamy p16, Patricia Hofmeester/Shutterstock p17, Jeffrey M. Frank/Shutterstock p19, USGS/Alamy p20, neelsky/Shutterstock p21, LOUISA GOULIAMAKI/Getty p22, BlueRingMedia/Shutterstock p24, Somjin Klong-ugkara/Shutterstock p26, Shutterstock p29, bonvoyagecaptain/Shutterstock p32, MarcelClemens/Shutterstock p34, vilax/Shutterstock p35, Kieran McCarthy p35, Budimir Jevtic/Shutterstock p36, Kieran McCarthy p37, Massimo Santi/Shutterstock p37, Niall Dunne/Alamy p38, MikeDrago.cz/Shutterstock p52, Aleksandrs Bondars/Shutterstock p53, yykkaa/Shutterstock p60, NASA p68, Manamana/Shutterstock p70, H.R.Photos/Shutterstock p71, trekandshoot/Shutterstock p71, Kieran McCarthy p71, Jose Gil/Shutterstock p72, Kieran McCarthy p75, Kieran McCarthy p76, USGS p77, OSi 2010/04/CCMA Clare County Council/Burrengeopark.ie p78, ROUSSELLE Xavier/Shutterstock p78, Ger Bosma/Alamy p79, Steve Weisberg/Shutterstock p79, scenicireland.com/Christopher Hill Photographic/Alamy p80, Stephen Saks Photography/Alamy p80, Michael Duff/Getty p85, Connacht Tribune p86, Jacques Langevin/Sygma/Getty p87, kuriaki1/Shutterstock p88, Nicola Pulham/Shutterstock p94, CPQ/Shutterstock p95, Jane McIlroy/Shutterstock p97, Breck P. Kent/Shutterstock p98, USGS p99, risteski goce/Shutterstock p100, Neil Mitchell/Shutterstock p101, ATIKAN PORNCHAIPRASIT/Shutterstock p101, Brisbane/Shutterstock p101, ESB p102, Copernicus/EMSR149 p103, Thomas Schnitzler/Shutterstock p108, Kieran McCarthy p112, Kieran McCarthy p113, emka74/Shutterstock p116, Melanie Lemahieu/Shutterstock p116, Tramont_ana/Shutterstock p116, Greenybot/Shutterstock p118, Sue Burton PhotographyLtd/Shutterstock p119, Sue Burton PhotographyLtd/Shutterstock p119, aerial photo OSi p120, Svet Nedvedeva/Shutterstock p122, Bildagentur Zoonar GmbH/Shutterstock p124, Bob JHare/Shutterstock p125, Geography Photos/UIG/Getty p125, USGS p127, Andrey Armyagov/Shutterstock p128, USGS p129, Kieran McCarthy p130, freeskyline/Shutterstock p130, Joe Cornish/Getty p131, Imfoto/Shutterstock p132, Tom Bean/Alamy p133, ESB p133, kolo5/Shutterstock p133, Andrej Blagojevic/Shutterstock p134, Barrow Coakley p134, Design Pics/Alamy p135, S.Borisov/Shutterstock p136, corbac40/Shutterstock p142, Design Pics Inc/Alamy p143, Education Images/UIG/Getty p144, Simon Turner/Alamy p144, Neil McAllister/Alamy p144, Pixeljoy/Shutterstock p146, Universal Images Group/Getty p147, Cloudia Spinner/Shutterstock p148, R.M. Nunes/Shutterstock p149, PJ photography/Shutterstock p150, Design Pics Inc/Alamy p153, Elena Arkadova/Shutterstock p153, Peter Turner Photography/Shutterstock p153, Esa Hiltula/Alamy p153, Chris Howes/Wild Places Photography/Alamy p153, David Wall/Alamy p153, morrison/Shutterstock p153, Simon Burt/Alamy p153, Design Pics Inc/Getty p157, Abrostrom/Shuttertstock p158, VLADYSLAV DANILIN/Shutterstock p164, pongpinun traisrisilp/Shutterstock p166, The Watchers p168, Michael Rosskothen/Shutterstock p169, Rudra Narayan Mitra/Shutterstock p175, Sergey Nivens/Shutterstock p176, NASA/Alamy p179, NASA p182, Orest lyzhechka/Shutterstock p183, Pavel L Photo and Video/Shutterstock p185, Stuart Aylmer/Shutterstock p186, Stan Pritchard/Alamy p188, Rainer Fuhrmann/Shutterstock p188, T.W. van Urk/Shutterstock p189, Drew McArthur/Shutterstock p192, NASA Earth Observatory/Joshua Stevens, using MODIS data from LANCE/EOSDIS Rapid Response p194, Getty p196, SUWIT NGAOKAEW/Shutterstock p198, EPA p202, Ocskay Bence/Shutterstock p203, BlueOrangeStudio/Shutterstock p204, Pierre Leclerc/Shutterstock p208, Oleg Anisimov/Shutterstock p213, Mike Mareen/Shutterstock p213, Taiga/Shutterstock p213, gabriel12/Shutterstock p213, MikRoman6/Shutterstock p213, Matthew Dixon/Shutterstock p213, Lucian BOLCA/Shutterstock p215, Wollertz/Shutterstock p218, Denis Zhitnik/Shutterstock p222, Shell Ireland p225, Cara-foto/Shutterstock p226, Scharfsinn/Shutterstock p230, Bloomberg/Getty p232, Aerovista Luchtfotografie/Shutterstock p234, underworld/Shutterstock p235, Vladseagull/Shutterstock p236, kakteen/Shutterstock p241, RanaPics/Alamy p243, Piotr Wawrzyniuk/Shutterstock p244, Gabriella Insuratelu/Shutterstock p246, Designpicsinc/Alamy p248, Howard Barlow/Alamy p249, Shutterstock p252, Hemis/Alamy p255, Lauren Smith - EyeEm /Getty p255, Alamy p256, erichon/Shutterstock p256, Yury Birukov/Shutterstock p259, Sean Pavone/Shutterstock p260, Testing/Shutterstock p262, Art Directors & TRIP/Alamy p264, Tacamex/Shutterstock p266, Mediacolor's/Alamy p269, clynt Garnhan Agriculture/Alamy p269, Mark Boulton/Alamy p270, Sean Sprague/Alamy p270, Brazil Photos/Getty p274, Bildagentur Z/Shutterstock p276, Pauline Thornton/Alamy p279, World Wide Picture Library/Alamy p282, robertharding/Alamy p283, Agencja Fotograficzna Caro/Alamy p287, Nicolas Economou/Shutterstock p288, Iakov Filimonov/Shutterstock p290, Cameron Whitman/Shutterstock p291, Glyn Genin/Alamy p293, Aldegonde/Shutterstock p296, André Quillien/Alamy p300, redbrickstock.com/Alamy p302, Michele Burgess/Alamy p303, Lynn Hilton/Alamy p303, Friedrich Stark/Alamy p305, Danylo Dzhepo/Shutterstock p306, Chronicle/Alamy p308, Michele Burgess/Alamy p310, Dinodia Photos/Alamy p312, Vecbit/Shutterstock p313, bodom/Shutterstock p313, ZUMA Press/Alamy p317, S. Forster/Alamy p317, Patryk Kosmider/Shutterstock p318, Liam Ashe p321, Colm Ashe p321, Osi p324, Nicola Pulham/Shutterstock p325, shutterupeire/Shutterstock p326, Irelandaerialphotography.com, John Herriott p327, Jose Ramiro Laguna/Shutterstock p332, Sweet Honey/Shutterstock p333, STLJB / Shutterstock p336, dotshock / Shutterstock p337, John Harriott p339, james walsh/Alamy p340, Phil Crean A/Alamy p340, Rihardzz/Shutterstock p341, chuyuss/Shutterstock p342, imageBROKER/Alamy p345, Sean Pavone/Alamy p346, Henry Westheim Photography/Alamy p348, David Soanes Photography/Getty p351, massimofusaro/Shutterstock p352, Ojo Images Ltd/Alamy p354, A ROOM WITH VIEWS/Alamy p354, Hero Images Inc/Alamy p354, Barrow Images p356, Barrow Images p358, ValeStock/Shutterstock p360, John_Walker/Shutterstock p364, krivinis/Shutterstock p365, JOSEP LAGO/AFP/Getty p368, Bernard Golden/Alamy p369, Michael Gottschalk Getty p372, Elisabetta Ravaioli p373, Age Fotostock/Alamy p375, Cartoonstock/Nilsson-Maki,Kjell p376, Irish Aid p378, Irish Aid p378, Irish Aid p379, Nurture Africa p380, watchara/Shutterstock p382, Alex Kolokythas Photography/Shutterstock p383, Enterprise Ireland, p386, Vincent MacNamara/Shutterstock p389, Peter Hermesfurian/Alamy p393, CRS PHOTO/Shutterstock p394.
Illustrations by Compuscript and Outburst Design.

Ordnance Survey maps and aerial photographs
Ordnance Survey Ireland Permit No. 9140 EDCO
©Ordnance Survey Ireland/Government of Ireland
Pages 41–69, 76, 95, 98, 113, 117, 128, 320, 323, 324, 328, 330, 334, 359

Ordnance Survey
Ireland
National Mapping Agency - www.osi.ie

Map section pages 396–403 © Collins Bartholomew Ltd 2018

The contents of this publication are believed correct at the time of printing. Nevertheless the publisher and or copyright owners can accept no responsibility for errors or omissions, changes in the detail given or for any expense or loss thereby caused. The representation of a road, track or footpath is no evidence of a right of way.

The publisher would like to thank the following for permission to reproduce the following material: Page 121, Ralph Riegel, 'Ireland 250 acres smaller after floods tear chunks off coastline', The Irish Independent, 10 March 2014; Page 124, 'Gigantic iceberg now floating free', www.esa.int, 17 July 2017; Page 141, Jonathan Watts, 'Third of Earth's soil is acutely degraded due to agriculture', The Guardian, 12 September 2017; Page 154, 'Ireland's Peatlands', www.antaisce.org. Used by permission; Page 240, Morgan Erickson-Davis, 'The world lost an area of tree cover the size of New Zealand last year', www.mongabay.com, 24 October 2017; Page 295, Aamna Mohdin, 'Not even a million migrants will reverse Germany's looming demographic decline', www.qz.com, 30 August 2016; Page 310, HT Brand Studio, 'From then to now: How India's battle for gender equality has changed over time', www.hindustantimes.com, 24 July 2017; Page 372, Peter O'Connell, 'Clare 'poorly served' by tourism industry', The Clare Champion, 25 August 2017; Page 397, Charlie Taylor, 'So much for the smart economy: Irish lack basic digital skills', The Irish Times, 3 March 2017.

While every care has been taken to trace and acknowledge copyright, the publishers tender their apologies for any accidental infringement where copyright has proved untraceable. They would be pleased to come to a suitable arrangement with the rightful owner in each case.

Contents

Digital Resources

The *Geography Now!* digital resources will enhance classroom learning by encouraging student participation and engagement. They support the New Junior Cycle Specification's emphasis on the use of modern technology in the classroom and are designed to cater for different learning styles.

To provide guidance for the integration of digital resources in the classroom and to aid lesson planning, they are **referenced throughout the textbook** using the following icons:

 Student website – www.edco.ie/geographynow – with interactive activities and quizzes

 A series of stimulating **videos**, covering a variety of different topics, allows students to observe geography in action

 Animations bring key diagrams from the textbook to life and reinforce the topic at hand

 PowerPoint presentations provide a summary of key chapters of the student textbook, highlighting main themes and topics.

Teachers can access the *Geography Now!* digital resources – which also includes **editable lesson plans** – via the *Geography Now!* interactive e-book, which is available online at **www.edcolearning.ie**.

Exploring the Physical World

Our restless Earth

Go to **www.edco.ie/geographynow** and try the interactive activities and quizzes.

Learning intentions

When you have completed this chapter you will be able to:

- State Earth's position in the solar system
- Describe the structure of Earth
- Examine the plates that make up Earth's crust
- Identify the seven main tectonic plates on a world map
- Describe the results of plates moving (fold mountains, volcanoes, earthquakes)
- Explain the concept of continental drift.

1.1 Describe the formation and global distribution of volcanoes, earthquakes, and fold mountains in the context of **plate tectonics** and **structure of the Earth**

You are also working towards:

1.10 Investigate a range of physical processes active in a chosen location and the connections between them

Key terms

crust

mantle

core

magma

plates

plate tectonics

convection currents

transform boundary

destructive boundary

constructive boundary

continental drift

Pangaea

The structure of Earth

Earth is one of the eight planets of our solar system.

GEO FACT

Our solar system is made up of the Sun and its eight planets. They are, in order from the nearest to the Sun: Mercury, Venus, Earth, Mars, Jupiter, Saturn, Uranus and Neptune.

Learning Activity

Curiosity Responsibility Numeracy

1.1 Work with a partner. As you work through the following, complete the Investigation sheet in your Activity Book (page 2).

Investigate answers to the following questions to the nearest million kilometres.

(a) How far is Earth from the Sun in kilometres (km)?

(b) What is the name of the imaginary line around the widest part of Earth?

(c) What is the circumference of Earth in kilometres?

(d) What length is the radius of Earth (the distance from the edge to the centre) in kilometres?

Earth was formed about **4.5 billion years** ago. At first it was a giant, boiling sea of molten (melted) material. As it began to cool, the heavier material sank, while the lighter material floated to the surface. As a result, Earth is made up of **three different layers**:

- The **crust** – the layer that we live on

- The **mantle**

- The **core** (outer and inner).

Figure 1.1 Earth is a sphere. It is shaped like a ball

The structure of Earth

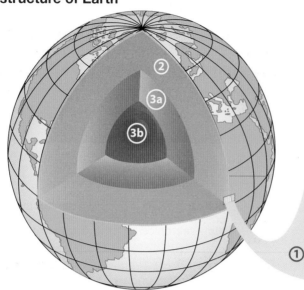

Figure 1.2 The layers that make up Earth

1 **The crust** Earth's outer skin. It is made up of solid rock. It can be up to 60 km thick beneath the continents, but as thin as 10 km under the oceans.

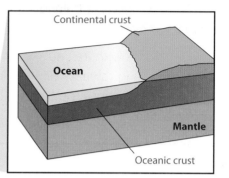

Continental crust

Ocean

Mantle

Oceanic crust

2 **The mantle** A layer of hot, soft rock that the crust floats on. The temperature in the mantle is about 4,000°C. As a result, the rock is in a molten or semi-molten state and is called **magma**.

3 **The core** This is at the centre of Earth. It is made of nickel and iron. At over 5,000°C, it is the hottest layer of Earth. The outer core **(3a)** is molten, while the inner core **(3b)** is under so much pressure that it is solid.

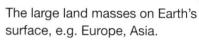

DEFINITION

Continents

The large land masses on Earth's surface, e.g. Europe, Asia.

Magma

The molten or semi-molten material that makes up Earth's mantle.

Plate tectonics

Earth's crust is not one continuous layer. It is broken up into different sections, called **plates**, which fit together like a jigsaw.

There are seven large plates and several smaller ones. They float on the semi-molten magma of the mantle. The edges of the plates meet at **plate boundaries**.

The plates are constantly moving. The theory that tries to explain the movements of the plates and the features that result is called **plate tectonics**. The plates are known as **tectonic plates**.

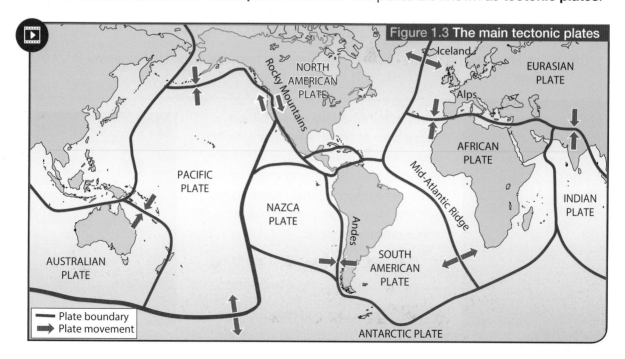

Figure 1.3 The main tectonic plates

Iceland

NORTH AMERICAN PLATE

Rocky Mountains

EURASIAN PLATE

Alps

AFRICAN PLATE

Mid-Atlantic Ridge

PACIFIC PLATE

NAZCA PLATE

Andes

INDIAN PLATE

AUSTRALIAN PLATE

SOUTH AMERICAN PLATE

ANTARCTIC PLATE

— Plate boundary
⟹ Plate movement

Learning Activity

 Curiosity

1.2 Answer these questions in your copy. With reference to figure 1.3 on the previous page:

(a) On which plate is Ireland located?

(b) Is the plate with Ireland on it moving towards or pulling away from the North American Plate?

(c) Which plate has the least land on it?

Plate boundaries

For most of the time, the plates are locked together and pressure builds up. When the pressure is eventually released, the plates move. The movement causes the boundaries to slide, collide or separate and this results, over millions of years, in:

■ Mountain building

■ Volcanic eruptions

■ Earthquakes.

We will look at each of these in the following chapters.

Table 1.1 gives the characteristics of each type of boundary.

Table 1.1 The three types of plate boundary

	Transform plate boundary	Destructive plate boundary	Constructive plate boundary
What happens	■ Plates **slide past** each other ■ Crust is neither created nor destroyed	■ Plates **collide** ■ Crust is **destroyed** ■ Huge pressure is built up and the **heavier plate is forced downwards** into the mantle where it melts	■ Plates **separate** ■ As the plates pull apart, **molten magma rises** from the mantle ■ It **cools and solidifies** ■ Crust is **created**
What you find there	■ Fault lines ■ Earthquakes	■ Fold mountains ■ Volcanic mountains ■ Earthquakes	■ Mid-ocean ridges ■ Volcanic islands ■ Volcanic mountains
Examples	The Pacific Plate is sliding past the North American Plate along the **San Andreas Fault**	The Nazca Plate is colliding with the South American Plate The Indian Plate is colliding with the Eurasian Plate	The North American Plate is separating from the Eurasian and African Plates

Learning Activity

 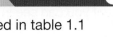 **Curiosity**

1.3 Match the following figures, **A**, **B** and **C**, to the type of boundary explained in table 1.1 (transform, destructive, constructive). Sketch the drawings into your copy with the correct headings.

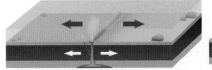

A

B

C

GEO FACT

North America and Europe are drifting further apart at a rate of about 2 cm per year, a distance of 20 km over a million years.

1.4 In groups of three, each of you select one boundary type and describe it to the others. Use objects (pieces of paper, pencils, etc.) to help you demonstrate the movement. Provide one example of your boundary type, identifying it on a world map, to help your partners to understand.

1.5 Examine figure 1.3 on page 4. Suggest why Ireland has no active volcanoes or large earthquakes. Discuss your answer with your group.

Why do plates move?

The plates float on the semi-molten magma in the mantle. The magma moves with a circular motion because of **convection currents**.

These convection currents cause the plates to move in different directions and at different speeds. You can see from the arrows on the map in figure 1.3 on page 4 the different directions the plates are moving in.

How do convection currents work?

The cycle for convection currents follows this pattern:

- The very hot core **heats the magma** in the mantle.

1.6 Answer these questions in your copy. Look at figure 1.3 on page 4 to help you.

    (a) The plate that Ireland is on has a constructive boundary with which other plate?

    (b) The plate that Ireland is on has destructive boundaries with which two plates?

    (c) Which two plates have a transform boundary?

GEO FACT

If you've ever watched a lava lamp, you've seen convection currents at work.

- The magma nearest the core gets hotter first. It **expands**, gets **lighter and rises** towards the top of the mantle.

- As it rises, it **cools**, because it is moving away from the heat source. It becomes **semi-molten**.

- The magma rises to the top of the mantle and **moves left or right** as it hits the bottom of the crust. This results in the circular motion of the material that you can see in figure 1.4.

- The **friction** between the crust and the moving magma drags the plates with it.

- As the magma continues to **cool** it becomes more solid and **heavier**. It begins to **sink** back towards the core.

- When it reaches the core it **reheats** and the cycle starts all over again.

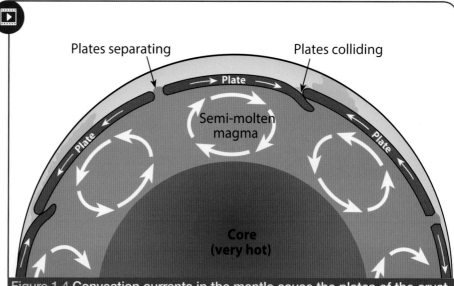

Figure 1.4 Convection currents in the mantle cause the plates of the crust to move

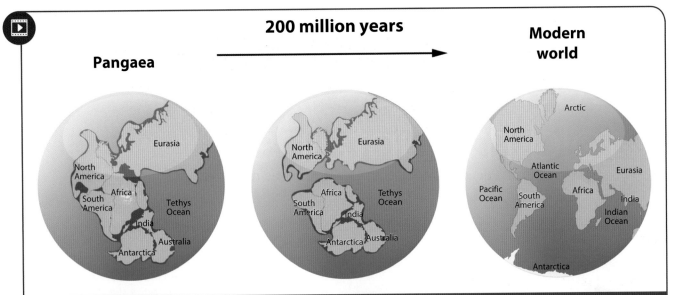

200 million years

Pangaea

Modern world

Figure 1.5 The continents as they might have looked about 200 million years ago, before continental drift (left); during the early stages of continental drift (centre); and a present-day map of the continents (right)

Continental drift

Earth's continents are **passengers on the plates** that float beneath them. As the plates move, they carry the continents with them. This movement is very slow and it has taken millions of years for the continents to reach where they are today.

The continents began as one large landmass, called **Pangaea**. It gradually began to break up. The individual sections started to drift apart, carried along on the moving plates. This process is known as **continental drift**.

Continental drift continues today. For example, Europe is slowly moving away from North America, while India continues to push northwards into Asia.

Learning Activity

Communicating Co-operating Curiosity Literacy

1.7 (a) In pairs, examine figures 1.3 on page 4 and 1.5 above. With the aid of an atlas or world map, identify the Mediterranean Sea. (See the map section starting on page 396.) Mark this on the blank world map on pages 6/7 of your Activity Book.

(b) Predict what will happen to the Mediterranean Sea over the next 50 million years. Discuss this with your partner; then share your thoughts with the rest of the class.

Reflecting on my learning

Reflecting Communicating Literacy

Write sentences using each of the following terms from this chapter. You may use more than one of the terms in your sentence if appropriate.

constructive boundary	core	magma	plate tectonics
continental drift	crust	mantle	plates
convection currents	destructive boundary	Pangaea	transform boundary

 PowerPoint summary

 **Revision**
Go to **www.edco.ie/geographynow** and try the interactive activities and quizzes.

Activity at plate boundaries – fold mountains

2

Go to **www.edco.ie/geographynow** and try the interactive activities and quizzes.

Learning intentions

When you have completed this chapter you will be able to:

- Describe how fold mountains are formed
- State periods of folding and give examples of the mountains that resulted
- Explain how people interact with fold mountains with reference to the Himalayas
- Consider how modern practices and technologies affect the traditional ways of mountain living.

1.1 Describe the
formation and
global distribution
of volcanoes,
earthquakes and
fold mountains
in the context of
plate tectonics and
structure of the Earth

2.1 Describe the
economic and
social impacts of
how we interact
with the occurrence
of volcanoes,
earthquakes and **fold
mountains**

**You are also working
towards:**

2.3 Identify how the
physical landscape
influences the
development of
primary activities

Key terms

fold mountains   syncline   Armorican folding

anticline   Alpine folding

How are fold mountains formed?

Fold mountains are found along **destructive plate boundaries**.

When two plates move towards each other and collide, the pressure forces the rocks to buckle and crumple upwards into a series of folds. This happens in the same way as a tablecloth wrinkles as it is pushed across a table.

The **upfolds** are called **anticlines** and the **downfolds** are called **synclines**.

Some examples of fold mountains are:

- The Himalayas in Asia
- The Alps in Europe
- The Andes in South America
- The Rocky Mountains in North America.

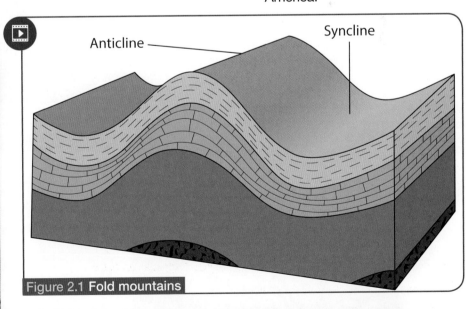

Figure 2.1 **Fold mountains**

Learning Activity

Curiosity   Responsibility

2.1 With the aid of an atlas or other form of research, find each of the mountain ranges mentioned above, and mark them on your blank world map on pages 6/7 of your Activity Book. (See the map section starting on page 396.)

Learning Activity

2.2 Conduct the following experiment at home.

(a) Find five towels (different coloured ones are best, if you have them); fold each one in half and lay them on top of each other. Get two boxes and place one either side of the towels. Now slowly and gently push the boxes towards each other.

(b) Write up your experiment in your copy. Include a diagram of what happens to the towels. Label your diagram with 'Anticline' and 'Syncline' to show the upfolds and downfolds.

(c) Conduct the experiment again and draw the pattern the towels make. Is it the same both times? Suggest a reason why or why not.

(d) Share your results with a partner. Do you get similar results? Suggest a reason why or why not.

How the Andes Mountains were formed

- The heavier **Nazca Plate** and the lighter **South American Plate** collided.

- The Nazca Plate was **pushed down** into the mantle.

- The rocks that lie on the plates were compressed and **forced upwards**.

- The layers of rock buckled and cracked into a series of **anticlines** and **synclines**.

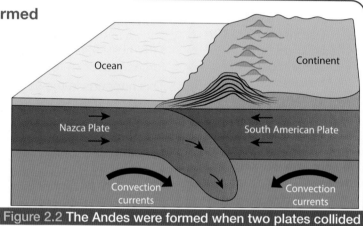

Figure 2.2 The Andes were formed when two plates collided

Learning Activity

2.3 Fossils of sea creatures have been found thousands of metres up in the Andes. How might this have happened? Discuss this with your partner and then share your thoughts with the rest of the class.

Link 🔗 Chapter 5: fossils – page 36

Figure 2.3 Folding has buckled the rocks to form anticlines and synclines. Note the faults that run up through the rock

DEFINITION

Fault
A crack or fracture in the crust where the rocks on either side have moved past each other.

Learning Activity

2.4 Examine the rock shown in figure 2.3. How can you tell that folding has taken place? (Remember the experiment you did with towels in learning activity 2.2.) Discuss your thoughts with your partner and share with the rest of the class.

Periods of folding

Armorican folding

Armorican folding took place about 250 million years ago when the Eurasian and African plates collided. While these mountains were once as high as the Alps, they have been severely worn down over the years.

Most of **Ireland's fold mountains** were formed during this period. They include:

- MacGillycuddy's Reeks
- The Galtees
- The Comeraghs
- The Knockmealdowns.

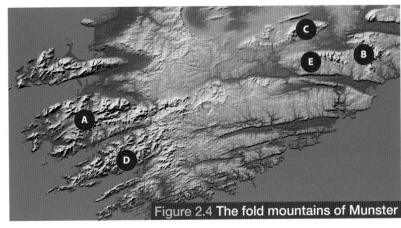

Figure 2.4 The fold mountains of Munster

Figure 2.5 The Galtees have been worn down by weathering and erosion over millions of years

Learning Activity

 Curiosity

2.5 The fold mountains of Munster (see figure 2.4) have an east–west trend. Examine figure 1.3 on page 4 and answer the following questions:

(a) Which plates caused these mountains?

(b) In which directions were these plates moving?

2.6 Using an atlas, identify the fold mountain ranges labelled A–E on figure 2.4. Write your answers in your copy.

A: Ma_____   B: Co_____   C: Ga_____   D: Ca_____   E: Kn_____

Alpine folding

Alpine folding happened only about 30 million to 35 million years ago. The mountains that were formed include:

- The Andes in South America
- The Rockies in North America
- The Himalayas in Asia.

These mountains are very high and steep, as they have not yet been worn down as much as older fold mountains.

Figure 2.6 **The young folds of the Alps are still very high**

How humans interact with fold mountains

Living and working in a mountainous area has its disadvantages as well as its advantages. It can be difficult to make a living in an area where there aren't many people and the land is not good for farming.

Learning Activity

 Literacy Curiosity Communicating Co-operating

2.7 The following extract is adapted from the website of Himalayan Voices, an organisation that provides information on the people living on these fold mountains.

(a) On your own, read the extract; then consider the questions below with your partner or small group.

Remoteness and harsh weather have affected how the Himalayan people live. Traditionally, resources have been used sustainably because of their limited availability. The main economic activities of the people are:

Agriculture Farmers have to deal with lack of water, small farms and a short growing season. In some areas, farmers move about, clearing the forest and moving between each piece of land to allow vegetation to grow. Previously they used each piece of land once every 10 years but they now use each piece of land for an unsustainable 2–3 years.

Animals Animals are kept for their milk, wool and meat. Communities move with their animals and families up the mountains during summer and return to the lower levels in the winter.

Trade Traditionally, trade fairs would be organised where animals, equipment and food would be exchanged without money (known as bartering), but now money is used. The introduction of markets has led to a decrease in local self-sufficiency.

Tourism Tourism is becoming more widespread. Annually, over a million tourists come to the region for trekking, sightseeing and wildlife watching. People work in hotels, as tour guides or in eco-tourism businesses.

The building of roads and airports has helped the Himalayan people. But it has also caused the destruction of natural resources. Many trees have been cut down and wild plants used for medicines have been pulled up before they can regrow.

DEFINITION

Self-sufficiency
Looking after your needs, such as food, yourself or within a community.

Sustainable
Can continue for a long time.

Eco-tourism
Tourism relating to wildlife and the natural environment, which supports conservation in the region.

Ecosystem
All the living things (animals and plants) in an area that interact with each other and rely on each other to live.

Learning Activity

Ecosystems have been destroyed. This has resulted in people moving away from the area. Although better education systems and access to television and the internet have provided more options for young people, many of them have left to go to urban areas in search of higher incomes and a 'better' lifestyle.

Questions

    (i)   State the three main ways people in the Himalayas earn a living.

    (ii)   Distinguish between the 'old' ways of making a living and the 'new' ways of making a living.

    (iii)   Describe the difficulties of farming on the mountains.

    (iv)   Explain how farming activities are now causing problems for the environment.

    (v)   Compare the way trade was carried out in the past to how it is conducted now.

    (vi)   Examine how the changes in trading have changed the way people now live.

    (vii)   Assess the way the modern world affects the environment in the region.

    (viii)   Evaluate the effects of tourism on the region. Do you think tourism is a good thing for the region, or is it a bad thing? Justify your answer.

(b) Appoint one of your group to be a note taker.

- The note taker should copy the following column headings onto a sheet of paper.
- Each member of the group will provide a point for your note taker to write in column one (Challenges young people in the Himalayas face). Keep going round the group until you can't think of anything else to add. Discuss each point to make sure you are in agreement.
- Do the same with column two. (How the lives of young Irish people compare).
- When you have finished the table, each of you make a copy of it.

Comparison of the lives of young people in the Himalayas with those of young people in Ireland	
Challenges young people in the Himalayas face	**How the lives of young Irish people compare**

Reflecting on my learning

  Reflecting Communicating Literacy

Write sentences using each of the following terms from this chapter. You may use more than one of the terms in your sentence if appropriate.

Alpine folding   Armorican folding   syncline

anticline   fold mountains

 PowerPoint summary

 Revision
Go to **www.edco.ie/geographynow** and try the interactive activities and quizzes.

Activity at plate boundaries – volcanoes

 Go to **www.edco.ie/geographynow** and try the interactive activities and quizzes.

Learning intentions

When you have completed this chapter you will be able to:

- Describe how volcanoes erupt
- Explain how volcanic eruptions result in new land
- Describe how volcanic mountains are formed
- Classify, using examples, active, dormant and extinct volcanoes
- Consider Iceland and its inhabitants as an example of how humans interact with volcanoes
- Consider Mount St Helens as an example of the environmental, human and economic impacts of volcanoes.

Key terms

mid-ocean ridge

geothermal energy

volcanic cone

Pacific Ring of Fire

eruption

vent

volcanic pipe

crater

lava

lava flow

mudflow

Volcanic activity

Most volcanic activity takes place along the **margins** or boundaries of plates. Volcanic activity can result in:

- Mid-ocean ridges and islands
- Volcanic cones.

Mid-ocean ridge

A mid-ocean ridge is an **underwater mountain range**. It is formed where two plates separate.

As the plates move apart, molten magma rises from the mantle and fills the gap between the plates. When the magma meets the cold seawater, it cools and becomes solid to form a new ocean floor. As the eruptions of magma continue in an endless cycle, the ocean floor is built up to form a long ridge of mountains.

The **Mid-Atlantic Ridge** runs north to south for the full 16,000 km length of the Atlantic Ocean. It is so high in places that it is exposed above sea level as islands. **Iceland** is one such island.

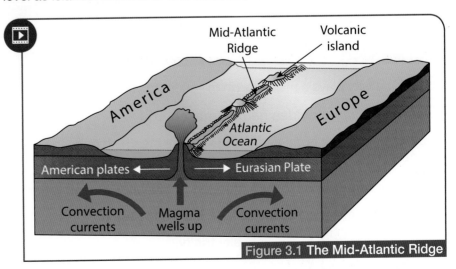

Figure 3.1 **The Mid-Atlantic Ridge**

15

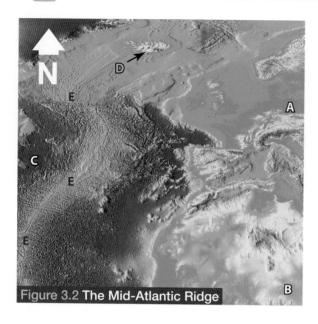

Figure 3.2 **The Mid-Atlantic Ridge**

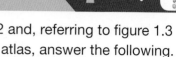

3.1 Examine figure 3.2 and, referring to figure 1.3 on page 4 and an atlas, answer the following. Check your answers with your partner's and share with the rest of the class.

(a) Identify the three plates marked A, B and C.

(b) Name the country marked D.

(c) Name the mountain range marked E.

(d) What type of plate boundary caused the mountain ridge to form?

(e) In what directions were the plates moving to cause the mountain range to form?

(f) Mark and name the location of the Mid-Atlantic Ridge on your blank world map on pages 6/7 of your Activity Book.

GEO FACT

The word **volcano** comes from the name of the Roman god of fire, Vulcan.

How humans interact with volcanoes

Iceland is one of the few places where the Mid-Atlantic Ridge is exposed above the ocean. It is only about 20 million years old, making it the youngest country on Earth.

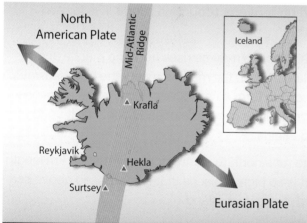

Figure 3.3 **Iceland is a volcanic island where the Mid-Atlantic Ridge rises above the surface of the ocean**

Figure 3.4 **Tourists in Iceland walking along the fissure (long, narrow opening) between the Northern American and Eurasian plates**

Volcanic activity plays a major part in the economy of Iceland in the following ways.

Volcanic activity provides geothermal energy

Geothermal energy is created by hot water or steam, from deep beneath Earth's surface, being converted into electricity. It works like this:

 Geothermal energy in Iceland

- **Magma** comes close to the surface and heats underground water to temperatures over 400°C.

- When the water reaches the surface, it turns to **steam**.

- The steam is used to generate **electricity**.

Geothermal energy provides almost 30% of Iceland's electricity needs. It is used to:

- Heat more than 85% of homes and offices
- Heat greenhouses, enabling farmers to grow flowers and vegetables all year round
- Provide power for factories
- Help keep the pavements free of ice in winter.

Volcanic activity is an attraction for tourism

Tourism is a big economic activity in Iceland.

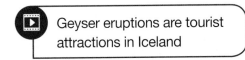
Geyser eruptions are tourist attractions in Iceland

Tourists come to see Iceland's **volcanic landscape**. Tours by helicopter and coach are organised to visit active volcanoes.

Some of the underground water comes to the surface as **hot springs** and **geysers**. Geysers are natural fountains of hot water and steam. These are said to have healing powers due to the minerals in the water and are natural spas. Many tourists visit these spas, such as the **Blue Lagoon**.

Figure 3.5 The Blue Lagoon, Iceland

Volcanic activity provides minerals and soil

Lava from deep within the earth contains minerals. Many of these are found in spa waters. Other minerals, such as sulfur and gypsum, were mined in the past.

All soils in Iceland owe their origin to volcanic activity. The materials expelled from the volcanoes break down to form soil rich in nutrients. While this is excellent for farming, the harsh climate creates difficulties.

Learning Activity

Curiosity Responsibility Literacy Creativity

3.2 Mark Iceland on your blank world map on pages 6/7 of your Activity Book.

3.3 Has anyone in your class visited Iceland or other volcanic site? Ask them to describe to the class what they saw and did while there.

3.4 Investigate holidays in Iceland. Would you like to visit? Using pictures and picture captions only, make a collage or picture series explaining why you would or would not like to visit. You may draw the pictures yourself or get them from the internet. You may create a slide show, computer document or paper presentation of your pictures.

GEO FACT

The Antrim–Derry plateau is the result of volcanic activity. Magma spewed out through a crack or fissure in Earth's crust, spread out and cooled. The **Giant's Causeway** is the best-known section of the plateau. Its six-sided columns of rock are a major tourist attraction. (See the photo (figure 5.4) on page 35.)

Volcanic mountains

Volcanic mountains are formed when molten magma emerges or **erupts** through a hole in the crust called a **vent**. They are generally found where plates are pulled apart or are in collision. Because the magma is under great **pressure** in the mantle, many eruptions are violent.

1 Magma finds its way towards the surface through an opening in the crust called a **vent**. When the magma reaches the surface, it is known as **lava**. Layers of lava build up around the vent, where it cools and hardens.

2 As the cone-shaped mountain builds up, the magma continues to make its way upwards through a **volcanic pipe**. Sometimes layers of **ash** also help to build the cone.

3 The lava continues to spill out of the volcano through an opening called a **crater**. Other materials, such as ash, gas, steam, rocks and boiling mud, can escape during an eruption.

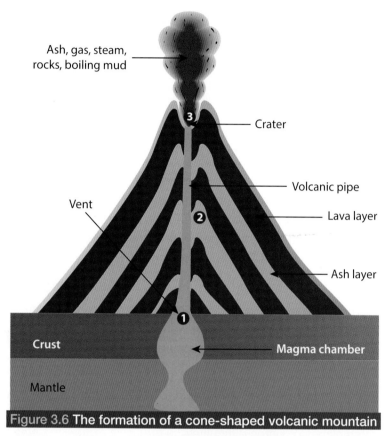

Figure 3.6 **The formation of a cone-shaped volcanic mountain**

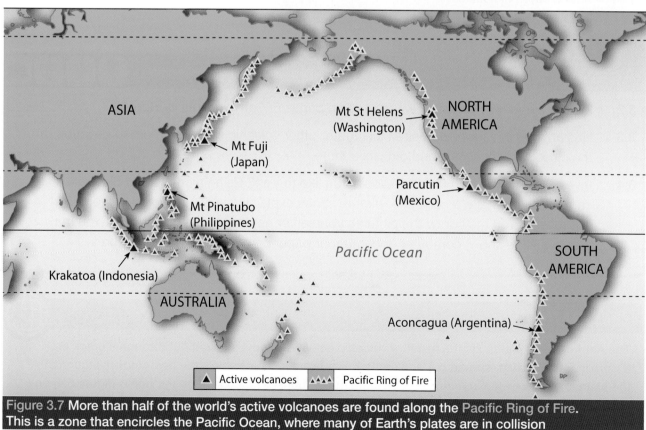

Figure 3.7 **More than half of the world's active volcanoes are found along the Pacific Ring of Fire. This is a zone that encircles the Pacific Ocean, where many of Earth's plates are in collision**

Learning
Activity  Curiosity

3.5 Examine figure 1.3 (page 4) and figure 3.7. Name two pairs of plates that collide on the Pacific Ring of Fire. What type of boundary occurs at each collision?

Life cycle of a volcano

Volcanoes do not erupt forever. Some stopped erupting a long time ago. Volcanoes can be classed as:

- **Active** The volcano is still erupting at regular intervals, e.g. Mount Etna (Sicily), Mount Vesuvius (Italy) and Mount St Helens (USA).

- **Dormant** The volcano has been quiet for hundreds of years but may erupt again. Mount St Helens had not erupted for over 120 years when it became active again in 1980.

- **Extinct** The volcano has not erupted in recorded times (thousands of years). Slemish Mountain in Co. Antrim is an extinct volcano.

GEO FACT

Stromboli, off Italy's Mediterranean coast, is a volcano that erupts so frequently that sailors have named it the **Lighthouse of the Mediterranean.**

Learning
Activity Curiosity

3.6 With the aid of an atlas or other reference, mark the approximate location of the volcanoes mentioned in the text (Mount Etna, Mount Vesuvius, Mount St Helens, Slemish Mountain, Stromboli) on the blank world map on pages 6/7 of your Activity Book.

 Figure 3.8 **This extinct volcano in the USA is now a national park**

Learning
Activity Curiosity Reflecting

3.7 Examine figure 3.8 above and answer the following questions. Agree your answers with your partner and then share with the rest of the class.

(a) Identify two pieces of information to suggest that this was a volcano.

(b) Identify two pieces of information that suggest that it is now extinct.

The impacts of an erupted volcano

Mount St Helens is a mountain peak in the **Cascade Range** in the USA. It was formed by a series of volcanic eruptions over thousands of years. By 1980, it had been **dormant** for so long that people living in the region thought it would never again erupt.

A series of earthquakes early in 1980 indicated that the mountain was beginning to rumble again. Soon **steam** and small **lava flows** began to appear from the crater. One side of the mountain began to bulge as **pressure** built up. It swelled outwards by over 100 metres before a massive eruption took place. Clouds of steam, gas and ash escaped in a huge volcanic explosion.

Results of the eruption

The environmental impact

- The force of the eruption **reduced** the height of the mountain by 400 metres.
- A **new crater**, almost 3 km wide, was created.
- **Forests were stripped** from hills. Trees of 2 metres in diameter were mown down as if they were blades of grass as far as 25 km from the volcano.
- The eruption **melted glacial ice** and snow at the summit. This water combined with ash to form **mudflows** that clogged shipping channels in nearby rivers.
- Almost **7,000 large animals** (deer, elk and bear) were **killed** in the blast.

The human impact

- The force of the blast and **poisonous gas** killed 57 people. Some were geologists, but the majority were so-called 'disaster tourists'.

The economic impact

- 12 million farmed fish were killed
- 200 homes were destroyed or extensively damaged
- 300 km of highway had to be rebuilt
- 25 km of railways had to be replaced
- Forests were destroyed up to 25 km from the volcano, as were camps for the loggers.

DEFINITION
Geologist
A scientist who studies rocks and soil.

DEFINITION
Logger
A person who harvests trees from forests.

Figure 3.9 **Mount St Helens on the day before the eruption. Identify the bulge on the mountain**

Figure 3.10 Mount St Helens shortly after the eruption. Explain the absence of forest and presence of large scars in the landscape at the foot of the mountain

Learning Activity

 Curiosity Responsibility Literacy Creativity

3.8 Create a poster on the impacts of the Mount St Helens eruptions in 1980. Include pictures. Use the information we have given here, and further research if you wish.

3.9 Investigate volcanic activity on Mount St Helens since 1980. What changes have occurred on the mountain?

Reflecting on my learning

 Reflecting Communicating Literacy

Write sentences using each of the following terms from this chapter. You may use more than one of the terms in your sentence if appropriate.

crater	lava	mudflow	volcanic cone
eruption	lava flow	Pacific Ring of Fire	volcanic pipe
geothermal energy	mid-ocean ridge	vent	

 PowerPoint summary

 Revision
Go to **www.edco.ie/geographynow** and try the interactive activities and quizzes.

Activity at plate boundaries – earthquakes

4

Go to **www.edco.ie/geographynow** and try the interactive activities and quizzes.

Learning intentions

When you have completed this chapter you will be able to:

- Explain how earthquakes occur
- Describe what happens during an earthquake
- Explain how the Richter scale is used to classify the strength of an earthquake
- Consider the Nepal earthquake of 2015 as an example of the environmental, human and economic impacts of earthquakes
- Explain how a tsunami occurs
- Consider the tsunami in Japan in 2011 as an example of the environmental, human and economic impacts of tsunamis.

1.1 Describe the formation and global distribution of volcanoes, **earthquakes**, and fold mountains in the context of plate tectonics and structure of the Earth

2.1 Describe the economic and social impacts of how we interact with the occurrence of volcanoes, **earthquakes** and fold mountains

You are also working towards:

1.10 Investigate a range of physical processes active in a chosen location and the connections between them

2.7 Investigate examples of how people interact with and manage surface processes

2.8 Investigate how people respond to a natural disaster

Key terms

plate boundary

fault line

focus

tremors

epicentre

aftershocks

seismograph

Richter scale

tsunami

What is an earthquake?

An **earthquake** is a sudden movement or trembling of Earth's crust. This movement takes the form of a series of shock waves or **tremors**.

Earthquakes occur at **plate boundaries**, where plates collide or slide past one another. Pressure builds up until one of the plates slips. This eases the pressure and a huge amount of **energy is suddenly released**. The earthquake has occurred.

1 Plates suddenly move along the **fault line**.

2 The **focus** is the point deep underground where the earthquake occurs.

3 Shock waves or **tremors** spread out from the focus, causing Earth's surface to shake (or quake) for a period. Most tremors last from a few seconds to up to a minute.

4 The tremors are usually strongest at the **epicentre**, the area on the surface directly above the focus.

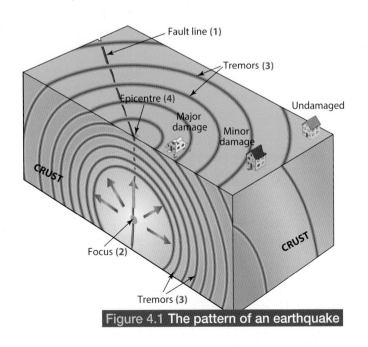

Figure 4.1 **The pattern of an earthquake**

23

Major earthquakes 2000–2017

Learning
Activity

Curiosity

4.1 At which two types of boundary do earthquakes occur: transform, destructive or constructive? Justify your answer to your partner and share with the rest of the class. (Refer to table 1.1 on page 5 to remind yourself of the boundary types.)

Aftershocks

Earthquakes rarely last for longer than one minute. Smaller tremors, called **aftershocks**, may occur in the hours or days after an earthquake. They often cause more damage than the original earthquake.

Learning
Activity

Communicating Curiosity

4.2 With your partner, discuss why aftershocks are likely to cause more damage than the original earthquake. Share your conclusions with the rest of the class.

Measuring earthquakes

Tremors from an earthquake can be detected and measured by a **seismograph** (the instrument), as shown in figure 4.2 below. A pen on the tip of the seismometer records the tremors on a rotating drum to produce a **seismogram** (the graph). The seismograph can detect tremors too small for a person to be aware of.

1 The base and frame of the **seismograph** vibrate during the earthquake.

2 The weight does not move because it is hanging freely from a thin wire.

3 A pen attached to the weight records the **tremors** (vibrations) on a rotating drum.

The Richter scale

Magnitude refers to the size of an earthquake. It is commonly described using the **Richter scale**. The scale is from 1 to 10, in steps of 0.1. Each increase of one unit on the scale means that the shaking is ten times more powerful. An example is given in table 4.1 below.

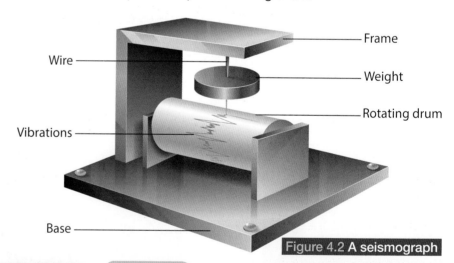

Figure 4.2 A seismograph

Labels: Frame, Wire, Weight, Rotating drum, Vibrations, Base

Table 4.1 An example of earthquake magnitude using the Richter scale	
Magnitude 3	
Magnitude 4	Magnitude 4 is 10 times stronger than magnitude 3
Magnitude 5	Magnitude 5 is 10 times stronger than magnitude 4 Magnitude 5 is 100 times (10 x 10) stronger than magnitude 3

Learning
Activity

Numeracy

4.3 **Earthquake A** measures 8 on the Richter scale and **Earthquake B** measures 5 on the Richter scale. Calculate how many times stronger Earthquake A is. Check your answer with your partner's and share with the rest of the class.

Today, scientists and geologists rarely use the Richter scale. They use laser technology that is more complicated and also more accurate. However, the Richter scale is still used in media reports of earthquakes.

GEO FACT

The largest earthquake ever recorded on Earth was a magnitude 9.5. This was in Chile in 1960.

Learning Activity

Communicating Literacy Responsibility Creativity

4.4 Although Ireland does not experience large earthquakes, occasionally we record small ones. Investigate the **Donegal earthquake** of August 2017. As you do this activity, complete the Research record in your Activity Book (page 19) to record what you have done.

    (a) Find out the following:

        (i) Where in the county did the earthquake occur?

        (ii) At what time did the earthquake occur?

        (iii) What was the strength of the earthquake on the Richter scale?

        (iv) How did people know that there was an earthquake?

        (v) What were the impacts of the earthquake?

    (b) Write a newspaper report or blog post, or record a news item on the Donegal earthquake.

    (c) Read or listen to the reports of the other people in your class or group. Make a note on page 20 of your Activity Book of what you liked about other people's reports that you might try to incorporate into your work when doing future activities.

GEO FACT

While more than 500,000 earthquakes occur each year, only about 50 are strong enough to cause damage.

The impacts of an earthquake

A very strong earthquake hit **Nepal** in April 2015. The epicentre was high in the **Himalayas**. The effects of the earthquake were felt up to 1,000 km away in China and India.

Nepal lies on the edge of the boundary between the **Indian Plate** and the **Eurasian Plate**. The Indian Plate is moving northwards at a speed of about 4 cm a year. A collision caused the solid rock on the surface of both plates to buckle and eventually build up to form the **Himalayas**.

As the plates continue to move, **immense pressure and stresses** build up in the rocks.

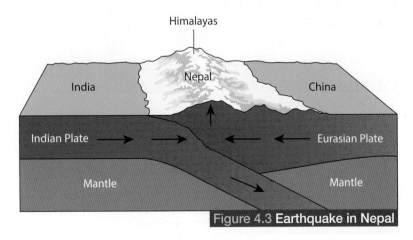

Figure 4.3 **Earthquake in Nepal**

Learning
Activity

🔍 Curiosity

4.5 With the aid of an atlas or other reference, mark the approximate location of the earthquake in Nepal on your blank world map on pages 6/7 of your Activity Book.

The earthquake

The main earthquake registered **7.9 on the Richter scale** and lasted for less than a minute. More than a hundred **aftershocks**, some measuring as big as 6.7, were felt in the days following the initial earthquake.

The environmental impact

- An area of Earth's crust, about 120 km long, was **moved forward** by about two metres.

- Hundreds of **landslides** occurred, some of them large enough to be visible from space. Villages and roads were buried.

- **Avalanches** and ice falls occurred in many of the climbing regions.

- **Harvests** were affected as people had only a short time to plant crops before the onset of the Monsoon rains.

The human impact

The greatest impact of the earthquake was felt in **poor, crowded urban areas**. These had lots of older and cheaply made buildings.

- More than 8,000 people are known to have died.

- More than 20,000 people were injured.

- 3.5 million people were made homeless.

> **GEO FACT**
>
> Satellite measurements indicate that Mount Everest is now 3 cm lower than it was before the earthquake.

Figure 4.4 Many of the buildings in Kathmandu, the capital of Nepal, were destroyed in the earthquake

Learning
Activity

🔍 Curiosity

4.6 Examine figure 4.4. Suggest two reasons why the building in the left background was not destroyed in the earthquake. Agree your reasons with your partner, and share with the rest of the class.

Learning Activity

4.7 Think about why an earthquake in a developing country is likely to cause more damage than one in a developed country. Consider the environmental impacts and the human impacts.

(a) Discuss your thoughts with your partner. In your copy, draw a spider diagram to represent any reasons you think of. Write each of your reasons on separate sticky notes or small pieces of paper.

(b) The first pair of students should put their sticky notes on the wall in a row. The next pair puts their sticky notes on the wall too. If one of your reasons is already hanging up, place your sticky note above or below it. Carry on round the class until all pairs have put their sticky notes on the wall.

(c) The entire class should read all the reasons. If other people wrote down reasons that you didn't think of, add them to your spider diagram in a different colour ink.

The economic impact

- The **cost of rebuilding** after the earthquake could be more than €8 billion. This cost is shocking for such a poor country.

- The **damage to cultural sites** and the deaths of climbers caught up in the earthquake harmed the tourism industry. Tourism employs more than a million people and is crucial to the Nepalese economy.

Responses to the earthquake

The government of Nepal was not well prepared for a disaster on this big scale.

- China, India and other countries provided immediate emergency aid and medical supplies.

- Within days, emergency rescue teams arrived from many other countries.

- Many aid organisations sent people to help with rescue operations and food distribution.

- Individuals from around the world donated to humanitarian organisations.

- International organisations provided money to support building programmes.

Learning Activity

4.8 **Walking debate** A lot of the aid money donated to the Nepalese earthquake fund by people around the world didn't reach the people it was intended for. Would it put you off donating to a disaster fund in the future if you knew that the funds didn't reach the people in need? Or would you still donate in the hope that the people in need would receive it?

(a) When your teacher tells you to move, go to the sign that reflects how you feel: Yes, Not sure, No.

(b) Each person should justify to the class why they have chosen their position. If a student's reason makes you change your mind about your first thoughts, move to join the other group.

(c) When everyone has decided on their position on this subject, discuss as a class whether it is right to donate money when you can afford it to a fund for a disaster that might not directly affect you.

Predicting and preparing for earthquakes

Predicting earthquakes is neither easy nor accurate. However, there are still some ways of checking the chances of an earthquake:

- **Laser beams** can be used to detect **plate movement**.

- A **seismograph** can be used to pick up advance **vibrations** in the Earth's crust.

Preparing for earthquakes is vital in many parts of the world. People living in earthquake zones can:

- Hold **earthquake drills**, practising what to do in the event of an earthquake

- Put together **emergency kits** and store them in their homes.

In areas where there is a high likelihood of earthquakes, **earthquake-proof buildings** have been constructed. In these:

- Heavy **furniture is bolted** to walls

- The foundations have rubber **shock absorbers**

- Concrete structures are **reinforced** with steel.

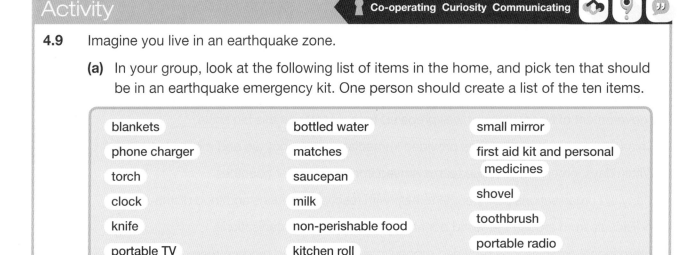

Learning Activity

Co-operating Curiosity Communicating

4.9 Imagine you live in an earthquake zone.

(a) In your group, look at the following list of items in the home, and pick ten that should be in an earthquake emergency kit. One person should create a list of the ten items.

blankets	bottled water	small mirror
phone charger	matches	first aid kit and personal medicines
torch	saucepan	
clock	milk	shovel
knife	non-perishable food	toothbrush
portable TV	kitchen roll	portable radio
toilet tissue	diary	spare batteries

(b) When all the groups' lists are completed, one person from the class or your teacher will read out each item on the list, and the note takers from each group will raise their hand if that item is on their group's list. Discuss as a class the reasons why any item that is not unanimously chosen or is not unanimously rejected should or should not be on the list.

Earthquakes resulting in tsunamis

A **tsunami** is a **huge wave** or series of waves. The waves can be as high as 60 metres. They are usually a result of an underwater earthquake or, occasionally, volcanic eruption.

When the ocean floor at a plate boundary rises or falls suddenly, it **displaces** the water above it and starts the **rolling waves** that grow to become a tsunami.

Tsunamis can move across the sea at **up to 800 km** an hour (that's how fast a jet plane can go). They lose very little energy as they travel. In the open ocean they are only about 30 cm high, but as they get to shallower water near the shoreline they slow down and begin to **grow** in energy and height. The tops of the waves move faster than the bottoms do, so the waves rise up and crash down on the land, engulfing anything in their way.

Impacts of a tsunami

The most powerful earthquake ever to hit **Japan**, measuring 9.0 on the Richter scale, had its **epicentre** under the Pacific Ocean, just 70 km off the coast. Here, the Pacific Plate pushes against and slides beneath the Eurasian Plate on which Japan sits.

Tsunami in the Pacific Ocean (Japan 2011)

For a long time the plates had been locked and stresses were building up. In March 2011 the tension became too great and the plates suddenly slipped past one another. The tremors lasted for about six minutes. The earthquake created a huge **tsunami**.

By the time they hit the coastline of Japan, the tsunami waves were between 6 and 10 metres high. The highest tsunami defence wall was only 5 metres. The waves travelled inland for up to 10 km.

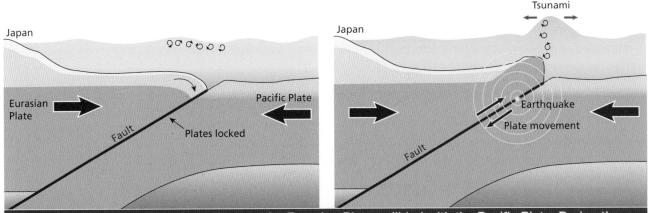

Figure 4.5 The earthquake occurred where the Eurasian Plate collided with the Pacific Plate. During the earthquake, the edge of the Eurasian Plate was pushed upwards by as much as 8 metres

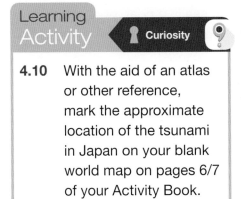

Learning Activity Curiosity

4.10 With the aid of an atlas or other reference, mark the approximate location of the tsunami in Japan on your blank world map on pages 6/7 of your Activity Book.

Figure 4.6 The aftermath of the tsunami in Japan (2011)

The environmental impact

- Entire towns were wiped off the map. At least 200,000 homes were damaged or destroyed.

- Roads, bridges and railways were washed away.

- Nuclear plants were shut down across the country as a safety measure. However, the cooling system of the Fukushima nuclear plant failed, leading to radiation leaks. This has resulted in a long-term health and environmental hazard.

- Many sea birds, fish and other wildlife died.

- Freshwater wildlife habitats were contaminated by seawater.

- 4.37 million chickens died because of difficulty getting food to them.

The human impact

- More than 500,000 people were evacuated from their homes. Four years later, about 230,000 people were still living in temporary accommodation.

 Homeless people in temporary shelter following the Nepal earthquake

- More than 18,000 people were killed or reported missing.

The economic impact

- This is likely to be the world's costliest natural disaster.

- Many of Japan's nuclear reactors remained closed for years because of stricter safety standards put into place after the tsunami. Japan relies on nuclear power, and so this has caused many problems.

- Farmland was ruined by salt left in the soil from the seawater. It could take many years to recover.

- The fishing industry of several regions was almost destroyed because 13,000 boats were damaged or destroyed and 440 fishermen were killed.

- Many manufacturing plants had to close temporarily or permanently because of damage and power cuts. Some of these businesses will never recover.

 Learning Activity

Curiosity Literacy

4.11 If an earthquake triggers a tsunami, would you be safer out at sea in a boat, or on the third floor of a building on the shore? Justify your answer to your partner and share with the rest of the class.

Responses to the tsunami

The Japanese government had excellent **disaster plans** in place. These involved the military, the police and medical staff. A tsunami **warning** was issued three minutes after the earthquake.

- The government disaster plans were immediately put into action.

- Nuclear power plants were shut down.

- People were kept informed by social media, such as Twitter.

- Many countries sent search and rescue teams to help look for survivors. They also offered other aid, such as blankets and food.

- Evacuation shelters were erected and the government arranged for food, blankets, etc. for them.

- Newspapers reported there was at first no disorder from the people of Japan. Later, though, reports began to come out of looting and thefts of cash from homes, businesses and banks.

- Many people from around the world donated money to aid organisations to help the survivors.

Learning Activity

Communicating Co-operating Curiosity Reflecting

4.12 **Walking debate** When there is a disaster in one part of the world, such as the tsunami in Japan, do you think it is right that governments from other counties should offer help to the country in difficulty?

(a) When your teacher tells you to move, go to the sign that reflects how you feel: Agree, Not sure, Disagree.

(b) Each person should justify to the class why they have chosen their position. If a student's reason makes you change your mind about your first thoughts, move to join the other group.

(c) When everyone has decided on their position on this subject, discuss as a class whether countries should help one another in times of disasters.

Reflecting on my learning

Reflecting Communicating Literacy

Write sentences using each of the following terms from this chapter. You may use more than one of the terms in your sentence if appropriate.

aftershocks	focus	seismograph
epicentre	plate boundary	tremors
fault line	Richter scale	tsunami

  PowerPoint summary

Revision
Go to **www.edco.ie/geographynow** and try the interactive activities and quizzes.

Rocks

5

Go to **www.edco.ie/geographynow** and try the interactive activities and quizzes.

Learning intentions

When you have completed this chapter you will be able to:

- Define the characteristics of rocks
- Group rocks according to how they were formed
- Explain how the different rock types were formed and name them
- Identify certain rocks from pictures and descriptions
- Name and identify locations in Ireland of different rock types
- Provide examples of what different rocks are used for.

Learning Outcomes

1.2 Distinguish between different categories of rock type, referring to composition and formation

2.2 Evaluate the environmental, economic, and social consequences of rock exploitation and energy resources.

Key terms

minerals · intrusive · sandstone
compressed · extrusive · bedding planes
cemented · crystals · heat
igneous · sediments · pressure
sedimentary · limestone · marble
metamorphic · permeable · quartzite
granite · fossils · slate
basalt · strata

What is rock?

Rock is the hard material that forms Earth's crust. All rocks:

- Are solid
- Occur naturally
- Are made up of one or more **minerals** that have been **compressed** and **cemented** together.

Rocks differ from each other in their:

- Mineral content
- Colour
- Hardness
- Texture (how they feel to the touch).

There are many different types of rock. They can be divided into **three groups**, according to **how they were formed**. These groups are:

- **Igneous** rocks
- **Sedimentary** rocks
- **Metamorphic** rocks.

We will look at each of these in the rest of this chapter.

There are many different rock types in each group.

Figure 5.1 Rocks are made up of one or more minerals

Igneous rocks

Igneous rocks are formed as a result of **volcanic activity**. Volcanic material cools down and solidifies, either within the crust or on the surface.

- **Intrusive** rocks are formed from material that **cooled inside the crust**.

- **Extrusive** rocks are formed from material that **cooled on the surface**.

We will look at two igneous rocks: **granite** and **basalt**.

Granite

Granite is an **intrusive** rock. It formed when molten magma forced its way into the crust. It **cooled very slowly** over millions of years, allowing large **crystals** to form. These crystals include quartz. It eventually came to the surface when the overlying rocks were worn away.

Granite varies in colour from black or grey to pink. Granite is found in the Mourne and Wicklow Mountains.

Learning Activity
 Curiosity

5.1 With your partner, identify the sample that shows gold and quartz. Justify your selection. Share your thoughts with the rest of the class.

GEO FACT

The word igneous comes from the Latin word for fire: ignis.

Link Chapter 3: page 18

DEFINITION

Crystal

A hard substance that is formed naturally when a liquid such as a mineral becomes solid due to pressure.

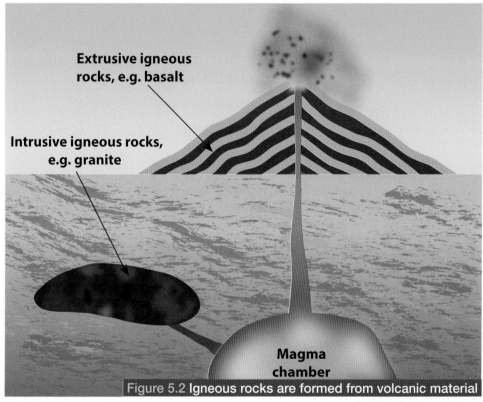

Extrusive igneous rocks, e.g. basalt

Intrusive igneous rocks, e.g. granite

Magma chamber

Figure 5.2 Igneous rocks are formed from volcanic material

Learning
Activity ⚷ Curiosity 🔍

5.2 On the geological map in your Activity Book (page 27), mark the Mourne Mountains and the Wicklow Mountains. Use an atlas or other reference to help you find them.

Figure 5.3 **Pink granite**

Basalt

Basalt is an **extrusive** rock. It formed when lava spread out across Earth's surface. The lava **cooled and solidified very quickly** because it was exposed to the air. As a result, basalt has **tiny crystals** that cannot be seen by the naked eye.

Basalt varies in colour from dark grey to black. It is found in the Antrim–Derry plateau. The most famous section of it is the **Giant's Causeway**. Here, as the lava cooled, it shrank and cracked to form six-sided columns.

Figure 5.4 **There are about 40,000 blocks of basalt in the Giant's Causeway**

Learning
Activity ⚷ Numeracy 🔢

5.3 Remembering your maths class:

(a) What is a two-dimensional six-sided shape called?

(b) What is a six-sided column called?

Learning
Activity ⚷ Curiosity 🔍

5.4 On the geological map in your Activity Book (page 27), mark the Giant's Causeway. Use an atlas or other reference to help you find it.

Learning
Activity ⚷ Reflecting Curiosity

5.5 Thinking back to your work on volcanoes, distinguish between molten magma and lava. In pairs, each of you write your definitions onto a piece of paper without using the words magma or lava. Hand the paper to your partner, and ask them to write the word next to the correct definition. When you have done this, pass the paper back to your partner and ask them to confirm your answers to their definitions.

5.6 Consider the words **intrusive** and **extrusive**. Why, do you think, are these words given to the two different types of igneous rock? Discuss this with your partner.

Sedimentary rocks

Sedimentary rocks are formed from the remains (**sediments**) of other rocks, plant life and animal life. These sediments are **deposited** on the beds of seas and lakes as well as on land. They are then **compressed** and **cemented** together.

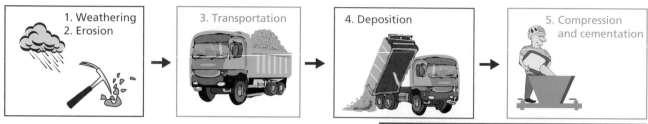

1. Weathering
2. Erosion

3. Transportation

4. Deposition

5. Compression and cementation

Figure 5.5 **The making of sedimentary rocks**

Figure 5.6 **Limestone containing fossils**

We will look at two sedimentary rocks: **limestone** and **sandstone**.

Limestone

Limestone is formed on the beds of shallow, warm seas from the **skeletons of tiny sea creatures, fish and shells**. These piled up over millions of years. The particles were **compressed** and **cemented** together. The remains of some of the skeletons are preserved in the rock as **fossils**.

Limestone varies in colour from white to grey. It is **permeable** (allows water to pass through it) and is laid down in layers, or **strata**.

Limestone is found in the Burren (Co. Clare) and under the soil and bogs that cover the Central Plain of Ireland.

Link 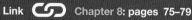 Chapter 8: pages 75–79

DEFINITION

Fossil

The remains or impression of a prehistoric plant or animal embedded and preserved in rock.

GEO FACT

Limestone is the most common rock in Ireland and is found in thirty-one of the thirty-two counties.

 Sandstone strata near the River Jordan

Learning Activity

Curiosity

5.7 On the geological map in your Activity Book (page 27), mark the Burren and the Central Plain. Use an atlas or other reference to help you find them.

Sandstone

Sandstone formed when large amounts of sand were worn away from Earth's surface and transported by wind and rivers. The sand was then deposited on the beds of lakes and seas, as well as in deserts. The deposits built up and were **compressed** and **cemented** to form sandstone.

Sandstone varies in colour from **brown** to **red**. The mountains of Munster, including MacGillycuddy's Reeks, the Galtees and Comeraghs, are made of sandstone.

Figure 5.7 Sandstone is laid down in layers called strata. The divisions between the strata are called bedding planes

GEO FACT

Coal is a sedimentary rock that formed from decayed vegetation. It is used for fuel.

Learning Activity

Curiosity

5.8   On the geological map in your Activity Book (page 27), mark MacGillycuddy's Reeks, the Galtees and Comeraghs. Use an atlas or other reference to help you find them.

Metamorphic rocks

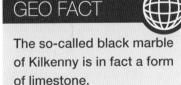

Metamorphic rocks are formed when existing igneous or sedimentary rocks come into contact with great **heat** and **pressure**. They can change in both shape and form.

We will look at two metamorphic rocks: **marble** and **quartzite**.

Marble

When molten magma forces its way into a body of limestone, it puts it under great heat and pressure. This changes the make-up of the limestone and it turns into **marble**.

Figure 5.8 Metamorphic rocks are formed when existing rocks are changed by heat and pressure

Pure marble is white, but when other minerals are present it can be red, green or black. Marble is a hard rock that also contains **crystals**.

Marble can easily be cut and polished. Marble is found in Rathlin Island (white), Connemara (green) and Cork (red).

GEO FACT

The so-called black marble of Kilkenny is in fact a form of limestone.

Link Chapter 22: pages 221–23

Figure 5.9 Quarrying large slabs of marble at Carrara in Italy. The artist Michelangelo used Carrara marble

Learning Activity

Curiosity

5.9   On the geological map in your Activity Book (page 27), mark Rathlin Island, Connemara and Cork. Use an atlas or other reference to help you find them.

Quartzite

Quartzite was formed when sandstone came into contact with magma deep in Earth's crust. This usually happened during periods of **folding**.

Link 🔗 Chapter 2: pages 9–13

Quartzite consists mainly of grains of quartz that are packed tightly together. It varies in colour from grey to white.

It is an extremely hard rock so it remains as a cap on some of Ireland's mountains. These include Croagh Patrick (Co. Mayo), Errigal (Co. Donegal) and the Great Sugarloaf (Co. Wicklow).

Figure 5.10 **Pilgrim Path on the quartzite slope of Croagh Patrick**

GEO FACT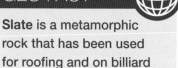

Slate is a metamorphic rock that has been used for roofing and on billiard tables.

Learning
Activity

🔑 Curiosity 💡

5.10 On the geological map in your Activity Book (page 27), mark Croagh Patrick (Co. Mayo), Errigal (Co. Donegal) and the Great Sugarloaf (Co. Wicklow). Use an atlas or other reference to help you find them.

Learning
Activity

🔑 Curiosity Communicating Reflecting Co-operating Responsibility

5.11 Work in pairs.

(a) Create a quiz for your partner by finding on the internet a picture of each of the six types of rocks we have talked about. Place these in a random order on a slide show or document. Ask your partner to identify the rock type. You can give hints, if you think the picture on its own is too hard.

(b) Mark your partner's quiz. Discuss the pictures to inform each other about the characteristics that show what type of rock it is.

(c) Complete the Peer feedback sheet (page 28) for your partner in their Activity Book.

Common rocks in Ireland

Figure 5.11 is a geological map. It shows where the most common rock types in Ireland can be found.

Learning Activity Curiosity Responsibility

5.12 Examine Figure 5.11 and answer these questions in your copy:

(a) Name the most common rock in Ireland.

(b) Name two counties (or areas) where the most common rock is found.

(c) Name and locate your own county on the geological map in your Activity Book (page 27).

(d) Name the most common rock type found in your county.

5.13 Search Google Images for a map of the bedrock of Ireland using the search words 'Ireland bedrock geology'.

(a) Identify the bedrock type in your area.

(b) Name the rock group to which it belongs.

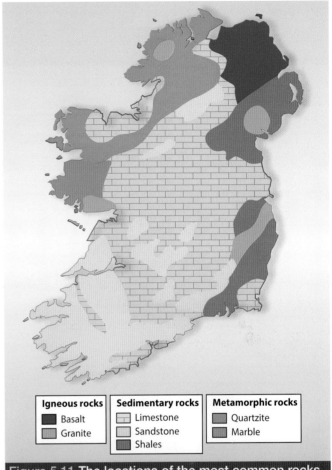

Igneous rocks	Sedimentary rocks	Metamorphic rocks
Basalt	Limestone	Quartzite
Granite	Sandstone	Marble
	Shales	

Figure 5.11 The locations of the most common rocks in Ireland

Reflecting on my learning
Reflecting Communicating Literacy

Write sentences using each of the following terms from this chapter. You may use more than one of the terms in your sentence if appropriate.

basalt	fossils	marble	sandstone
bedding planes	granite	metamorphic	sedimentary
cemented	heat	minerals	sediments
compressed	igneous	permeable	slate
crystals	intrusive	pressure	strata
extrusive	limestone	quartzite	

 PowerPoint summary

 Revision
Go to **www.edco.ie/geographynow** and try the interactive activities and quizzes.

Maps and photographs

Learning intentions

When you have completed this chapter you will be able to:

- Describe how symbols and colour are used to present information on OS maps
- Accurately locate features on OS maps and aerial photographs
- Use the skills of measurement and drawing on OS maps and aerial photographs
- Interpret the physical landscape in OS maps and aerial photographs.

Learning Outcome

Graphicacy

Graphicacy is the ability to construct, read and interpret a range of images including maps, photographs, tables, graphs and charts. The skills you learn in this chapter will be useful for many other topics in your study of geography and in other areas of your life.

Key terms

map	grid reference	aerial photograph
scale	co-ordinates	vertical aerial photograph
Ordnance Survey	compass points	oblique aerial photograph
Discovery Series	cardinal points	foreground
legend	contours	middle ground
straight-line distance	spot height	background
curved-line distance	triangulation pillar	street plan
area	gradient	historic map
National Grid	cross-section	satellite image
	sketch map	

Ordnance Survey maps

A **map** is a drawing or plan of part or all of Earth's surface. **Ordnance Survey Ireland (OSi)** is the **national mapping agency** for Ireland. All Ordnance Survey (OS) maps in Ireland will have been created by this organisation (or its OS predecessors).

Maps:

- Are drawn to **scale**

- Use **colours, symbols and labels** to represent features found on the landscape.

Scale

Scale is the ratio or relationship between a distance on the map and the corresponding distance on the ground.

Maps are drawn to different scales, depending on the amount of information that is required and the area of ground that the map must cover.

Figure 6.1 **Small-scale** maps show a large area but have little detail. This map, centred on Kilkenny, is drawn to a scale of 1:400,000

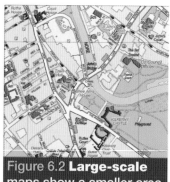

Figure 6.2 **Large-scale** maps show a smaller area but have great detail. This map, showing the centre of Kilkenny, is drawn to a scale of 1:7,000

Learning
Activity

Curiosity Communicating

6.1 Examine the maps in figures 6.1 and 6.2. Identify one purpose for which each map could be used. Discuss this with your partner and share with the rest of the class.

Discovery Series of maps

OSi publishes a series of maps called the **Discovery Series**. These maps are drawn at a scale of **1:50,000**. This means that each centimetre on the map represents 50,000 centimetres (or 500 metres) on the ground.

Learning
Activity

Curiosity Numeracy

6.2 State how many centimetres represent 1 km on the ground on a Discovery Series map.

Scale on a map

Scale on a map may be shown in three ways:

1 Representative fraction (RF)

2 Linear scale

3 Statement of scale.

Figure 6.3 **The Discovery Series** of maps are designed for tourists and leisure activities. They are drawn to a scale of 1:50,000. This map shows the centre of Kilkenny

1 Representative fraction (RF)

The scale is written as a ratio. In this case, the scale is 1:50,000.

2 Linear scale

The scale is shown along a ruled line that is divided into kilometres and miles. One section of the linear scale divides miles and kilometres into tenths.

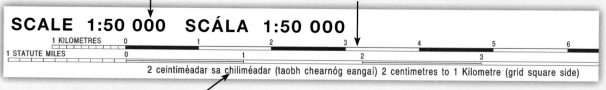

SCALE 1:50 000 SCÁLA 1:50 000

1 KILOMETRES   0   1   2   3   4   5   6
1 STATUTE MILES   0   1   2   3

2 ceintiméadar sa chiliméadar (taobh chearnóg eangaí) 2 centimetres to 1 Kilometre (grid square side)

3 Statement of scale

The map gives a written description of the scale. In this case, 2 centimetres on the map represent 1 kilometre on the ground.

Figure 6.4 The three methods of showing scale on the Discovery Series maps all say the same thing, but in different ways

Learning
Activity

 Curiosity Numeracy

6.3 (a) State how many centimetres represent 5 km on the ground on a Discovery Series map.

(b) A straight village street has houses along its length for 0.75 km. State how many centimetres this is on a Discovery Series map.

(c) A road through a mountain pass is a 6 km drive. The road has many bends. State whether the road will be shown on a Discovery Series map at a length of 12 cm, less than 12 cm, or more than 12 cm. Justify your answer.

(d) Compare your answers with your partner's and share with the rest of the class.

OS map legend

OS maps use **symbols** to show information on a map. All the symbols used can be found in the map **legend** (see page 63).

The symbols are used to represent both natural features (such as beaches, mountains and rivers) and built features (such as roads, buildings and airports). The symbols vary from map to map, depending on the scale.

Measuring distance

Scale is the same for all parts of a map. This is important because it enables us to measure distances on the map.

Straight-line distance

Straight-line distance is the shortest distance between any two points. It is often referred to 'as the crow flies'.

To measure a straight-line distance between two points on a map:

1 Place a strip of paper on the map so that its edge passes through the two points.

2 Mark the edge of the paper where it touches the two points on the map.

3 Place the paper against the linear scale on the map and read the distance in kilometres (km).

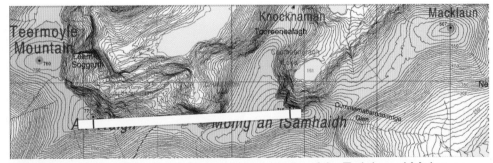

6.5a Measure the distance between the summits of An Traigh and Moing an tSamhaidh, Co. Kerry. Place a strip of paper on the map and mark it at the two points.

6.5b Place the strip of paper against the scale so that the first mark is at zero (0).

6.5c

- Move the paper strip to the left until the second mark touches a number (in this case, 2).

- Count the tenths to the left of the zero (in this case, 7).

- The distance between the summits is 2.7 km.

Figure 6.5 Measuring straight-line distance (as the crow flies) on a map

Learning
Activity

Curiosity Numeracy

6.4 **(a)** Examine the map in figure 6.5a. Calculate the straight-line distances between these summits:

  (i) Teermoyle and Macklaun

  (ii) Teermoyle and Knocknaman.

(b) Compare your answers with your partner's and share with the rest of the class.

Curved-line distance

Curved-line distance is used to measure a distance along any line that is not straight, e.g. roads, railways and rivers.

To measure a curved-line distance between two points on a map:

1 Place the edge of your paper strip at the start point and put a pencil mark on both the map and the paper (A).

2 Hold the edge of the paper along the line until you reach the first bend or turn. Put a pencil mark on both map and paper (B).

3 Keep the marks at (B) in line with one another. Move the paper strip so that it is in line with the next section of the line. Put a pencil mark on both map and paper (C).

4 Repeat this process until you have measured the required distance.

5 Place the paper strip on the linear scale and read the distance in kilometres.

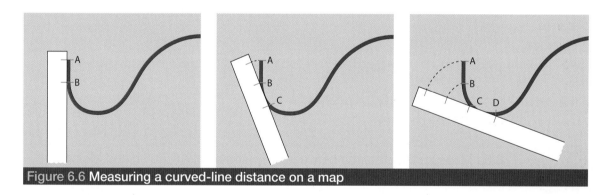

Figure 6.6 Measuring a curved-line distance on a map

Learning
Activity

Curiosity Numeracy

6.5 Calculate the length, in kilometres, of the section of the R352 in figure 6.15 (page 49).

Calculating area

Two types of area can be measured on an OS map:

- A regular-shaped area such as the actual map extract

- An irregular-shaped area such as an island, lake or mountain.

GEO FACT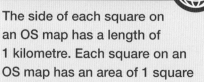

The side of each square on an OS map has a length of 1 kilometre. Each square on an OS map has an area of 1 square kilometre (km²).

To calculate the area of a map extract

1 Count the number of squares along the base of the map.

2 Count the number of squares along the vertical side of the map.

3 Multiply the two totals. This gives you the area of the map extract in square kilometres (km^2).

Example

Calculate the area of the map extract shown in figure 6.7.

Number of grid squares along base of map = 5

Number of grid squares up the side of the map = 6

Total number of squares = 5 × 6 = 30

Area of map extract = 30 km^2

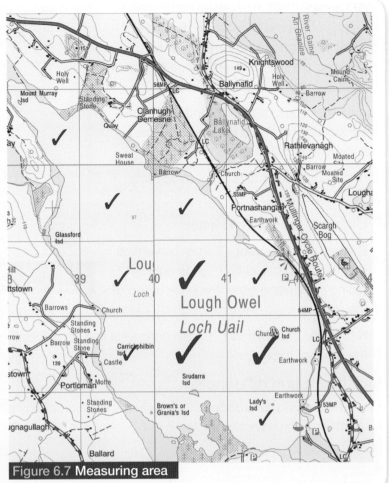

Figure 6.7 Measuring area

To calculate the area of an irregular shape

1 Count all the complete squares.

2 Count each square where the shape covers half or more of its area. Ignore those squares where the shape takes up less than half its area.

3 Add the totals from steps 1 and 2 to find the total area in square kilometres (km^2).

Example

Calculate the area of the lake in the map extract shown in figure 6.7.

Number of complete squares = 3
Number of areas that take up half or more of a square = 7
Total number of squares = 3 + 7 = 10
Area of lake = 10 km^2

Learning Activity

Curiosity Numeracy

6.6 Calculate the land area in the map extract shown in figure 6.7.

The National Grid

The **National Grid** covers Ireland and some of its sea areas. It consists of twenty-five squares called **sub-zones**, each named by a letter of the alphabet. Each sub-zone is 100 km by 100 km in area.

Learning Activity

Curiosity

6.7 State the letter square that your school is in. Check your answer with your partner's and share with the rest of the class.

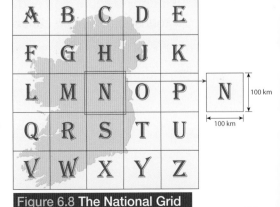

Figure 6.8 The National Grid

Finding location with grid references

The sides of each sub-zone are divided into 100 equal parts by a series of lines. These lines are called **co-ordinates** and are numbered from 00 to 99.

We use these co-ordinates together with the sub-zone letter to find a location on a map. This location is called a **grid reference**.

Grid references are made up of three parts (call them **LEN**):

- **L** refers to the sub-zone **letter**.
- **E** refers to the **easting**. This is the vertical line. Its value is read from left to right (going east) along either the base or top of the map.

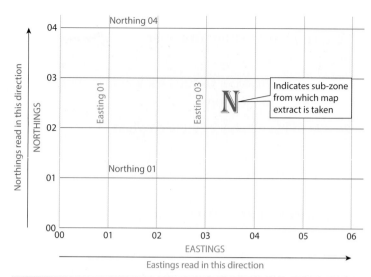

Figure 6.9 **A grid reference consists of a sub-zone letter, an easting and a northing (LEN)**

- **N** refers to the **northing**. It is the horizontal line. Its value is read from bottom to top (going north) along the sides of the map.

Four-figure grid references

A **four-figure grid reference** will give you the location of any single **square** on the map. The easting and the northing each have two digits.

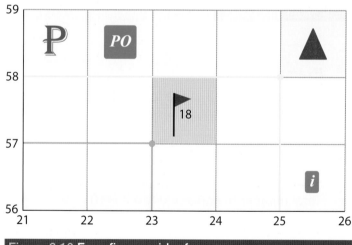

Figure 6.10 **Four-figure grid references**

Golf course

Sub-zone:	P
Easting:	23
Northing:	57
Grid reference:	P 23 57

Hostel

Sub-zone:	P
Easting:	25
Northing:	58
Grid reference:	P 25 58

Learning Activity

Curiosity Numeracy

6.8 Examine figure 6.10 and state the four-figure grid references for the post office (PO) and tourist information centre (*i*). Check your answer with your partner's and share with the rest of the class.

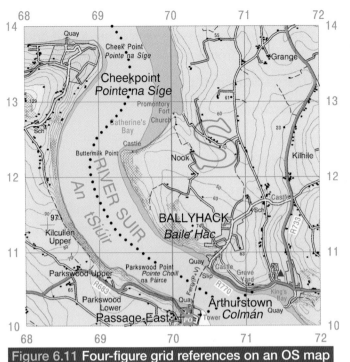

Figure 6.11 Four-figure grid references on an OS map

The following are examples of four-figure grid references from figure 6.11.

Ballyhack

Sub-zone:	S
Easting:	70
Northing:	11
Grid reference:	S 70 11

Cheekpoint

Sub-zone:	S
Easting:	68
Northing:	13
Grid reference:	S 68 13

Learning Activity

Curiosity Numeracy

6.9 Examine figure 6.11. Give a four-figure grid reference for:

(a) Passage East

(b) Arthurstown

(c) Buttermilk Point

(d) Promontory Fort.

GEO FACT

In a four-figure grid reference, the easting and northing cross at the bottom left corner of the square.

Six-figure grid references

A **six-figure grid reference** gives a more exact location than a four-figure grid reference. It refers to a definite **point** within a grid square.

Imagine that each side of the grid square is divided into ten equal parts, as in decimal measurement. This will then give a third digit for both the easting and the northing (see figure 6.12).

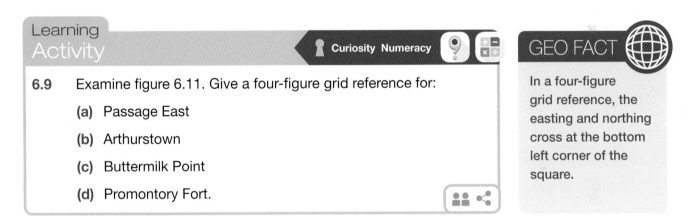

The sub-zone letter is **P**
The easting is **23.5**
The northing is **42.7**
Ignore the decimal point when writing the grid reference.
The six-figure grid reference for **X** is **P 235 427**.

Figure 6.12 Getting a six-figure grid reference

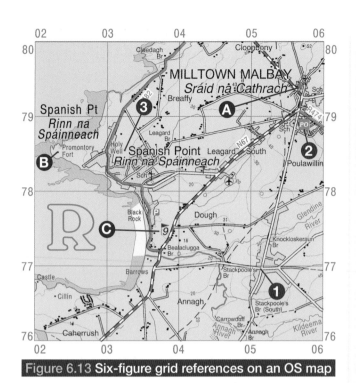

Figure 6.13 **Six-figure grid references on an OS map**

The following are examples of six-figure grid references from figure 6.13.

Garda Station (A)

Sub-zone:	R
Easting:	05.6 (written 056)
Northing:	79.4 (written 794)
Grid reference:	R 056 794

Promontory Fort (B)

Sub-zone:	R
Easting:	02.3 (written 023)
Northing:	78.5 (written 785)
Grid reference:	R 023 785

Golf course (C)

Sub-zone:	R
Easting:	03.7 (written 037)
Northing:	77.5 (written 775)
Grid reference:	R 037 775

Learning Activity

Curiosity Numeracy

6.10 Examine figure 6.13.

(a) Give a six-figure grid reference for the following:

    (i) Crossroads **1**   (ii) Post office **2**   (iii) Holy Well **3**.

(b) Identify the feature at each of these six-figure grid references:

    (i) R 036 777   (ii) R 023 766   (iii) R 040 772

(c) Check your answers with your partner's and share with the rest of the class.

Directions

Directions on a map are described by using **compass points**. The four main points of the compass – **north**, **east**, **south** and **west** – are called the **cardinal points**.

If the spaces between the cardinal points are divided, four more compass points are created. These are NE, SE, SW and NW.

A further division creates eight more minor compass points.

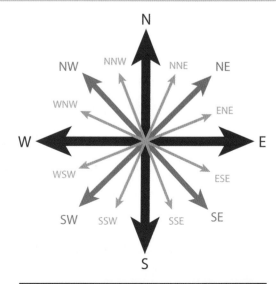

Figure 6.14 **Points of the compass shown on a compass rose**

Learning Activity

Curiosity Communicating

6.11

(a) State what the letters NE, SE, SW and NW stand for.

(b) State the direction that lies between:

(i) E and NE

(ii) SW and W

(iii) N and NE.

(c) Check your answers with your partner's and share with the rest of the class.

(d) (i) Close your books and draw a diagram showing the cardinal points of the compass.

(ii) Check your diagram with your partner's.

(iii) Give your partner two compass points (other than the cardinal points) to draw on their diagram.

(iv) Check each other's diagrams.

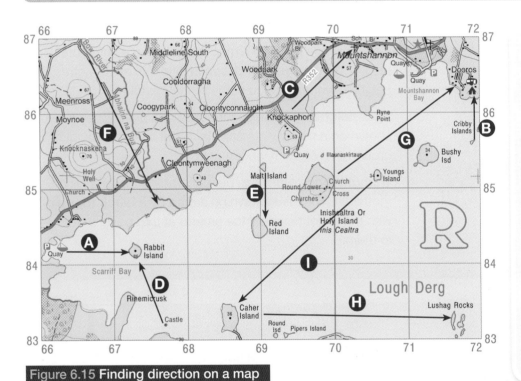

Figure 6.15 Finding direction on a map

The following are examples of directions from figure 6.15.

A: Rabbit Island lies to the **east** of the quay.

B: The camping site lies to the **north** of Cribby Islands.

C: The R362 runs in a **north-easterly** direction.

D: Rabbit Island lies to the **north-west** of the castle.

Learning Activity

Curiosity Communicating

6.12

(a) Examine figure 6.15 and complete the following directions in your copy.

E: Red Island lies to the _____ of Malt Island.

F: Abhainn na Bua flows in a _____ direction.

G: The caravan park lies to the _____ of Holy Island.

H: Lushag Rocks lie to the _____ of Caher Island.

I: Caher Island lies to the _____ of Youngs Island.

(b) Check your answers with your partner's and share with the rest of the class.

Height

Height (or altitude) on an Ordnance Survey map is shown in **metres above sea level**. Height is shown on a map in four ways:

1 Colour

2 Contours

3 Spot heights

4 Triangulation pillars.

Figure 6.16 Triangulation pillar on the summit of Nephin Mountain, Co. Mayo

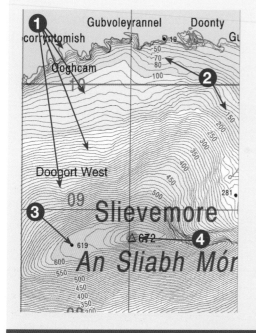

1 **Colour coding** gives a general picture of height. Different shades of green are used to show lowland areas under 200 metres in height. Cream indicates land between 200 and 300 metres. Next come various shades of brown, with the shade becoming darker as height increases.

2 **Contours** are **lines** on a map that join places of equal height. They are usually drawn at intervals of 10 metres. The height is written next to some of the contours.

3 **Spot heights** give the exact height of a point. They are shown on a map by a small **black dot** with the height of the ground at that point written next to it.

4 **Triangulation pillars** can be found at the top of a hill or mountain. They are shown on a map by a **black triangle** with the exact height of the ground at that point written next to them.

Figure 6.17 **Showing height on an OS map**

Learning Activity

 Curiosity Communicating Co-operating

6.13 Work in pairs. Examine an Ordnance Survey map of your area.

(a) Identify your school on the map.

(i) State the six-figure grid reference for your school.

(ii) Determine the height above sea level at which your school is built. Justify your answer.

(iii) Share with the rest of the class.

(b) Identify your homes on the map.

(i) State the six-figure grid references for your homes.

(ii) Determine the heights above sea level at which your homes are built. Justify your answers.

(c) Each of you calculate the difference in height between your home and your school.

(d) Identify a triangulation pillar on the same map on which your school appears.

(i) State its height above sea level.

(ii) State its four-figure grid reference. Share with the rest of the class.

Slope

Slope is also called **gradient**. Changes in slope are identified by the spacing of the contours.

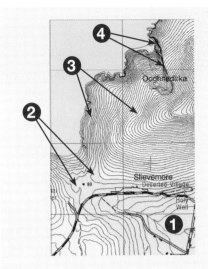

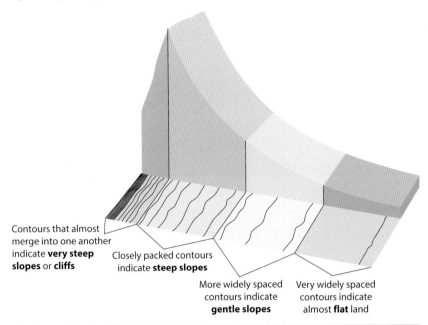

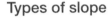

Contours that almost merge into one another indicate **very steep slopes** or **cliffs**

Closely packed contours indicate **steep slopes**

More widely spaced contours indicate **gentle slopes**

Very widely spaced contours indicate almost **flat** land

Figure 6.18 The spacing of contours gives an indication of how steep or gentle a slope is

1 **Flat land** is indicated by an absence of contours.

2 **Gentle slopes** are indicated by contours that are widely spaced.

3 **Steep slopes** are indicated by contours that are closely packed together.

4 **Cliffs** are indicated by contours that are 'on top of one another'.

Figure 6.19 Different slopes on an OS map

Types of slope

There are three types of slope. They can be identified by the pattern of the contours.

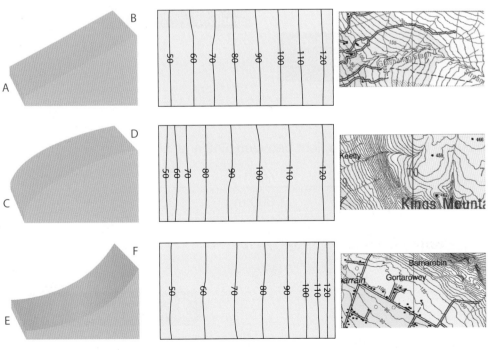

Even slope: The contour pattern shows evenly spaced contours.

Convex slope: This slope is steep at the bottom (closely packed contours) and gentle at the top (widely spaced contours).

Concave slope: This slope is gentle at the bottom (widely spaced contours) and steep at the top (closely packed contours).

Figure 6.20 We can identify the type of slope from the contour pattern

Learning Activity

6.14 **(a)** State which section of figure 6.21 shows:

   (i)   An even slope

   (ii) A convex slope

   (iii) A concave slope

   (iv) A level area.

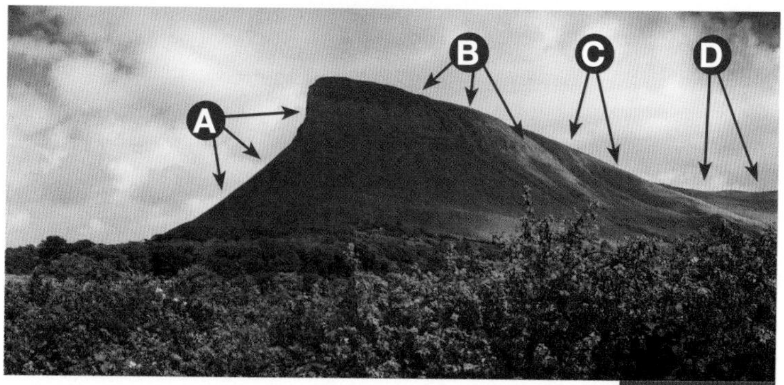

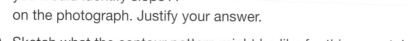

Figure 6.21

(b) State how, on an OS map, you would identify slope A on the photograph. Justify your answer.

(c) Sketch what the contour pattern might be like for this mountain.

(d) Check your answers with your partner's and share with the rest of the class.

Calculating gradient

We can give a more accurate description of the slope by expressing it as a ratio. It is calculated as follows:

$$\frac{\text{The difference in height between any two points}}{\text{The distance between the points}}$$

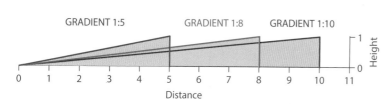

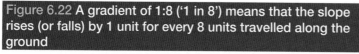

GRADIENT 1:5   GRADIENT 1:8   GRADIENT 1:10

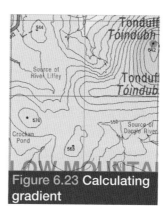

Figure 6.23 Calculating gradient

Figure 6.22 A gradient of 1:8 ('1 in 8') means that the slope rises (or falls) by 1 unit for every 8 units travelled along the ground

Example

Examine figure 6.23. **Calculate the average gradient between .642 and .563.**

$$\frac{\text{Difference in height}}{\text{Distance between points}} = \frac{642 - 563 \text{ m}}{1.8 \text{ km}} = \frac{79 \text{ m}}{1,800 \text{ m}} = \frac{1}{22.8}$$

This can be written as 1:22.8 (there is a gradient of 1 in 22.8).

Learning Activity

6.15 Calculate the average gradient between:

   (a) .642 and .570

   (b) .544 and .563.

Cross-sections

A **cross-section** shows a section of landscape that is viewed from the side as if it was cut through with a knife. It gives us a very good idea of the general shape, height and slope of that section of landscape.

Cross-sections are usually drawn on **graph paper** from a line that links two points on a map.

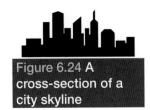

Figure 6.24 A cross-section of a city skyline

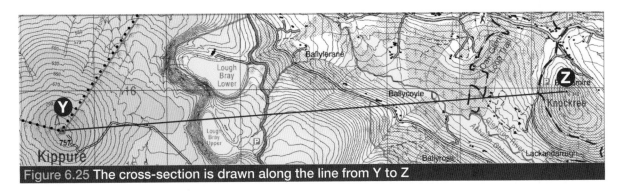

Figure 6.25 The cross-section is drawn along the line from Y to Z

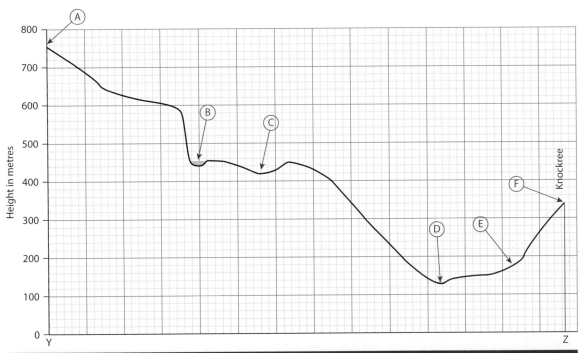

Figure 6.26 A cross-section drawn from Y to Z on the map extract above (figure 6.25)

Learning Activity

Curiosity Communicating

6.16   Examine the map (figure 6.25) and the cross-section (figure 6.26).

    (a) Name the mountain peak at A.

    (b) State the name of the lake at B.

    (c) Name the road at C.

    (d) Name the river at D.

    (e) State the type of vegetation at E.

    (f) State the height of the hilltop at F. Justify your answer.

    (g) Check your answers with your partner's and share with the rest of the class.

Drawing a sketch map from a map extract

A **sketch map** is a roughly drawn map that shows the basic details.

To draw a sketch map of an Ordnance Survey map extract follow these steps:

1 Always use a **pencil**.

2 Draw a frame that is the **same shape** as the map extract. It may be smaller than the map extract.

3 Give the sketch a **title** and indicate **north** with a direction arrow.

4 Draw the **coastline** (if there is one on the map extract).

5 Insert features. **Identify** each feature by name or by a legend or key.

Hint

In order to help you to position the features correctly, draw the sketch map on **graph paper**. Each square on the graph paper will correspond to a square on the map.

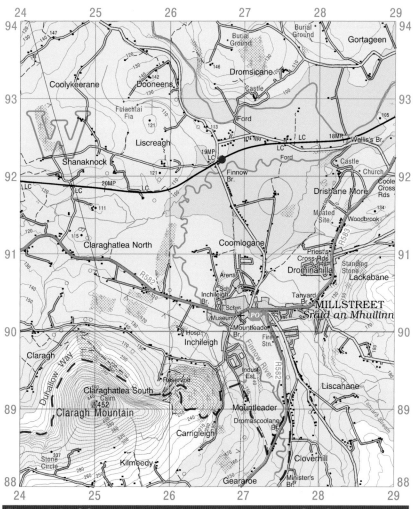

Figure 6.27 OS map extract of the Millstreet area, Co. Cork

Example

Draw a sketch map of the Millstreet area from the map in figure 6.27, showing the following features:

- A river
- A named road
- The built-up area of Millstreet
- An area of land above 200 metres in height
- The railway
- An antiquity
- A tourist attraction.

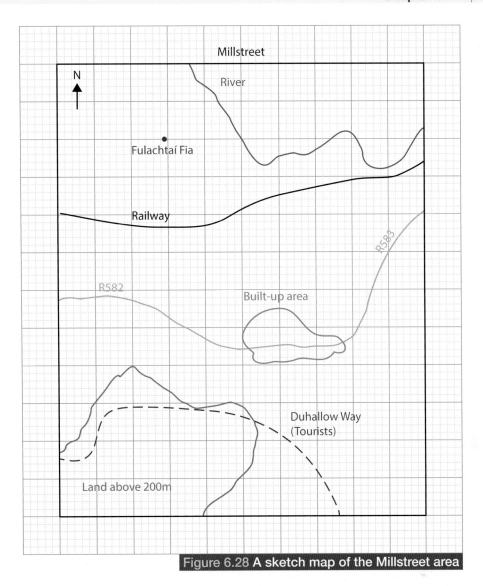

Millstreet

N

River

Fulachtaí Fia

Railway

R583

R582

Built-up area

Duhallow Way
(Tourists)

Land above 200m

Figure 6.28 A sketch map of the Millstreet area

Learning
Activity

Curiosity

6.17 Draw a sketch map of the Millstreet area from the map in figure 6.27.

On it show and name the following features:

- The Finnow River

- The R582 (both sections)

- The railway station

- An area of woodland

- A castle

- The Post Office

- Claragh Mountain.

Map revision

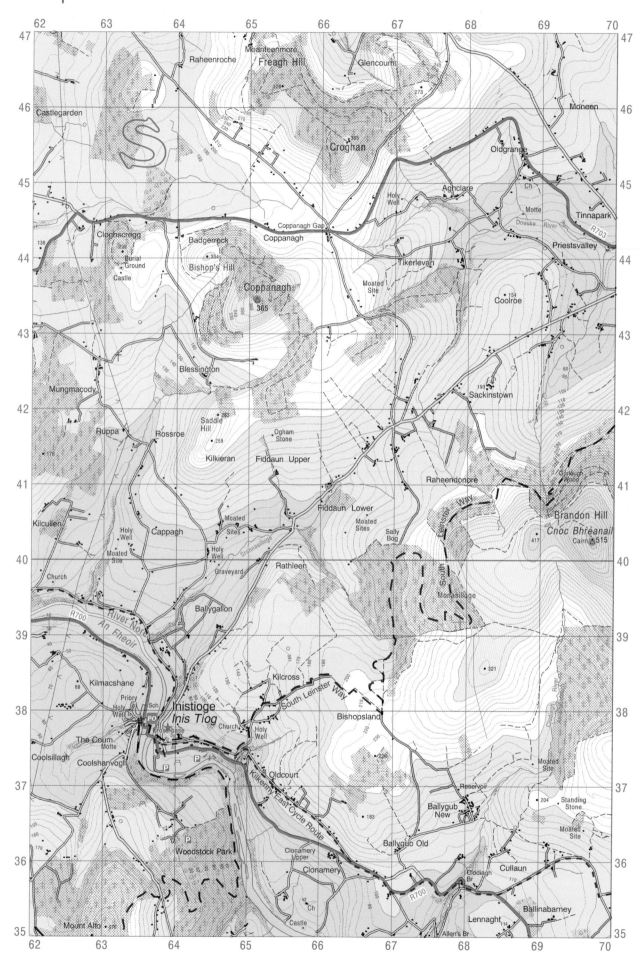

Learning Activity

The following questions all refer to the OS map extract of Co. Kilkenny in figure 6.29.

Write answers to the following in your copy.

6.18 State whether each of (a) to (d) is true or false. Justify each answer.

(a) Freagh Hill lies to the north on the map.

(b) An area of woodland is shown in the south-west of the map extract.

(c) Brandon Hill lies to the south-east on the map.

(d) The Leinster Way runs to the south of Brandon Hill.

6.19 Identify each of the following directions (all locations are hilltops, shown in brown):

(a) Freagh Hill lies to the _____ of Coppanagh Hill.

(b) Coppanagh Hill lies to the _____ of Brandon Hill.

(c) Brandon lies to the _____ of Mount Alto.

(d) Brandon Hill lies to the _____ of Croghan.

(e) Croghan lies to the _____ of Bishop's Hill.

6.20 (a) State four ways in which height is shown on this map extract.

(b) Identify the name and height of the highest point on the map.

(c) Identify the two hilltops that have a height of 365 metres.

(d) State two ways in which height is shown at each of these locations:

(i) S 651 434   (ii) S 621 345.

6.21 Complete the following sentences by selecting the correct answers from the brackets:

(a) The higher slopes of Brandon Hill are (gentle / steep).

(b) The slope in grid square S 63 45 is (gentler / steeper) than that in G 64 45.

(c) The grid square with the gentlest slope in the map extract is (S 63 39 / S 63 45).

(d) The slope in S 65 37 is (even / convex / concave).

(e) The slope in S 64 42 is (even / convex / concave).

(f) The slope in S 68 39 is (even / convex / concave).

6.22 (a) Calculate the straight-line distance, in kilometres, from the top of Brandon Hill to the top of Coppanagh.

(b) Calculate the length, in kilometres, of the section of the R703 shown on the map.

6.23 Prepare a sketch map of the area shown on the OS map. On it, show and name:

(a) The River Nore

(b) The R703

(c) The summit of Brandon Hill

(d) An area of land above 300 metres in height

(e) The built-up area of Inistioge

(f) A riverside parking area

(g) A castle

(h) An area of woodland.

6.24 (a) Swap your copy with your partner and together check each other's answers to questions 6.18 to 6.23.

(b) If you do not agree with an answer, discuss the question and try to reach agreement.

(c) Join with another pair and share your answers.

(d) Help each other with any questions you are still not sure about.

Figure 6.29 (opposite) Inistioge OS map extract, Co. Kilkenny

Aerial photographs

An **aerial photograph** is a view of the land surface taken from the air.

Aerial photographs provide a great deal of information about the landscape, especially when they are used alongside OS maps.

There are two types of aerial photograph: vertical aerial photograph and oblique aerial photograph.

Vertical aerial photograph

A **vertical aerial photograph** is taken with the camera pointing **directly downwards** at the ground.

- It shows a view taken from directly above the landscape.

- The dominant feature is the **roofline of buildings**.

- It does not show the horizon.

- The scale on a vertical aerial photograph is true throughout the whole photograph.

Oblique aerial photographs

An **oblique aerial photograph** is taken with the camera pointing **downwards at an angle**.

- It gives a view that is similar to viewing the landscape from the top of a high hill or a very tall building.

- It shows both the **roofline** and the **sides** of buildings.

- It may also show the horizon.

- Features at the bottom (foreground) of the photograph appear much larger than those at the top (background) of the photograph.

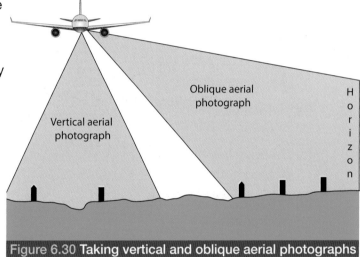

Figure 6.30 **Taking vertical and oblique aerial photographs**

Figure 6.31 **Vertical aerial photograph of Wexford**

Figure 6.32 **Oblique aerial photograph of Wexford**

Locating features on photographs

Divide the photograph into nine equal sections. The names given to these sections depends on the type of photograph.

Figure 6.33 The vertical aerial photograph will have an arrow that points to the north. Use compass directions (see page 48) to describe the location of features

Figure 6.34 To describe location on an oblique aerial photograph, use the names of the nine sections as shown in the picture

Learning Activity
Curiosity

6.25 Examine the vertical aerial photo in figure 6.33.

   (a) State the location of each of the following:

      (i) Factory

      (ii) Open fields

      (iii) School

      (iv) Church.

   (b) Check your answers with your partner's and share with the rest of the class.

Learning Activity
Curiosity

6.26 Examine the oblique aerial photo in figure 6.34.

   (a) State the location(s) of each of the following:

      (i) Factory

      (ii) Open fields

      (iii) School

      (iv) Church.

   (b) Check your answers with your partner's and share with the rest of the class.

Identifying the season

It is possible to identify the season when an aerial photograph was taken by using the following pointers.

Summer in the northern hemisphere

- Deciduous trees have full foliage.
- High summer sun casts short shadows.
- Cattle are seen grazing in the fields.
- Ripening crops are identified by bright colours.
- Bales of hay or silage may be seen in the fields.

Winter in the northern hemisphere

- Deciduous trees have lost their foliage.
- Low winter sun casts long shadows.
- Cattle have been moved indoors.
- Fields have been freshly ploughed.
- Chimney smoke from houses indicates cold weather.

Curiosity

6.27 State the evidence that the photograph in figure 6.35 was taken in the summer. Discuss the evidence with your partner, and share with the rest of the class.

Figure 6.35 **The Irish countryside in the summer**

Drawing a sketch map of an aerial photograph

To draw a sketch map of an aerial photograph, follow these steps.

1 Always use a pencil (or coloured pencils).

2 Draw a frame the same shape as the photograph. It may be smaller than the photograph.

3 Give the sketch map a title.

4 Divide the photo and sketch map frame into nine sections (using a light pencil).

5 Draw the coastline (if there is one on the map).

6 Draw the outline of the required features in a shape similar to the original.

7 Identify each feature either by name or by using a labelled key.

Example
Draw a sketch map of the area shown on the photograph. On it show and name the following:

- The town square
- A church
- A clump of trees
- A cemetery
- Polytunnels
- A terrace of houses
- An antiquity.

Hint: Remember to draw light lines to divide the photograph frame into nine sections. This makes it easier to locate features on the sketch.

Figure 6.36 **Aerial photograph of Kilfinane, Co. Limerick**

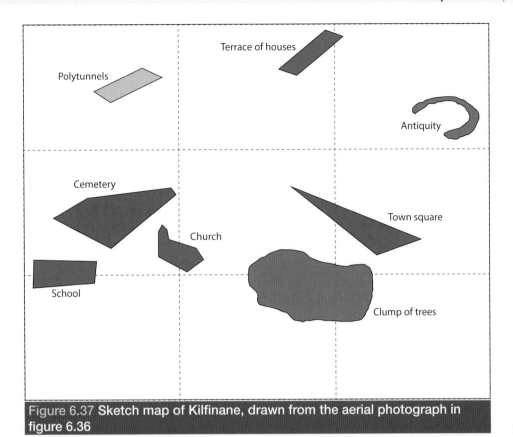

Figure 6.37 **Sketch map of Kilfinane, drawn from the aerial photograph in figure 6.36**

Figure 6.38 **Blarney, Co. Cork**

Learning
Activity

Curiosity Communicating

The following questions refer to the aerial photograph Blarney of Co. Cork in figure 6.38.

Write answers to the following in your copy.

6.28 State the type of aerial view of the photograph: vertical or oblique? Justify your answer.

6.29 State the location of each of the following:

(a) The car park at A

(b) The church at B

(c) Pasture at C

(d) The houses at D

(e) The school at E

(f) The shops at F.

6.30 Identify:

(a) Two types of vegetation in the left background.

(b) The large building in the centre middle ground.

(c) Recreation type in the right background.

6.31 Prepare a sketch map of the area shown in the photograph. On it show and name the following features:

(a) Two connecting streets

(b) An old factory building

(c) A church

(d) A car park

(e) A line of shops

(f) A clump of trees

(g) A housing estate.

6.32 (a) Swap your copy with a partner and together check each other's answers to questions 6.28 to 6.31.

(b) If you do not agree with an answer, discuss the question and try to reach agreement.

(c) Join with another pair and share your answers.

(d) Help each other with any questions you are still not sure about.

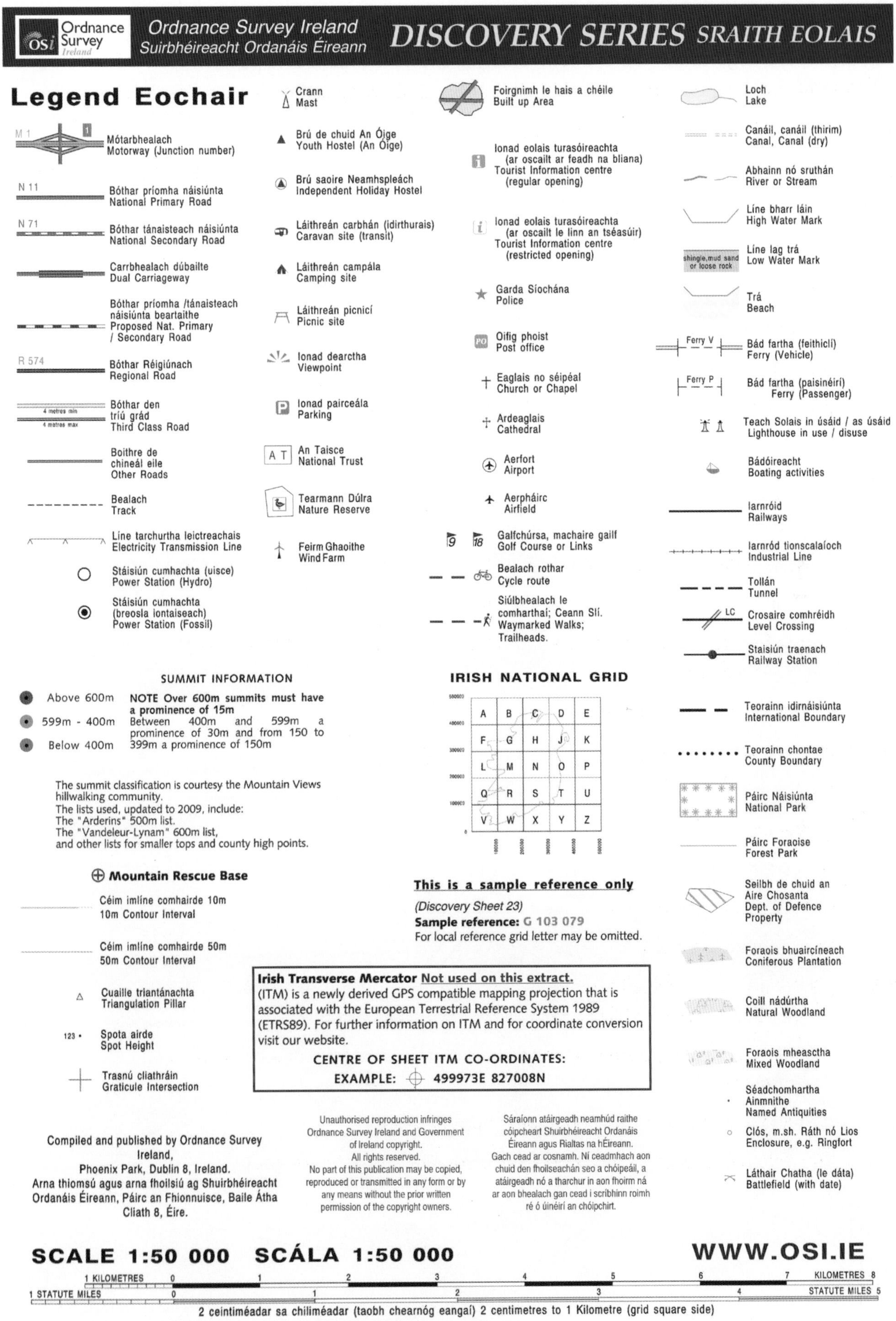

Ordnance Survey Ireland
Suirbhéireacht Ordanáis Éireann

DISCOVERY SERIES *SRAITH EOLAIS*

Legend Eochair

M 1 ▭	Mótarbhealach Motorway (Junction number)
N 11	Bóthar príomha náisiúnta National Primary Road
N 71	Bóthar tánaisteach náisiúnta National Secondary Road
	Carrbhealach dúbailte Dual Carriageway
	Bóthar príomha /tánaisteach náisiúnta beartaithe Proposed Nat. Primary / Secondary Road
R 574	Bóthar Réigiúnach Regional Road
4 metres min / 4 metres max	Bóthar den tríú grád Third Class Road
	Boithre de chineál eile Other Roads
	Bealach Track
	Líne tarchurtha leictreachais Electricity Transmission Line
○	Stáisiún cumhachta (uisce) Power Station (Hydro)
◉	Stáisiún cumhachta (breosla iontaiseach) Power Station (Fossil)

⌇	Crann Mast
▲	Brú de chuid An Óige Youth Hostel (An Óige)
ⓐ	Brú saoire Neamhspleách Independent Holiday Hostel
⛟	Láithreán carbhán (idirthurais) Caravan site (transit)
⛺	Láithreán campála Camping site
⊓	Láithreán picnicí Picnic site
⤋	Ionad dearctha Viewpoint
P	Ionad pairceála Parking
A T	An Taisce National Trust
	Tearmann Dúlra Nature Reserve
⟟	Feirm Ghaoithe Wind Farm

	Foirgnimh le hais a chéile Built up Area
i	Ionad eolais turasóireachta (ar oscailt ar feadh na bliana) Tourist Information centre (regular opening)
i	Ionad eolais turasóireachta (ar oscailt le linn an tséasúir) Tourist Information centre (restricted opening)
★	Garda Síochána Police
PO	Oifig phoist Post office
†	Eaglais no séipéal Church or Chapel
✟	Ardeaglais Cathedral
✈	Aerfort Airport
✦	Aerpháirc Airfield
9 ▸18	Galfchúrsa, machaire gailf Golf Course or Links
— — 🚲	Bealach rothar Cycle route
— — -K̂	Siúlbhealach le comharthaí; Ceann Slí. Waymarked Walks; Trailheads.

	Loch Lake
	Canáil, canáil (thirim) Canal, Canal (dry)
	Abhainn nó sruthán River or Stream
	Líne bharr láin High Water Mark
shingle,mud sand or loose rock	Líne lag trá Low Water Mark
	Trá Beach
Ferry V	Bád fartha (feithiclí) Ferry (Vehicle)
Ferry P	Bád fartha (paisinéirí) Ferry (Passenger)
� X	Teach Solais in úsáid / as úsáid Lighthouse in use / disuse
	Bádóireacht Boating activities
	Iarnróid Railways
	Iarnród tionscalaíoch Industrial Line
	Tollán Tunnel
LC	Crosaire comhréidh Level Crossing
●	Staisiún traenach Railway Station
— —	Teorainn idirnáisiúnta International Boundary
••••••	Teorainn chontae County Boundary
* * *	Páirc Náisiúnta National Park
	Páirc Foraoise Forest Park
	Seilbh de chuid an Aire Chosanta Dept. of Defence Property
	Foraois bhuaircíneach Coniferous Plantation
	Coill nádúrtha Natural Woodland
	Foraois mheasctha Mixed Woodland
·	Séadchomhartha Ainmnithe Named Antiquities
○	Clós, m.sh. Ráth nó Lios Enclosure, e.g. Ringfort
⤬	Láthair Chatha (le dáta) Battlefield (with date)

SUMMIT INFORMATION

		NOTE Over 600m summits must have a prominence of 15m
●	Above 600m	
●	599m - 400m	Between 400m and 599m a prominence of 30m and from 150 to 399m a prominence of 150m
●	Below 400m	

The summit classification is courtesy the Mountain Views hillwalking community.
The lists used, updated to 2009, include:
The "Arderins" 500m list.
The "Vandeleur-Lynam" 600m list,
and other lists for smaller tops and county high points.

⊕ **Mountain Rescue Base**

	Céim imlíne comhairde 10m 10m Contour Interval
	Céim imlíne comhairde 50m 50m Contour Interval
△	Cuaille triantánachta Triangulation Pillar
123 •	Spota airde Spot Height
┼	Trasnú cliathráin Graticule Intersection

IRISH NATIONAL GRID

A	B	C	D	E
F	G	H	J	K
L	M	N	O	P
Q	R	S	T	U
V	W	X	Y	Z

This is a sample reference only

(Discovery Sheet 23)
Sample reference: G 103 079
For local reference grid letter may be omitted.

Irish Transverse Mercator Not used on this extract.
(ITM) is a newly derived GPS compatible mapping projection that is associated with the European Terrestrial Reference System 1989 (ETRS89). For further information on ITM and for coordinate conversion visit our website.

CENTRE OF SHEET ITM CO-ORDINATES:
EXAMPLE: ⊕ 499973E 827008N

Compiled and published by Ordnance Survey Ireland,
Phoenix Park, Dublin 8, Ireland.
Arna thiomsú agus arna fhoilsiú ag Shuirbhéireacht Ordanáis Éireann, Páirc an Fhionnuisce, Baile Átha Cliath 8, Éire.

Unauthorised reproduction infringes Ordnance Survey Ireland and Government of Ireland copyright.
All rights reserved.
No part of this publication may be copied, reproduced or transmitted in any form or by any means without the prior written permission of the copyright owners.

Sáraíonn atáirgeadh neamhúd raithe cóipcheart Shuirbhéireacht Ordanáis Éireann agus Rialtas na hÉireann.
Gach cead ar cosnamh. Ní ceadmhach aon chuid den fhoilseachán seo a chóipeáil, a atáirgeadh nó a tharchur in aon fhoirm ná ar aon bhealach gan cead i scríbhinn roimh ré ó úinéirí an chóipchirt.

SCALE 1:50 000   SCÁLA 1:50 000

WWW.OSI.IE

1 KILOMETRES 0 1 2 3 4 5 6 7 KILOMETRES 8
1 STATUTE MILES 0 1 2 3 4 STATUTE MILES 5

2 ceintiméadar sa chiliméadar (taobh chearnóg eangaí) 2 centimetres to 1 Kilometre (grid square side)

Figure 6.39 Map legend for the 1:50,000 series of OS maps

Street maps

A street map is a large-scale map of a town or city. It shows the name and position of all the streets in the area covered.

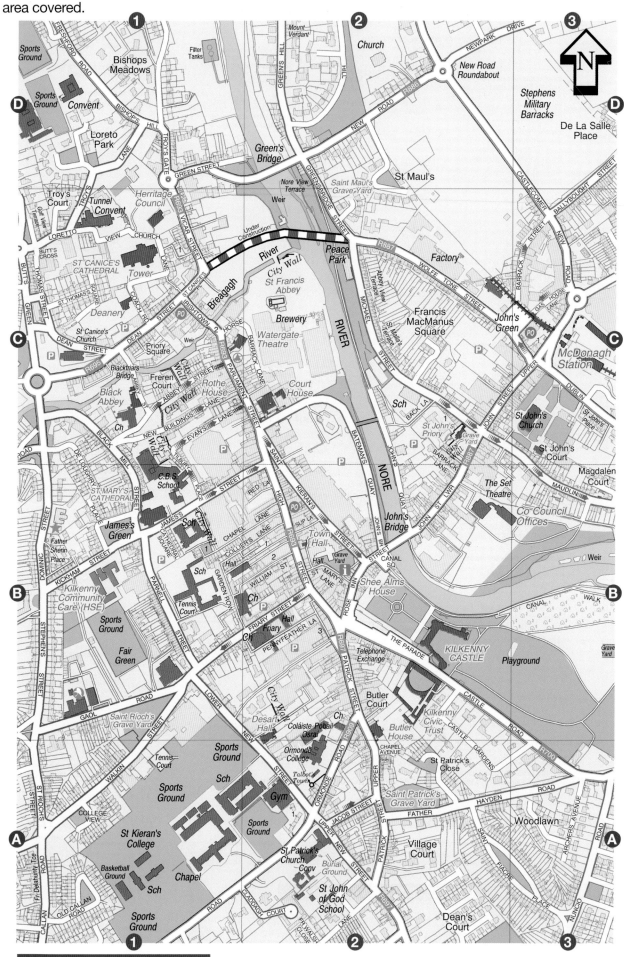

Figure 6.40 Kilkenny street map

Learning Activity

Curiosity Responsibility Communicating

The following questions refer to the Kilkenny street map in figure 6.40.

Write answers to the following in your copy.

6.33 Prepare a sketch map of the area shown on the map. On it show and name:

(a) Two named rivers

(b) Two schools

(c) Two industries

(d) The railway station

(e) The castle

(f) A road under construction.

6.34 Starting at John's Bridge (2B), travel in a south-westerly direction until you reach a junction. Take the road that goes in a south-easterly direction.

(a) State the name of this street.

(b) State one tourist attraction near this street.

(c) Suggest one reason why this is an attractive place to visit.

6.35 Select any three streets on the map and suggest a reason why each one got its name.

6.36 State three pieces of evidence from the map that suggest that Kilkenny is a very old town.

6.37 State what is indicated by the arrows on Friary Street (2B) and Saint Kieran's Street (2B).

6.38 A road and bridge are under construction to link St Canice's Place (1C) with Wolfe Tone Street (2C). Suggest one advantage and one disadvantage of building a large road here.

6.39 Name and locate (by a nearby street name or a map reference) one example of each of the following:

(a) Residential area

(b) Public transport

(c) Recreation

(d) Religion.

6.40 **(a)** Swap your copy with a partner and together check each other's answers to questions 6.33 to 6.39.

(b) If you do not agree with an answer, discuss the question and try to reach agreement.

(c) Join with another pair and share your answers.

(d) Help each other with any questions you are still not sure about.

Historic maps

Between 1829 and 1842 Ordnance Survey Ireland completed the first ever large-scale survey of an entire country. Noted for their accuracy, these maps are regarded by map makers as amongst the finest maps ever produced. They were produced in a variety of scales. The most detailed was at a scale of 25 inches to 1 mile (approx. 1: 2,500).

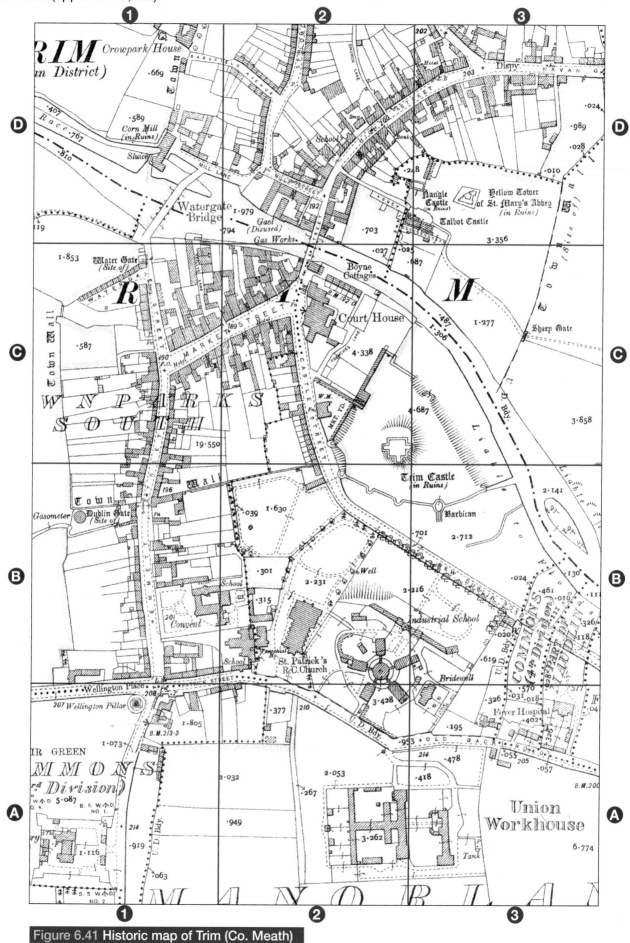

Figure 6.41 **Historic map of Trim (Co. Meath)**

Learning
Activity

Curiosity Responsibility Communicating

The following questions refer to the Trim historic street map in figure 6.41.

Write answers to the following in your copy.

6.41   Prepare a sketch map of the area shown on the map. On it show and name:

   (a)   The river

   (b)   Trim Castle

   (c)   The castle walls

   (d)   A barbican

   (e)   A section of the town wall.

6.42   Suggest two reasons why the castle was built at this location.

6.43   Using evidence from the map, suggest why each of the following streets received its name:

   (a)   Water Gate (site of) (1C)

   (b)   Mill Lane (1D, 2D)

   (c)   Castle Street (2B, 2C)

   (d)   Market Street (1C, 2C).

6.44   Assess why much of the land near the river was not built on in the past.

6.45   Assess the map for evidence to confirm that these functions were available in Trim in the past. Use a grid reference to locate each piece of evidence.

   (a)   Religious

   (b)   Legal

   (c)   Medical

   (d)   Trade

   (e)   Industry

   (f)   Defence.

6.46   **(a)**   Swap your copy with a partner and together check each other's answers to questions 6.41 to 6.45.

   (b)   If you do not agree with an answer, discuss the question and try to reach agreement.

   (c)   Join with another pair and share your answers.

   (d)   Help each other with any questions you are still not sure about.

Satellite images

Satellite images are photographs that are taken from space by cameras in a network of satellites that continually orbit Earth.

Satellite images have many uses, including:

- Finding out how a natural disaster has affected an area
- Showing change over time (e.g. deforestation, ice melt, urban growth)
- Helping to forecast and track weather conditions.

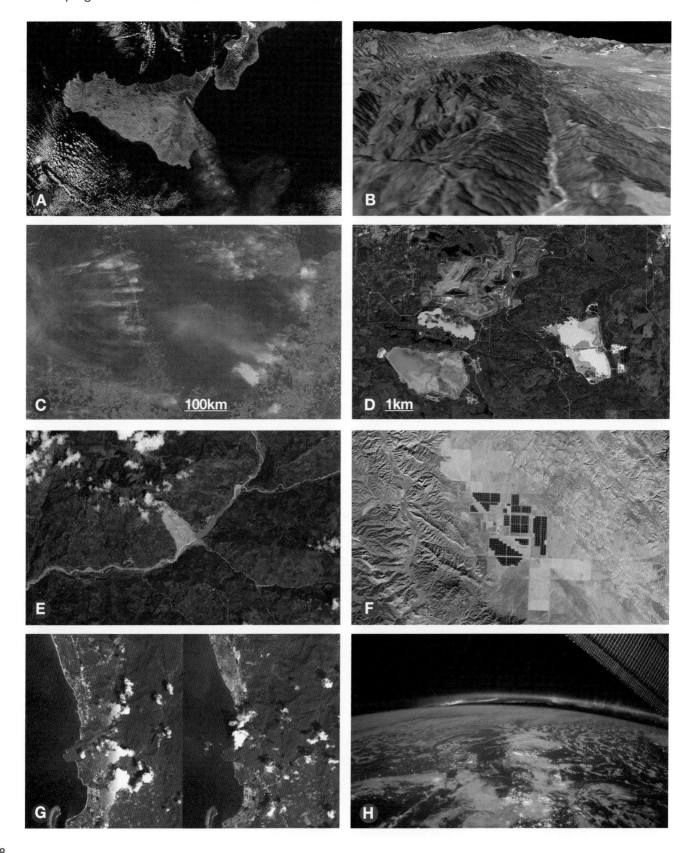

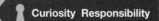

Learning Activity

Curiosity Responsibility

6.47 The following captions are for the satellite images on the previous page.

   (a) Match each caption to one of the images labelled A–H.

      (i)   Large-scale opencast mine and waste ponds

      (ii)   Ireland and Britain at night

      (iii) Landslides following an earthquake in Nepal

      (iv) San Andreas Fault in California

      (v)   Forest fires in the Amazon

      (vi) Lava flow and plume of smoke and ash from an eruption of Mount Etna

      (vii) Solar energy farm in a Californian desert

      (viii) Tsunami – before and after

   (b) Check your captions with your partner's and share with the rest of the class.

6.48 In pairs, examine the satellite image of Ireland and Britain at night.

   (a) With the aid of an atlas, identify any four urban centres in the image.

   (b) The green band in the background is the Aurora Borealis. Explain what this is; research as necessary.

Reflecting on my learning

Reflecting Communicating Literacy

Write sentences using each of the following terms from this chapter. You may use more than one of the terms in your sentence if appropriate.

aerial photograph	foreground	satellite image
area	gradient	scale
background	grid reference	sketch map
cardinal points	historic map	spot height
compass points	legend	straight-line distance
contours	map	street plan
co-ordinates	middle ground	triangulation pillar
cross-section	National Grid	vertical aerial photograph
curved-line distance	oblique aerial photograph	
Discovery Series	Ordnance Survey	

 PowerPoint summary

An introduction to denudation

7

Learning intentions

When you have completed this chapter you will be able to:

● Outline the process of denudation.

1.10 Investigate a range of physical processes active in a chosen location and the connection between them

Key terms

denudation   mass movement   regolith

weathering   erosion

What is denudation?

Denudation is the process of breaking up and removing the rocks on the surface of Earth. The three main processes of denudation are **weathering**, **mass movement** and **erosion**.

Weathering

Weathering is the **breakdown and decay** of rocks that are exposed to the weather. There are two types of weathering:

- Mechanical weathering
- Chemical weathering.

Mass movement

Mass movement is the **movement of loose material** (called **regolith**) down a slope under the influence of gravity. It occurs at different speeds:

- Slow (soil creep)
- Fast (landslide, rockfall, bogburst, mudflow).

Erosion

Erosion is the **wearing away** of rocks and the **removal** of the materials that result. The main agents (causes) of erosion are:

- Moving water
- Moving ice
- Moving air.

Figure 7.1 **Denudation**

PowerPoint summary

DEFINITION

Regolith
The loose layer of rock and soil on the surface of Earth.

Learning Activity

Curiosity Communicating

7.1 Erosion is caused by the movement of something. Consider what each of the following could be and compare your ideas with your partner's. Then share with the rest of the class.

(a) Moving water   **(b)** Moving ice   **(c)** Moving air

Weathering

8

 Go to **www.edco.ie/geographynow** and
try the interactive activities and quizzes.

Learning intentions

When you have completed this chapter you will be able to:

- Explain what is meant by weathering
- Distinguish between mechanical weathering and chemical weathering
- Identify where freeze-thaw action has taken place
- Describe how carbonation takes place to decay rocks
- Identify a karst landscape and its landforms
- Examine tourism in an environmentally sensitive landscape.

Key terms

weathering   carbonation   grike

erosion   joint   swallow hole

mechanical weathering   bedding plane   cave

freeze-thaw   karst   stalactite

frost action   Burren   stalagmite

scree   limestone pavement   pillar

chemical weathering   clint   responsible tourism

Mechanical weathering

Mechanical weathering (also called physical weathering) is the breaking down of rocks into smaller pieces. The pieces are not removed and remain in place. The most common type of mechanical weathering is freeze-thaw.

Freeze-thaw

Freeze-thaw is the break-up of rock by **frost action**. It occurs where:

- There is **precipitation** (rainfall) and

- The **temperature** rises above and falls below freezing point (0°C).

These conditions occur in Ireland during winter months, especially in upland areas. They also occur in snow-covered mountain ranges such as the Alps.

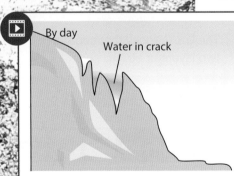
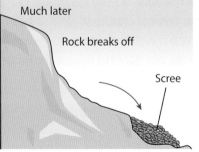

Figure 8.1 **Freeze-thaw action**

By day

During the day, water seeps into joints (cracks) in the rock.

By night

The temperature drops below freezing point (0°C). The water freezes and expands. This makes the crack bigger and puts strain on the rock.

Over time

After repeated freezing and thawing of water, over many years, the rock splits. Sharp jagged pieces, called **scree**, break off. They roll down the mountainside and collect in piles at the bottom of the slope.

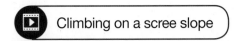 Climbing on a scree slope

Learning Activity

 Curiosity Co-operating

In pairs, one of you think about questions 8.1 and 8.3, and the other think about questions 8.2 and 8.4. The person who has question 8.1 tells the other person what they think is the answer. Does your partner agree or disagree? Discuss the questions with another pair of students if you are unsure of your answers. Reach agreement on the answer before moving on to the next question.

8.1 Consider why freeze-thaw does not occur when the temperature remains above freezing point (0°C). Explain the reason.

8.2 Is freeze-thaw more likely to happen in the lowlands of the Midlands, or in upland areas of the Wicklow mountains? Justify your answer.

8.3 Where in a town or city might you see the results of freeze-thaw action?

8.4 Trees can cause mechanical weathering. Suggest how this would happen.

Chemical weathering

Chemical weathering occurs when rocks decay or are dissolved by chemicals. The most common type of chemical weathering is **carbonation**.

Carbonation

The process of **carbonation** is as follows.

 Link Science: Chemical World

- When rain falls it takes in **carbon dioxide** as it passes through the air.

- The carbon dioxide mixes with the rainwater, turning it into a weak **carbonic acid**.

- Limestone contains **calcium carbonate**. The weak acid rain reacts with the calcium carbonate and slowly dissolves it.

- It then **washes it away** in solution.

The make-up of the limestone makes all this easier. It is **permeable**, so the rainwater can easily pass through it. It also has vertical cracks (called **joints**) and horizontal **bedding planes**, which make it easier for the water to pass through. (This is shown on figures 8.2 and 8.3 on the opposite page.)

> **DEFINITION**
>
> **Bedding plane**
> The line in rocks that separates two layers or strata.

Learning Activity

 Curiosity Responsibility Reflecting

8.5 What **type** of rock is limestone? Make a note of this in your copy.

8.6 All liquids and gases have a short-hand way of writing their names; this is called a **chemical formula**. You will learn about these in your science course. Look up the chemical formulas for the following and write them in your copy:

(a) Oxygen   (b) Water   (c) Carbon   (d) Carbon dioxide.

Karst landscapes

The effects of carbonation are best seen in a limestone landscape, especially one where the soil cover has been removed and the rock is exposed to the weather. These areas are better known as **karst landscapes**, called after the limestone region of Slovenia.

Ireland's best-known karst region is the Burren in Co. Clare.

The Burren landscape

The Burren is a karst landscape of world importance. Its name comes from the Irish word for **rocky place**.

Most of the soil cover of the Burren was removed by erosion, leaving the limestone exposed. Weathering by **carbonation** has created a remarkable landscape, both on the surface and under the ground.

Figure 8.2 Rocks showing strata (layers), bedding planes and joints (cracks)

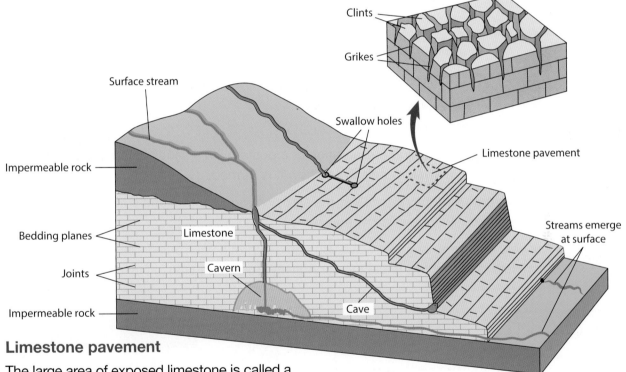

Figure 8.3 The surface features of a karst region include a limestone pavement, clints, grikes and swallow holes

Limestone pavement

The large area of exposed limestone is called a **limestone pavement**. It generally takes the form of almost flat terraces, but may also have steep cliff edges.

As the rainfall seeps through the rock, it picks out the weakest points and weathers them by **carbonation**.

The joints or cracks in the limestone are widened and deepened to form deep gashes called **grikes**.

The blocks of limestone that remain are called **clints**.

Swallow hole

When a river flows onto a bare limestone surface, the water begins to dissolve the limestone by carbonation.

The water widens the joints and bedding planes, opening them up.

The river disappears from the surface and begins to flow underground.

The passage through which the river disappears is called a **swallow hole**.

Figure 8.4 Clints and grikes on a limestone pavement in the Burren

Learning Activity

Reflecting Creativity

8.7 Work with a partner for this question.

(a) Individually, create a slide presentation or a poster with a series of labelled drawings to explain what a swallow hole is and how it is formed.

(b) Ask your partner if they can follow the steps of your diagram and if they feel better informed about what a swallow hole is.

(c) Ask your partner to suggest ways you could improve your presentation or poster. Complete the feedback sheet in your Activity Book (page 49).

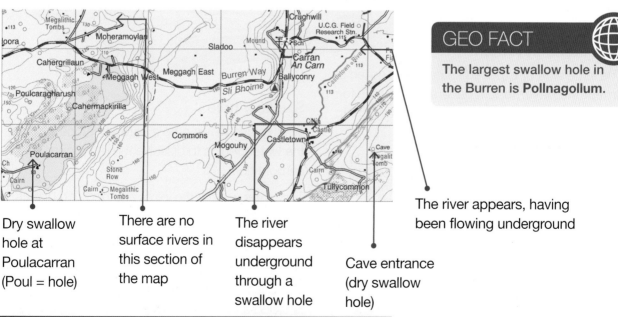

GEO FACT

The largest swallow hole in the Burren is **Pollnagollum**.

Dry swallow hole at Poulacarran (Poul = hole)

There are no surface rivers in this section of the map

The river disappears underground through a swallow hole

Cave entrance (dry swallow hole)

The river appears, having been flowing underground

Figure 8.5 Identifying surface features of a karst region on an Ordnance Survey map

1 As the river flows underground, the carbonic acid in the water dissolves the limestone to cut out a long passage called a **cave**.

2 Sometimes the cave gets big enough to form a large chamber called a **cavern**.

3 When water containing dissolved limestone seeps through the limestone to the cave or cavern, some drops hang from the roof for a while.

Some of the water evaporates, leaving behind tiny deposits of **calcite** (calcium carbonate) attached to the roof. These deposits build up slowly over thousands of years and hang from the roof in icicle-like shapes called **stalactites**.

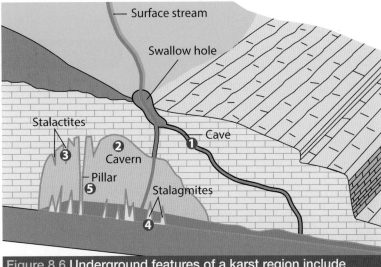

Figure 8.6 Underground features of a karst region include caves, caverns, stalactites, stalagmites and pillars

4 When a drop of water falls to the floor of the cave, it leaves behind a tiny amount of calcite. These deposits build up over time to form cone-shaped features called **stalagmites**.

5 As the stalactites and stalagmites continue to grow, they may join up to form **pillars**.

Remember

Stala**c**tites: **c** for ceiling.

Stala**g**mites: **g** for ground.

Learning Activity

Curiosity

8.8 Examine the photo at figure 8.7. Identify the features labelled A, B and C and note them in your copy, together with a sketch for each feature.

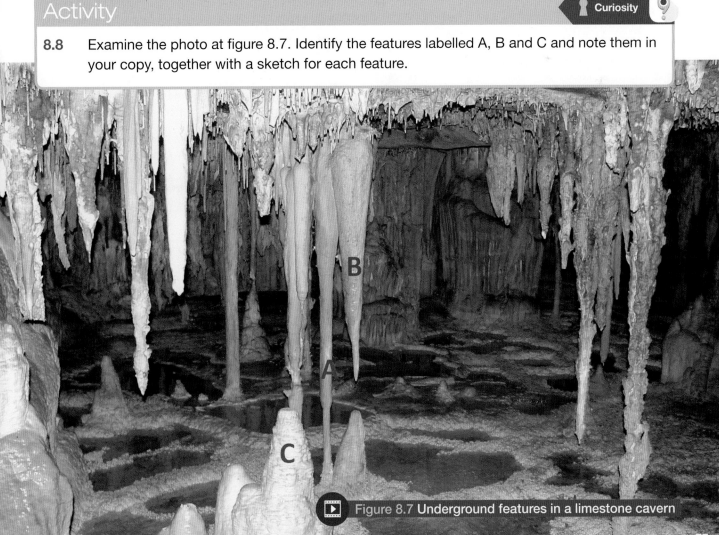

Figure 8.7 Underground features in a limestone cavern

Interrelationships between the physical world and tourism

Link Chapter 38: pages 362–73

Places that are interesting in terms of geology and heritage result in tourism. People naturally want to see these interesting sites and businesses grow up around them. But in order to protect the sites for future generations, we have to manage them very carefully. This requires a balance between preservation, business and visitors.

DEFINITION

UNESCO

United Nations Educational, Scientific and Cultural Organization

Geopark

A site of geological importance. Its tourism industry is carefully managed.

The Burren

The Burren in Co. Clare, largely because of its karst landscape, is one of Ireland's most important tourist destinations. Along with the nearby Cliffs of Moher, the Burren was declared a **UNESCO Global Geopark** in 2011. Part of the Burren, centred on Mullaghmore, had already been declared a **National Park** in 1991.

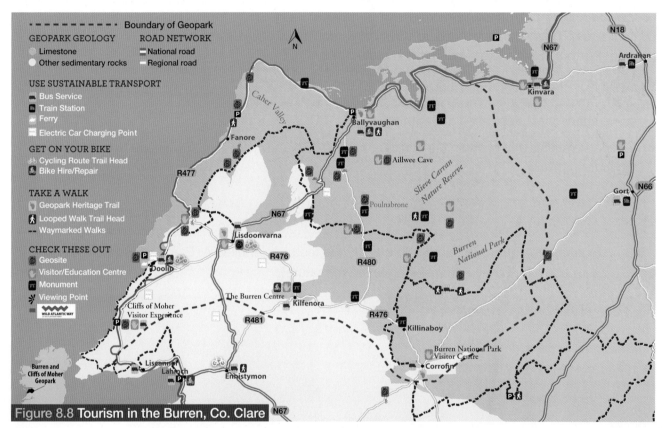

Figure 8.8 **Tourism in the Burren, Co. Clare**

The Burren has a wide range of attractions for tourists, including:

Landscape The Burren has a wide variety of scenery to attract tourists, cavers, walkers and rock climbers. These include the karst landscape, Aillwee Cave, the Cliffs of Moher and the Burren Way. The Burren coastline is on the **Wild Atlantic Way**.

History The Burren has a wide variety of monuments and archaeological sites. They include high crosses, dolmens, ring forts and churches. They provide evidence that the Burren has had a long history of settlement.

Figure 8.9 **Poulnabrone dolmen is one of the many historical monuments in the Burren**

Figure 8.10 The Burren is the only place in Ireland or Britain where the green moth is found

Figure 8.11 Flowers growing in a grike on the limestone pavement

Flora The flora (plant life) of the Burren is remarkable because it has plants that are normally found in widely separate parts of Europe. Alpine, Mediterranean and native plants grow side by side. Orchids, ferns and avens are among the rare plants found there.

Fauna The fauna (wildlife) is also varied. It includes animals such as the pine marten and wild goat. Insects include many butterflies and the green moth, which is not found anywhere else in Ireland or in Britain.

Responsible tourism in the Burren

Tourism makes a valuable contribution to the economy of the Burren. This tourist activity can also pose a threat to the fragile environment. Because of this, the growth of tourism in the Burren must be carefully managed.

This can be achieved by **responsible tourism**. This involves paying attention to environmental, economic and social issues that matter to the people of the area. This makes better places for people to live in as well as better places for people to visit. If tourism makes only a positive impact on an area, it will be **sustainable** in the long term.

Learning
Activity

Co-operating Communicating Literacy Creativity

8.9 Consider the benefits and problems that tourism can bring to the Burren and its surrounding area, or to a rural tourist area with which you are familiar. With your partner, construct two spider diagrams:

(a) One to show the benefits that tourism brings to the area

(b) One to show the disadvantages that tourism has on the area.

Compare these with the diagrams the other groups in the class have drawn. Add to your diagrams if other people have thought of things you haven't.

Learning
Activity

Communicating Co-operating

8.10 One of the ways that people enjoy the Burren is to travel by coach. Very often, this is by day trip from cities such as Dublin or Cork.

    (a) Consider, on your own, the impact this has on:

        (i) The tourists

        (ii) The Burren environment

        (iii) Burren businesses

        (iv) People who live and work in the area.

    (b) With your partner, analyse the impacts of this type of travel by drawing up a table of advantages and disadvantages for each group.

    (c) Each pair then gives one point to the rest of the class, going round the class until there are no more comments. Add any points you have missed to your table.

    (d) There may be some points that some people think are an advantage and others will think are a disadvantage. Discuss with the rest of the class why a particular point could be an advantage or a disadvantage, and vote on which side of the table it should appear.

Marble Arch

The Marble Arch Global Geopark is the world's first UNESCO Global Geopark that crosses an international border. It takes in a large area of mountainous uplands (Cuilcagh Mountains) and gently sloping lowlands in counties Fermanagh and Cavan.

The highlights of the park include:

- Marble Arch caves – tour and boat trip
- Cuilcagh Mountains – boardwalk to summit (666 m)
- Shannon Pot – source of the River Shannon
- Castle Archdale Forest Park.

Figure 8.12 One of the unusual aspects of the cave system is a boat trip on an underground river

Figure 8.13 The entrance to the caves at the geopark

Learning
Activity

 Curiosity Responsibility Creativity

8.11 **(a)** On the geological map in your Activity Book (page 27), mark the Marble Arch Global Geopark. Use an atlas or other reference to help you find it.

(b) **(i)** Find and open the Marble Arch Geopark website.

(ii) Investigate the attractions listed above.

(iii) Create a poster or flier to point out the benefits of a Junior Cycle student visiting the geopark as part of their geography studies.

Learning
Activity

Responsibility Curiosity Creativity Reflecting

8.12 Research the seven principles of **Leave no trace**.

(a) Create a poster informing people of what this initiative is and what the seven principles are. Put all the posters around the room.

(b) Pick one poster that someone else has created that you particularly like, and make notes in your Activity Book (page 49) on what it is about the poster that you like and how you can incorporate these features into your own work.

Reflecting on my learning

Reflecting Communicating Literacy

Write sentences using each of the following terms from this chapter. You may use more than one of the terms in your sentence if appropriate.

bedding plane	freeze-thaw	pillar
Burren	frost action	responsible tourism
carbonation	grike	scree
cave	joint	stalactite
chemical weathering	karst	stalagmite
clint	limestone pavement	swallow hole
erosion	mechanical weathering	weathering

PowerPoint summary

 Revision
Go to **www.edco.ie/geographynow** and try the interactive activities and quizzes.

9

Go to **www.edco.ie/geographynow** and try the interactive activities and quizzes.

Learning intentions

When you have completed this chapter you will be able to:

- Explain what is meant by mass movement
- Outline the factors that influence mass movement
- Classify the types of mass movement
- Identify the effects of soil creep
- Consider the effects on people of landslides and mudflows
- Assess how human activities affect mass movement.

1.3 Analyse the processes and effects of weathering and **mass movement** on our landscape

1.10 Investigate a range of physical processes active in a chosen location and the connection between them

Key terms

mass movement

gravity

gradient

soil creep

terracettes

landslide

mudflow

bogburst

lahar

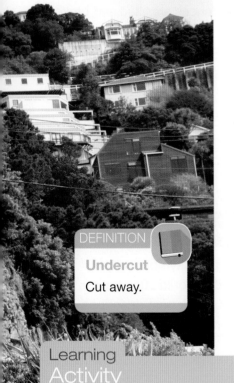

DEFINITION
Undercut
Cut away.

Mass movement

Mass movement refers to the movement of loose material, called **regolith**, downslope under the influence of **gravity**. This loose material includes loose rock produced by weathering, as well as soil and mud.

Factors that influence mass movement

Gradient Gradient is a measure of the **steepness** of a slope. Mass movement is most likely when the gradient is steep. It is also **fastest**. On more gentle slopes, soil and rock will move very slowly.

Water After heavy rainfall, water makes the regolith **heavier** and also acts as a **lubricant**. This makes the material more likely to move downhill.

Vegetation The **roots** of trees and plants bind the soil together. This prevents or slows down mass movement.

Human activity People can cause mass movement by interfering with slopes. This may occur when the base of a slope is **undercut** during road building. The steeper slope means that material is more likely to collapse.

Learning Activity

Curiosity Communicating Co-operating

9.1 Consider other ways that human activity can contribute towards mass movement. (Hint: these might include deforestation, traffic vibrations and quarry blasting.) Select one and discuss this with your partner and then share your thoughts with the rest of the class.

Types of mass movement

Mass movements are grouped according to the **speed** at which they occur and the **moisture** they contain. They may be **fast** or **slow**; they may be **wet** or **dry**. The movements are summarised in table 9.1.

Table 9.1 Types of mass movement

Speed	Moisture	Type of mass movement
Slow	Dry	Soil creep
Fast	Dry	Landslides
Fast	Wet	Mudflows

Soil creep

Soil creep is the slow movement of soil down a slope under the influence of gravity.

Creep is the **slowest** type of mass movement. The soil sometimes moves less than 1 cm a year. It is so slow that you can't see it happening. However, you can see its **effects on the landscape**, as shown in figure 9.1.

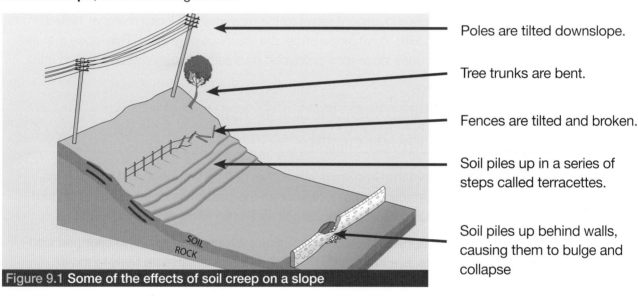

Poles are tilted downslope.

Tree trunks are bent.

Fences are tilted and broken.

Soil piles up in a series of steps called terracettes.

Soil piles up behind walls, causing them to bulge and collapse

Figure 9.1 Some of the effects of soil creep on a slope

Learning Activity

Communicating Co-operating

9.2 Look at figure 9.1. Think about why soil creep occurs slowly. On a sticky note, write a label that could be added to figure 9.1 to explain this. Everybody should stick their label to the wall. Read all the labels and put a tick on the one you think best describes soil creep. Write in your copy the label that has the most ticks, or write on a new sticky note and attach it to figure 9.1 in your textbook.

Landslides

A **landslide** takes place when large amounts of loose rocks and soil **suddenly** slide down a steep slope. They occur when slopes become unstable, and are most common in **upland** and **coastal** areas.

 Small landslide

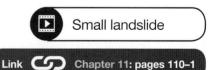 Link Chapter 11: pages 110–1

Most landslides occur when slopes are **undercut**, either by sea erosion or human activities such as quarrying and road building.

Figure 9.2 **A landslide in Sierra Leone, August 2017**

They also occur after heavy rainfall because the water loosens the grip that the **regolith** has on the rock beneath it. When the ground eventually gives way, the loose, wet soil moves downslope. It can travel rapidly and is capable of causing intense damage.

GEO FACT

Shock waves and vibrations from earthquakes and volcanic eruptions can trigger landslides.

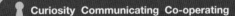

Learning
Activity

Curiosity Communicating Co-operating

9.3   Experts forecast that climate change will mean bigger storms and more rain in the future. Do you predict climate change will result in more or fewer landslides, or will there be about the same number as now?

(a) Note your reasoning for your answer in your copy and share what you have written with your partner.

(b) Discuss your thoughts with the rest of the class. Write in your copy good points that others make that you had not thought of. Has anyone's thoughts caused you to change your prediction?

 Small mudflow

Mudflows

Mudflows are flows of water that can contain rock, earth, silt, peat and other materials. They are the fastest forms of mass movement. The material can travel several kilometres from its starting point. The two main types of mudflow are:

- Bogburst
- Lahar.

Bogburst

A **bogburst** occurs in upland areas when **peat** (turf) becomes saturated with water **after heavy rainfall**. The peat loses its grip on the bedrock and begins to slide down the slope. The bogburst gains speed, forming a **slurry** that is strong enough to destroy everything in its path. Buildings and roads are damaged. Wildlife habitats are destroyed and rivers may be polluted.

Bogburst in the Slieve Aughty Mountains (Co. Galway) 2003

A construction company was engaged in preparing the ground for a large wind farm. It removed the coniferous trees on the site. In order to expose the bedrock, it also moved large areas of peat, and piled it into huge mounds.

A long spell of dry weather in summer was followed by heavy downpours in late autumn.

The peat became saturated, lost its grip on the bedrock and slid down the slope, following the course of a small stream. It caused a major fish kill, blocked roads and contaminated water supplies.

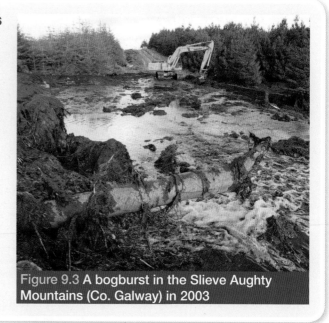

Figure 9.3 A bogburst in the Slieve Aughty Mountains (Co. Galway) in 2003

Learning Activity

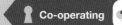 Co-operating

9.4 Does our description of the Slieve Aughty Mountain bogburst suggest to you that the greatest factor in the bogburst was nature, human activity or a combination of both? Discuss the options with the rest of the class and take a raised-hand vote on the views of everyone.

Lahar

A **lahar** is a type of mudflow that results after a **volcano erupts** in a **snow-capped mountain** region.

A sudden thaw of mountain snow due to a volcanic eruption can send a torrent of **mud, ash and hot water** down the slope of the volcano. As the water picks up more mud and rocks, it begins to look like a fast-flowing river of concrete.

 Lahar: the volcano of Nevado del Ruiz

The volcano of Nevado del Ruiz, a snow-capped mountain high in the Andes, erupted in 1985. The mountain was cloud-covered at the time, so the eruption went unnoticed.

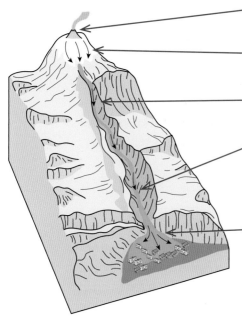

- The volcano of Nevado del Ruiz erupted, throwing out huge amounts of ash and steam.
- The heat from the eruption melted the snow on the volcano.
- The meltwater rushed down the mountainside, picking up ash, soil and rocks on its way.
- Water + ash or soil = mudflow. The mud was up to 20 metres deep in places. It raced through the valley at speeds of up to 80 km per hour. Heavy rains also increased the size of the mudflow.
- The town of Armero was built on the plain at the foot of the mountain. It lay directly in the path of the mudflow, which struck just before midnight.

Figure 9.4 From eruption to lahar to destruction

Impact of the mudflow

It was the world's most deadly mudflow in the twentieth century. More than 21,000 people were killed. The death toll was so high because it occurred when people were asleep.

More than 5,000 homes were destroyed and a further 6,000 people were made homeless.

The cost of the disaster was $1 billion – a huge amount for a country that was not wealthy.

Figure 9.5 The town of Armero in the foothills of the Andes after it was destroyed by a lahar

---

Learning Activity

 Curiosity Communicating

9.5 The Geological Survey of Ireland (GSI) keeps a database of all landslides, mudflows and bogbursts in Ireland.

Consider how this information could be used and discuss your ideas with your partner. Agree on three ways in which this data might be useful.

Share your thoughts with the rest of the class.

Reflecting on my learning

 Reflecting Communicating Literacy

Write sentences using each of the following terms from this chapter. You may use more than one of the terms in your sentence if appropriate.

bogburst	lahar	mudflow
gradient	landslide	soil creep
gravity	mass movement	terracettes

 PowerPoint summary

 Revision
Go to **www.edco.ie/geographynow** and try the interactive activities and quizzes.

Agents of erosion – rivers

10

Go to **www.edco.ie/geographynow** and try the interactive activities and quizzes.

Learning intentions

When you have completed this chapter you will be able to:

- Outline how rivers shape the land
- Describe the features of rivers
- Distinguish between the three stages of a river: youthful, mature, old
- Define how river landforms are created
- Identify river landforms on an Ordnance Survey map
- Locate Ireland's main rivers on a map of Ireland
- Explain how people interact with rivers, particularly in relation to hydroelectric power
- Offer reasons for why the river Shannon is prone to flooding in certain areas
- Assess the exploitation of water, with particular reference to the Shannon–to–Dublin pipeline.

1.5 Explain how the processes of erosion, transportation and deposition shape our **fluvial**, marine and glacial landscapes

You are also working towards:

1.10 Investigate a range of physical processes active in a chosen location and the connections between them

2.4 Assess the exploitation of water, fish stocks, forestry and soil as natural resources

2.7 Investigate examples of how people interact with and manage surface processes

Key terms

drain

landform

channel

bed

bank

youthful stage

mature stage

old stage

erosion

transportation

deposition

hydraulic action

abrasion

attrition

load

V-shaped valley

interlocking spurs

waterfall

plunge pool

gorge

meander

floodplain

alluvium

oxbow lake

levee

delta

distributary

dam

flooding

hydroelectric power (HEP)

surface water

groundwater

Rivers: shapers of our land

Rivers **drain** rainwater from land and lakes and carry it to the sea. In doing so, they shape the landscape, creating **landforms** (or features) along the way.

Rivers flow in **channels**. The bottom of the channel is called the **bed** and the sides of the channel are called the **banks**.

Some features are common to most rivers. These are shown in table 10.1.

Table 10.1 Features of a river	
Feature	**Definition**
Source	The point where a river begins
Course	The route taken by a river as it flows into the sea
Tributary	A small river or stream that joins a larger one
Confluence	The place where two rivers meet
Mouth	The place where a river enters the sea
Estuary	The part of a river mouth that is tidal
Drainage basin	The area of land that is drained by a river and its tributaries
Watershed	The boundary between two drainage basins, often marked by hills or mountains

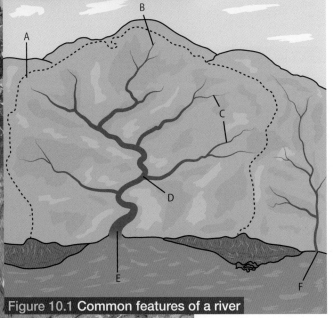

Figure 10.1 **Common features of a river**

Learning
Activity

Reflecting Curiosity Co-operating

10.1 Examine figure 10.1 on the previous page. On your own, match features A–F with the features explained in table 10.1. Check your answers with your partner. Check that everyone in the class agrees.

The three stages of a river

A river is often divided into three parts or **stages** as it flows from its source to its mouth. These are the **youthful** (or upper) stage, the **mature** (or middle) stage and the **old** (or lower) stage. Each stage has different features, as shown in table 10.2.

Table 10.2 The stages of a river	Youthful stage	Mature stage	Old stage
The river	■ Is small ■ Has a steep gradient	■ Is bigger ■ Has a gentler gradient	■ Is much bigger ■ Has an almost flat gradient
The valley has	■ Steep sides ■ A narrow floor	■ Gently sloping sides ■ A wider floor	■ Very gently sloping sides ■ A wide flat floor

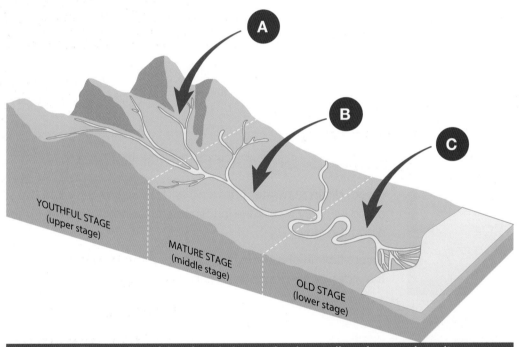

Figure 10.2 The gradient (slope) and shape of a river valley change along its course

Learning
Activity

Curiosity

10.2 State which of these pictures belong at each of the labels A–C on figure 10.2.

(i)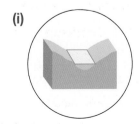

(ii)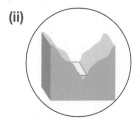

(iii)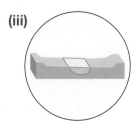

10.3   State at which stage of the river it is likely to flow:

(a) Fastest

(b) Slowest.

Justify each of your answers to your partner and then share with the rest of the class.

The work of rivers

As a river follows its course, it changes the landscape by the following processes:

- **Erosion** (wearing material away from the surface)

- **Transportation** (removing the material that it has eroded)

- **Deposition** (dropping the material it was transporting).

Erosion

The river **erodes** its bed and banks when:

- The force of the moving water breaks off material from the banks and bed of the river (**hydraulic action**).

- The material carried along by the river hits its banks and bed, wearing them away (**abrasion**).

- The material is worn down, smoothed and rounded as the stones bounce off each other (**attrition**).

- Acids in the water dissolve some rocks such as limestone (**solution**).

These methods are shown in figure 10.3.

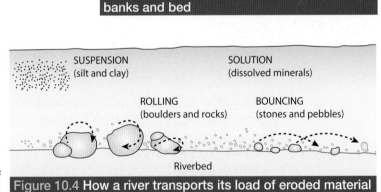

Figure 10.3 How a river erodes material in its banks and bed

Transportation

A river **transports** its **load** downstream in a number of ways:

- The largest load – boulders and rocks – is **rolled** along the bed of the river.

- The smaller particles – stones and pebbles – are **bounced** along the bed of the river.

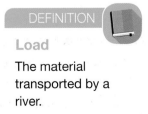

Figure 10.4 How a river transports its load of eroded material

- The lightest particles – silt and clay – are carried along, **suspended** in the water.

- Dissolved materials are carried in **solution**.

Deposition

The river drops or **deposits** its load when:

- It **loses speed** and has less energy

- Its **volume decreases**

- It enters a **flat** or gently sloping plain

- It **flows** into a lake or sea.

DEFINITION 📖

Load

The material transported by a river.

Learning
Activity

Curiosity Communicating

10.4 State at which stage of the river each of the following occurs.

(a) Most erosion

(b) Most deposition.

Justify your answers to your partner and then share with the rest of the class.

Learning
Activity

Literacy Communicating Co-operating

10.5 In small groups (ideally three people), create and play the following game. The pieces of paper should be playing-card sized; you will need twenty-seven pieces of paper (the cards). The aim of the game is to match words with their definitions and the type of process it describes, e.g. Transportation : Solution : Carrying dissolved materials.

(a) Create the game

(i) Each person takes three blank cards and writes on them one each of the following words: Erosion, Transport, Deposition.

(ii) On nine cards, one person writes one each of the following phrases: Hydraulic action, Abrasion, Attrition, Solution (dissolved), Rolled, Bounced, Suspended, Solution (carried), Deposits (drops) its load.

(iii) Turn the nine cards from part (ii) face down, and deal them among your group. On separate pieces paper write a definition of the words (in your own words) that you have been dealt. Don't show the others.

(iv) Mix up all twenty-seven cards and make a stack of them, face down.

(b) Play the game

(i) The first person takes the top card and lays it face up on the table where everyone can see it.

(ii) The second person takes the top card and, if it relates to the card already face up, places it face up alongside; if it doesn't relate, place it on the table face up below the card already there.

(iii) Continue going round the table in this way. When one person completes a line with their card, they gather their row and place it in front of them.

(iv) The winner is the person with the most stacks in front of them at the end of the game.

River landforms

Table 10.3 Landforms of a youthful river

The **youthful (or young) river** has a small volume of water and flows down a steep gradient. It may turn into a raging torrent after heavy rainfall. It uses most of its energy to **erode** the landscape. As a result, a number of features (or **landforms**) are created.

Landform	V-shaped valley	Interlocking spurs	Waterfall
Description	**Narrow floor** and **steep sides** (see figures 10.6 and 10.7)	A **series of ridges** that **jut** out from both sides of a young river valley and **lock into** one another like the teeth of a zip (see figures 10.6 and 10.7)	The river flows or **falls over a vertical slope** (see figure 10.8)
Formation	■ The river **carries** stones and rocks in its water ■ The force of the water and the grinding of rocks and stones cut down into the riverbed, and deepen it by **vertical erosion** ■ Meanwhile, **weathering** breaks up rock and soil on the valley sides. They eventually collapse and the material slides into the river ■ The material is eventually worn down and **transported** by the river	■ When the river meets **hard or resistant rocks**, it is unable to erode through them ■ Instead, it **winds** and bends to avoid them ■ At the same time, the river continues to erode **downwards** ■ In this way, the river develops a **zigzag** course	See figure 10.9. ■ Forms where a band of **hard** (or resistant) rock lies on top of a band of **softer** rock ■ Over thousands of years, the softer rock is **eroded** more quickly than the hard rock ■ Over time, the slope becomes **steeper** and a waterfall is formed ■ As the water drops over the waterfall, it carries its load with it. This helps the waterfall to erode a deep hole called a **plunge pool** ■ The falling water cuts under the waterfall to form an **overhang** of hard rock. This eventually collapses ■ The process repeats itself so that the waterfall **retreats upstream** to form a **gorge**
Examples	Youthful stage of the rivers: ■ Moy ■ Lee ■ Liffey ■ Slaney	Youthful stage of the rivers: ■ Moy ■ Lee ■ Liffey ■ Slaney	■ Aasleagh Falls (Co. Mayo) ■ Torc Waterfall (Co. Kerry) ■ Glencar Falls (Co. Sligo)

Learning
Activity

 **Curiosity Reflecting**

10.6 Answer this in your copy.

(a) Reproduce figure 10.5, and add the following labels in the correct places against numbers 1–5 on the diagram:

(i) The weathered and eroded material is removed by the river

(ii) The river is cutting downwards by vertical erosion

(iii) The riverbed is worn away by the force of the water and its load of rocks and stones

(iv) Weathering breaks up and loosens rock and soil

(v) The weathered material moves downslope by mass movement

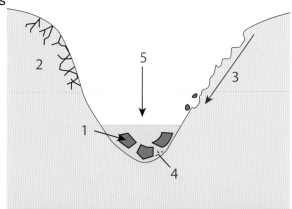
Figure 10.5 How a V-shaped valley is formed

(b) Under your diagram, write a definition of mass movement.

Link **Chapter 9**

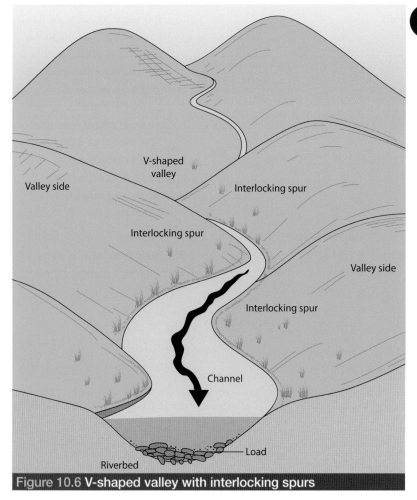
Figure 10.6 V-shaped valley with interlocking spurs

Figure 10.7 A V-shaped valley with interlocking spurs

Figure 10.8 Waterfall and gorge at Niagara Falls. The tourist boat is called The Lady of the Mist; can you suggest why?

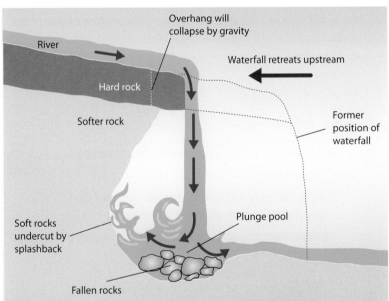

River

Overhang will collapse by gravity

Waterfall retreats upstream

Hard rock

Softer rock

Former position of waterfall

Soft rocks undercut by splashback

Plunge pool

Fallen rocks

Figure 10.9 **How a waterfall is formed**

GEO FACT

Niagara Falls is one of the world's most famous waterfalls. It is only about 50 metres high but is over 1 km wide. It retreats upstream by about 1 metre a year.

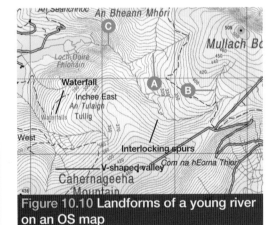

Figure 10.10 **Landforms of a young river on an OS map**

 Waterfall and gorge at Iguazu Falls on the Brazil-Argentina border

Learning Activity

Curiosity Communicating

10.7 Examine the landforms labelled on the Ordnance Survey map at figure 10.10.

(a) Identify and write in your copy the landforms identified by labels A–C.

(b) Explain how you identified the landform at labels A–C.

(c) Discuss your answers with your partner and then share with the rest of the class.

Table 10.4 Landforms of a mature river

The **mature river** has a **greater volume** of water now that many tributaries have joined it. It flows over a **gentler slope** (gradient) and has a **large load** of material to transport. As a result, it flows more **slowly** than in the youthful stage.

Landform	Wider valley	Meanders	Floodplain
Description	Sides are less steep and the valley floor is wider and almost flat and has a gentle gradient	Curves or bends that develop along the mature (and old) course of a river	The level area of land on either side of a mature (and old) river. It has a covering of very fine clay called **alluvium**
Formation	• At this stage, the river begins to swing from **side to side**, removing the interlocking spurs • As a result, the valley floor is widened by **lateral** (sideways) **erosion** • Weathering and mass movement continue, so the valley sides become **less steep**	See figure 10.11. • As the water flows around a slight bend, the water at the outer bank is deeper and flows more quickly. As a result, it has more power to **erode** the bank • The water at the inner bank is shallower and flows more slowly. As a result, the river **deposits** some of its load there • Erosion and deposition continue and the **meander** becomes more prominent	See figure 10.12. • The river may become swollen and **overflow its banks** after a period of heavy rain • As it spreads over the level land on either side of the river, it quickly loses its energy and **deposits its load** of alluvium • Over many periods of flooding, a thick layer of alluvium builds up to form the **floodplain**
Examples	Along the **mature** course of the rivers: • Nore • Boyne • Barrow	Along the **mature** course of the rivers: • Shannon • Moy • Avoca	Along the **mature** course of the rivers: • Shannon • Liffey • Boyne • Suir

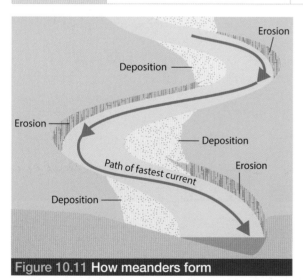

Erosion
Deposition
Erosion
Deposition
Erosion
Path of fastest current
Deposition

Figure 10.11 How meanders form

 Floodplain and meanders along the mature course of a river

GEO FACT

Well-developed meanders and wide floodplains are also found in the old stage of a river.

DEFINITION

Alluvium

Material (clay, silt and sand) transported and deposited by a river when it floods.

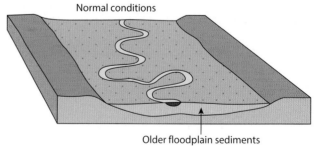

Normal conditions

Older floodplain sediments

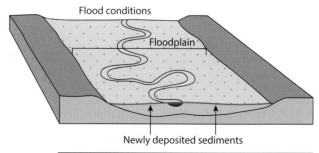

Flood conditions

Floodplain

Newly deposited sediments

Figure 10.12 How a floodplain is formed

Learning Activity

 Curiosity

10.8 Examine the river in the photo on the right.

(a) Identify the landforms at X and Y.

(b) State at which points (A, B, C and D) erosion is taking place, and at which points deposition is taking place.

Table 10.5 Landforms of an old river

The **old river** transports a **large load of alluvium** as it flows over land that is almost **level**. As a result, it **flows slowly** and has little spare energy. If some of this energy is lost or if the load becomes too great, the load is **deposited**.

Landform	Oxbow lake	Levee	Delta
Description	A horseshoe-shaped lake that was **once part of a river meander**, but is now cut off from the river (see figure 10.15)	Raised banks of **alluvium** that build up along the sides of an old river	A triangular or fan-shaped area of land found **where a river flows into the sea** (or a lake) (see figure 10.18)
Formation	See figure 10.13. ■ Erosion takes place on the outer banks of the river where **two meanders are close together** ■ Slowly the **neck** of land between two meanders gets narrower ■ During a flood, when the river has more energy, the neck of land is finally **cut through** ■ When this happens, a new, straighter river channel is created. The meander is **abandoned** ■ The river has little energy at this stage and **deposits** some of its load of **alluvium** ■ Both ends of the meander are cut off from the river channel to form an **oxbow lake**	See figure 10.14. ■ When a river **floods** and begins to spread out over the floodplain, it quickly loses its energy and begins to **deposit its load** ■ Most of the load, especially its **heavier particles**, is deposited **close to the banks** of the river. The lighter particles are carried further ■ After many periods of flooding, these deposits build up to form **levees**	See figure 10.17. ■ When a river flows into the sea, it loses its speed and **deposits its load** ■ If a river has a big load, the tides and currents may not be strong enough to carry it all out to sea ■ The mouth of the river becomes clogged and the river breaks up into smaller channels called **distributaries** ■ The deposits build up gradually and eventually rise above sea level to form a **delta**
Examples	Along the old stage of the rivers: ■ Mississippi ■ Liffey ■ Moy	Along the old stage of the rivers: ■ Mississippi ■ Liffey ■ Moy	At the mouths of the rivers: ■ Nile ■ Po ■ Mississippi ■ Amazon

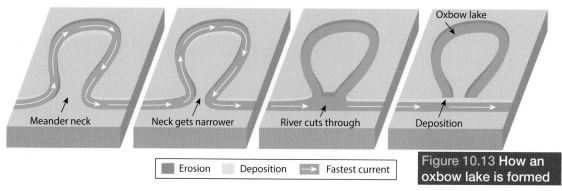

Meander neck | Neck gets narrower | River cuts through | Deposition

Oxbow lake

Erosion   Deposition   → Fastest current

Figure 10.13 How an oxbow lake is formed

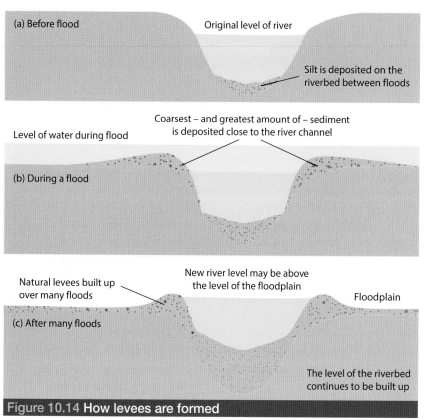

(a) Before flood   Original level of river

Silt is deposited on the riverbed between floods

Coarsest – and greatest amount of – sediment is deposited close to the river channel

Level of water during flood

(b) During a flood

New river level may be above the level of the floodplain

Natural levees built up over many floods

Floodplain

(c) After many floods

The level of the riverbed continues to be built up

Figure 10.14 How levees are formed

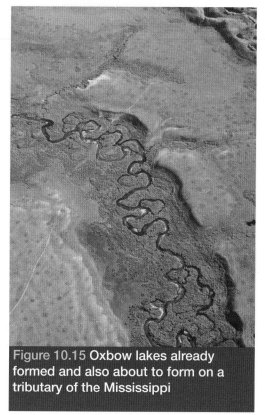

Figure 10.15 Oxbow lakes already formed and also about to form on a tributary of the Mississippi

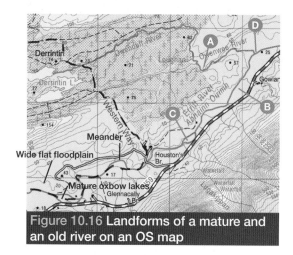

Figure 10.16 Landforms of a mature and an old river on an OS map

▶ Oxbow lakes, meanders and floodplain along the old stage of a river

Learning Activity

🔑 Curiosity   Communicating

10.9 Examine the landforms labelled on the Ordnance Survey map at figure 10.16.

   (a) Identify and write in your copy the landforms identified by labels A–D.

   (b) Explain how you identified the landform at labels A–D.

   (c) Check your answers with your partner's and share with the rest of the class.

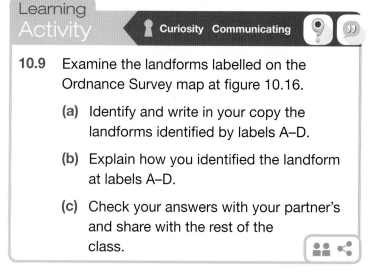

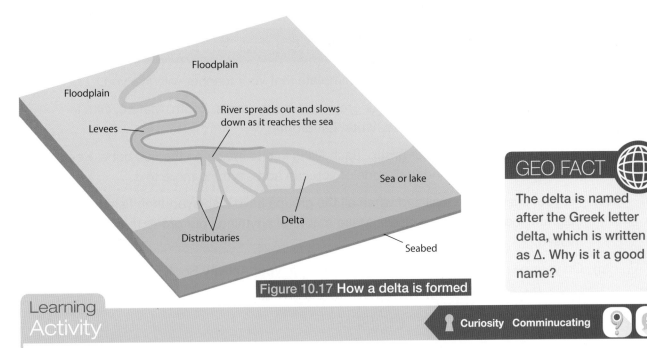

Figure 10.17 **How a delta is formed**

GEO FACT

The delta is named after the Greek letter delta, which is written as Δ. Why is it a good name?

Learning Activity

Curiosity Comminucating

10.10 Consider why some rivers do not have a delta at their mouths. Share your thoughts with your partner. Discuss your conclusions with the rest of the class.

Learning Activity

Curiosity Reflecting

10.11 Using an atlas or other reference source, find all the rivers in Ireland given as examples in tables 10.3, 10.4 and 10.5. Draw these onto the blank map of Ireland in your Activity Book (page 68).

10.12 Using an atlas or other reference source, find all the rivers given as examples in tables 10.3, 10.4 and 10.5 that are not in Ireland, and note in your copy which countries they are in.

GEO FACT

The Amazon is the world's greatest river. It discharges almost 150 billion litres of water into the Atlantic Ocean every minute.

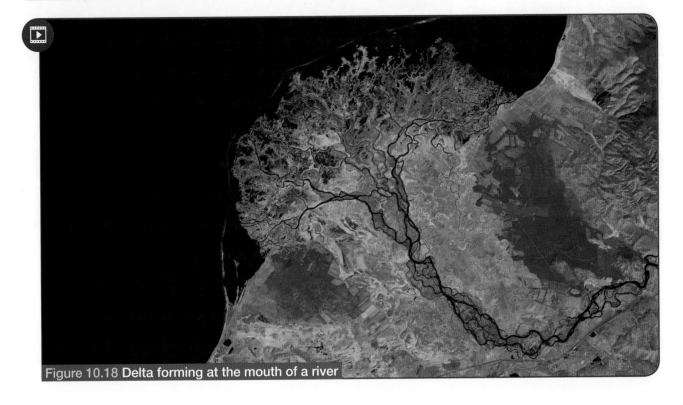

Figure 10.18 **Delta forming at the mouth of a river**

Learning Activity

Reflecting Communicating Co-operating

10.13 Work in small groups. Use the fish bone template that your teacher will give you.

    (a) In the top three boxes, one of your group fills in the words: Youth, Mature, Old. In each of the bottom three boxes, write: Landform.

    (b) Pass the sheet around your group, each filling in one space on the fish bone. Keep passing the sheet around until none of you can add anything more to it.

    (c) Fix your sheet to the wall and when all the groups have displayed their fish bone diagram, look at everyone else's. Make a note of anything your group may have missed.

    (d) On your own, complete the activity summary in your Activity Book (page 60).

People and river processes

People interact with two main aspects of river processes:

- Flow of the river

- Flooding.

Modifying the flow of the river

People have always attempted to control the flow of rivers. Rivers have been shaped by people in many ways, big and small, to suit human needs.

Building dams

A **dam** is a barrier, usually made of concrete, that is built across a river to **control the flow of water**. Dams are usually constructed to **store water** in a **reservoir** or artificial lake. The water from the reservoir is used for a variety of purposes, such as irrigation, recreation and water supply for household and business use.

The water can also be directed to flow through turbines in the dam, producing **hydroelectric power (HEP)** for use in homes and industries. During periods of heavy rainfall, excess water can be released in a controlled way.

Figure 10.19 Dam, with a HEP station on a river in Brittany

DEFINITION

Dam

A barrier built across a river to raise the level of the river on the upstream side.

Alluvium that would normally be deposited in the lower stage of the river's course will instead be deposited behind the dam. This might cause the dam to silt up, while soils further downstream in the floodplain lose a source of fertility.

Building levees

The levees found along the lower course of many large rivers **prevent flooding** of the floodplain, except when the level of the river is very high. Sometimes natural levees are **raised by river engineers** by adding soil or rocks on top. **Artificial levees** are also built. In both these cases, the aim is to **prevent flooding**.

This **interference** with natural processes by people can create a new problem. The water is now confined within a narrow channel so water level is higher and the water is flowing faster. This increases the **flood risk** further downstream. As more **pressure** is put on levees, they may collapse, leading to even more severe flooding.

Figure 10.20 **Levee on a river in Yorkshire, UK after breaking, leading to large-scale flooding**

Dealing with flooding

▶ Serious flooding after the River Thames burst its banks

Flooding is a **natural process** that occurs regularly, especially after heavy rainfall. Most of it occurs in the lower course of the river, on the appropriately named **floodplain**. People's activities also play a part in the flooding of land and homes in two main ways.

Deforestation

Trees and vegetation **intercept** rainfall and store it. They also **slow down** the water so that it soaks into the ground. A healthy soil with a rich humus layer can absorb a lot of water, while the trees and plants also take up water. This reduces the volume of water entering a river at any one time.

Link 🔗 Chapter 13: pages 139–42

When the trees and vegetation are removed, the rate of **surface run-off** on valley slopes rapidly increases, especially following heavy rainfall. The level of the river rises very quickly, leading to flooding of the floodplain.

Rapidly flowing water also causes **soil erosion**, leading to **silting** in the river bed.

Figure 10.21 **The river in the foreground is laden with sediment following heavy rainfall and soil erosion**

Building on floodplains

In the past, people who lived on floodplains were within the agricultural system and they expected and prepared for flooding. Nowadays, developers find the level land easy and attractive to build on and don't want to waste it. Building increases the area that is covered by concrete and tarmac.

Figure 10.22 **Large-scale flooding in Brisbane. This suburb was built on the floodplain of the river**

Learning Activity

🏆 Curiosity Communicating 📍 💬

10.14 Consider the consequences in relation to rainfall of concreting over more and more land. Discuss your thoughts with your partner and then share with the rest of the class.

Case study: the River Shannon

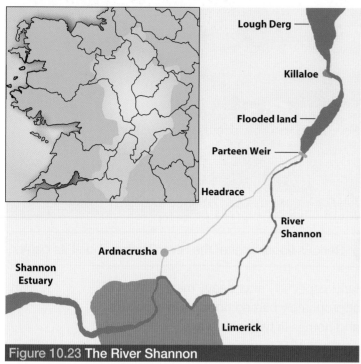

Figure 10.23 The River Shannon

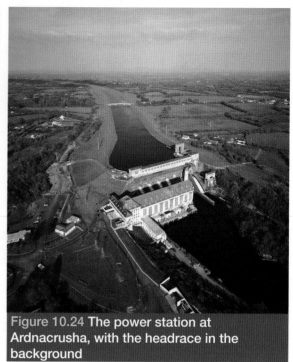

Figure 10.24 The power station at Ardnacrusha, with the headrace in the background

The Shannon is the longest river in Ireland. For most of its course, the River Shannon has a very **gentle gradient**.

It also receives large amounts of water from **tributaries** such as the Inny, Suck and Brosna. The Shannon and its tributaries drain an area of almost 16,000 km².

The Shannon hydroelectric scheme

The **Shannon Scheme** was a plan by the Irish government in the 1920s to provide a cheap, reliable and plentiful supply of electricity for the country.

The main aspects of the scheme are:

- **Parteen Weir** The raising of the water levels created a large **reservoir** south of Killaloe. The weir diverts much of the flow of the River Shannon into a **headrace canal** leading to the power station at Ardnacrusha.

- **The headrace canal** This canal brings water from the weir at Parteen to the dam at Ardnacrusha.

- **Ardnacrusha dam** This is where electricity is generated, using the water in the headrace canal. The water rapidly spins the **blades** in the turbines. These are connected to generators that make electricity as they spin.

DEFINITION

Weir

A low barrier that serves the same purpose as a dam but also allows water to flow over its top.

Benefits and disadvantages

Table 10.6 Benefits and disadvantages of the Shannon dam and weirs

Benefits	Disadvantages
• They enable the generation of **HEP**. This is a clean source of renewable energy • They are used to **manage the risk of flooding** in the lower Shannon catchment area	• Thousands of hectares of **farmland** were lost when the artificial lake was created • Families had to evacuate their homes and be **relocated** elsewhere • New roads and bridges had to be built, while others were buried beneath the water

Learning
Activity

Curiosity   Responsibility

10.15 Research, using the internet or other information source, how many hydroelectric power plants there are now in Ireland.

Flooding on the Shannon

The River Shannon is liable to serious flooding. Some flooding now occurs every winter and for some period every second summer on average.

Causes

- The river has a very **gentle gradient** so water is slow to leave the channel.

- The river channel is both **narrow and shallow** in places. Silt from bogs along its course has settled on the bed. Vegetation has blocked some of the lower channel.

- There are narrow **choke points** where water leaves the lakes on the Shannon.

- The huge **floodplains** are barely above normal water levels in places. During the building boom, construction took place on some of the floodplains.

The 2015 floods

The **worst flooding** ever experienced along the Shannon took place in late December 2015 and early January 2016. It followed very heavy rainfall that was three times the average for the period. The rainfall resulted from six back-to-back storms that began in November. The ground soon became saturated and most water flowed quickly from the land as run-off.

The floods affected both rural areas and urban areas that included Carrick-on-Shannon and Athlone.

The effects

- Four hundred homes were abandoned after being flooded. Another 150 homes were marooned and cut off by floodwaters.

- Shops were flooded and stock destroyed.

- Roads were flooded, with many impassable for weeks.

- Large areas of floodplain were flooded. Animals had to be moved to higher ground. Stocks of winter feed were destroyed.

Flooding would have been more extensive but for the widespread use of **sandbags**. Nevertheless, the cost of repairing the damage caused by the floods was more than €100 million.

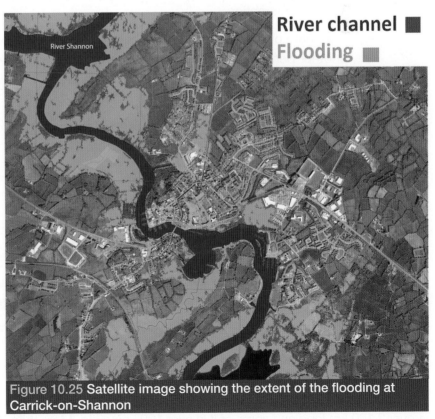

Figure 10.25 Satellite image showing the extent of the flooding at Carrick-on-Shannon

Learning Activity

Curiosity Communicating Literacy Responsibility

10.16 Do you think that flooding is going to increase in Ireland in the future?

(a) Consider your answer to this question. Justify your answer to the person sitting next to you.

(b) On a separate piece of paper, write a short paragraph on why you think flooding in Ireland is going to increase, decrease, or stay the same in the future.

(c) Work in small groups. Write the question on one sheet of paper. Each person in your group should then place their paragraph on the desk underneath the question so you can see all of them, just like you would if you were reading an online discussion board. Place a sticky note next to each one. Read all the answers from people in your group. Write an 'upvote' tick on the sticky note next to the answer you think is best.

(d) Take the answer(s) with the most upvotes and fix it to the wall, underneath the question. Read all the new answers and place an 'upvote' tick to the answer you think is best or with which you most agree. Which answer has the most 'upvotes'?

People and rivers

People exploit (use) rivers in other ways besides using their water for power.

Learning Activity

Communicating Co-operating Curiosity

10.17 In small groups, discuss how rivers and their landforms are used by people for earning a living and for recreation.

(a) Nominate one person to be the chairperson, to lead your discussion. Nominate another person to be the secretary, to write notes. Between you, compile a list of ways rivers might be used, and next to each entry say whether this is likely to be in a youthful river, a mature river or an old river.

(b) Nominate one or two people to create a poster showing the ways a river might be used by people. Everyone should provide ideas and, if necessary, find pictures to include.

(c) Put your posters around the wall and read those by the other groups.

Water supply

Water resources are abundant in Ireland. More than 80% of our drinking water comes from **surface water** – rivers and lakes. The remainder comes from **groundwater** – wells and springs.

Irish Water is responsible for the production and distribution of most of the water used in homes and industry.

The largest public water scheme in the country is in the Dublin Region.

The water is **purified** in four plants and distributed through a network of pipes. The pipework is over 2,100 km long and some of it is over 100 years old. More than a quarter of the purified water is lost through leaks in the system.

Learning
Activity

Curiosity Responsibility Numeracy

10.18 Investigate the following questions relating to the Dublin Region's water supply. Write your answers in your copy.

    (a) On average, how much water is delivered to the Dublin Region per day?

    (b) How many million litres are delivered to the Dublin Region in a year?

    (c) What are the two main sources of the water delivered to the Dublin Region?

    (d) From which mountains are these water sources fed?

By 2050, the Dublin region will require an additional 350 million litres of water per day. Simply fixing leaks will not deliver the additional water needed, nor can the additional water supply be sourced locally. Irish Water needs to find a way to make up for the shortfall.

Irish Water proposes to extract water from the **River Shannon** at Parteen. A planning application was lodged in 2017. If granted, the scheme will be completed within four years.

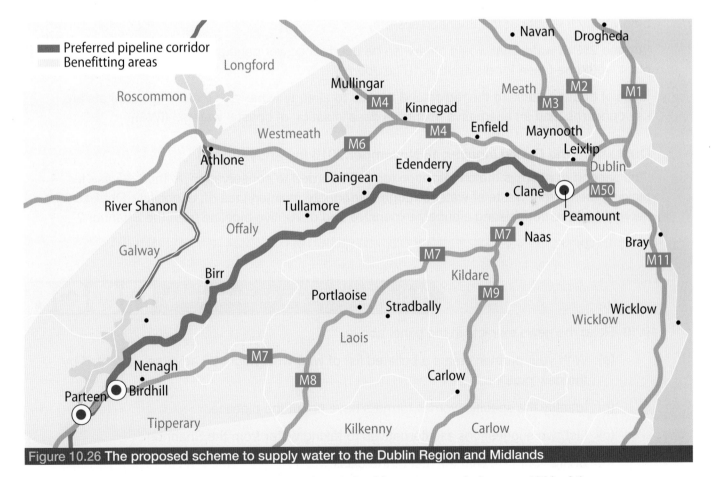

Figure 10.26 **The proposed scheme to supply water to the Dublin Region and Midlands**

The proposed scheme will deliver a **secure** and **sustainable** water supply for over 40% of the country's population up to 2050. The scheme will involve:

- The removal of up to 350 million litres of water per day from the River Shannon at **Parteen**

- Purifying the water at a treatment plant at **Birdhill**, Co. Tipperary

- Transporting the water via a 170 km pipeline to a reservoir at **Peamount**, on the outskirts of Dublin. From there, it will link into the existing pipeline network

- Providing the potential to serve treated water to towns and communities along the route from **Shannon to Dublin**.

There are, however, concerns, as these news extracts show:

Quote from the *Irish Farmers Journal*, 14 November 2016 (by Amy Nora Fitzgibbon)

'There will be a 50 m width corridor for construction and a permanent 20 m corridor under which the pipe will lie.'

IFA environent and rural affairs chair Thomas Cooney, speaking to the *Irish Farmers Journal*, 14 November 2016

'The working width of the project will be some 50 m, which, to put it into perspective, is the width of O'Connell Street in Dublin. The pipe itself will be about 2 m across, which is the width of a double door.'

'Farmers want to know if it will damage their underground culverts [underground drainage channels], affect drainage or if they will be able to build anywhere near or around the pipe. This gives rise to issues around devaluation of land and also questions around the ownership of the land.'

Quotes from www.afloat.ie, 26 November 2015

'Critics have expressed "deep concern" over its potential effects on boating tourism and biodiversity throughout the Shannon system.'

'Around 2% of water that would otherwise be used for power generation at the Ardnacrusha plant would be taken for distribution.' (*The Journal*)

'Loss of boating traffic to the region and threats to already vulnerable waterways habitats are key concerns [and an alternative might be] desalinisation of coastal waters.' (IWAI)

Quote from the *Dublin Inquirer*, 16 November 2016 (by Andy Storey)

'The second concern is the prioritization (or not) afforded to conservation. Is there a case for tackling the current waste of water through inadequate maintenance of, especially, Dublin's pipe network, *before* considering a hugely expensive and disruptive pipeline from the Shannon?'

Learning Activity

Curiosity Communicating Co-operating Literacy

10.19 Read the news extracts in the panel above.

    (a) With your partner, create a bulleted list of who/what might be adversely affected by the new pipeline.

    (b) Identify the specific worries farmers have about the pipeline.

    (c) List two suggestions as alternatives to taking water from the Shannon.

    (d) Share your lists with the rest of the class.

10.20 In the quote from the *Dublin Inquirer*, the writer asks whether leaks in the network should be fixed as a first step. Discuss your thoughts about this with your partner, then debate the subject with the rest of the class.

Reflecting on my learning

Reflecting Communicating Literacy

Write sentences using each of the following terms from this chapter. You may use more than one of the terms in your sentence if appropriate.

abrasion	erosion	mature stage
alluvium	flooding	meander
attrition	floodplain	old stage
bank	gorge	oxbow lake
bed	groundwater	plunge pool
channel	hydraulic action	surface water
dam	hydroelectric power (HEP)	transportation
delta	interlocking spurs	V-shaped valley
deposition	landform	waterfall
distributary	levee	youthful stage
drain	load	

PowerPoint summary

Revision
Go to **www.edco.ie/geographynow** and try the interactive activities and quizzes.

Agents of erosion – the sea

11

Go to **www.edco.ie/geographynow** and
try the interactive activities and quizzes.

Learning intentions

When you have completed this chapter you will be able to:

- Consider the ways the sea destroys the coastline
- Describe different types of wave and how they affect the coastline
- Explain how landforms are formed as a result of coastal erosion
- Consider the ways the sea builds up the coastline
- Explain how landforms are formed as a result of coastal deposition
- Identify coastal landforms on Ordnance Survey maps
- Provide examples of where particular coastal landforms can be found in Ireland
- Describe various forms of coastal protection.

1.5 Explain how the processes of erosion, transportation and deposition shape our fluvial, **marine** and glacial landscapes

You are also working towards:

1.10 Investigate a range of physical processes active in a chosen location and the connections between them

2.4 Assess the exploitation of water, fish stocks, forestry and soil as natural resources

2.7 Investigate examples of how people interact with and manage surface processes

Key terms

swash	wave-cut platform	sand spit
backwash	sea cave	lagoon
destructive waves	sea arch	sand bar
constructive waves	sea stack	tombolo
hydraulic action	blowhole	sea wall
compressed air	longshore drift	rock armour
bay	beach	groyne
headland	sand dunes	gabion
sea cliff	storm beach	

Sea: the destroyer

The coastline is constantly changing. This is due to the action of waves as they **erode**, **transport** and **deposit** material along the coastline.

Waves

When wind blows over the smooth surface of the sea, it causes ripples in the water and these grow into **waves**. The size of the wave increases with the **strength of wind** and the **distance of sea** over which it passes.

When waves reach shallow water, they **break** or tumble onto the shore. The frothy water that rushes onto the shore is called the **swash**. The water that runs back out from the wave is called the **backwash**.

- A **destructive wave** is one where the backwash is stronger than the swash and material is **eroded**.

- A **constructive wave** is one where the swash is stronger than the backwash and material is **deposited**.

GEO FACT

Storm waves hit the coast with forces of up to 30 tonnes per square metre.

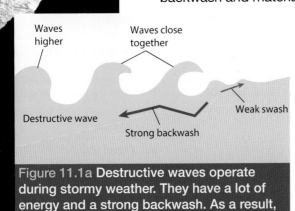

Figure 11.1a Destructive waves operate during stormy weather. They have a lot of energy and a strong backwash. As a result, these waves cause **erosion**

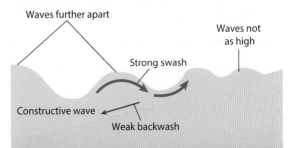

Figure 11.1b Constructive waves operate in calm weather. They have limited energy and most of it is used by the swash to transport and **deposit** material

109

How waves erode

Waves **erode** by the four **processes** shown in figure 11.2.

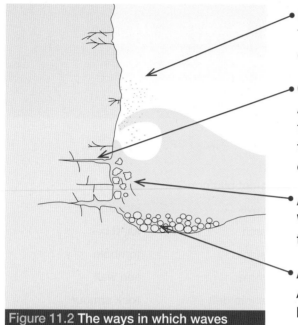

Figure 11.2 The ways in which waves erode the coastline

• **Hydraulic action**
This is the power of the water as it pounds against the coast. It is strongest during storms.

• **Compressed air**
Air is trapped in cracks in the rock and compressed by the waves. This increases the pressure on the rock. When the wave retreats, the air expands like an explosion. This can shatter the rock.

• **Abrasion**
Waves pick up rocks and stones and hurl them against the coast. This breaks off even more rock.

• **Attrition**
Attrition occurs when rocks and stones that have been broken off the coast are swirled around by the waves. They collide with and rub off one another. They are worn down to rounder and smoother particles.

Learning
Activity

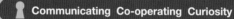 Communicating Co-operating Curiosity

11.1 Consider answers to the following questions, and then discuss them with your partner and agree your responses. Share your thoughts with the rest of the class.

(a) Identify which of the processes named in figure 11.2 are also ways in which river landforms are created.

(b) For the process(es) that are not part of the creation of river landforms, explain why this is.

(c) Will the processes be stronger in rivers or in the sea? Justify your answer.

Landforms of coastal erosion

A number of landforms are created as a result of coastal erosion.

Bays and headlands

Table 11.1 Bays and headlands		
	Bay	**Headland**
Description	A wide, curved opening into the coast	A neck of high land that juts out into the sea
Formation – where there are bands of different rock along the coast	**Soft** rock, such as shale, is eroded very quickly by the processes mentioned above	**Hard** rock, such as sandstone, is eroded much more slowly
Examples	▪ Dublin Bay ▪ Galway Bay	▪ Mizen Head ▪ Malin Head
If the headlands are big, they shelter the bay and a small **beach** may form in the bay		

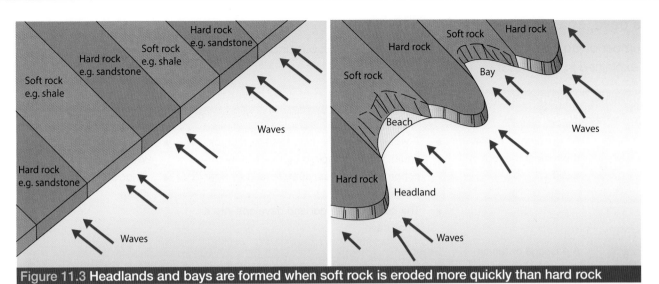

Figure 11.3 **Headlands and bays are formed when soft rock is eroded more quickly than hard rock**

> **GEO FACT**
>
> **Headlands** are also known as **points**, e.g. Rosses Point.

Sea cliff

Table 11.2 Sea cliff	
	Sea cliff
Description	A vertical or steep slope on the coast
Formation	▪ **Destructive waves** attack the coast and cut into the rock, eroding a **notch** ▪ When the notch becomes deeper, the overhanging rock above it will collapse under its own weight ▪ As the processes of **undercutting and collapse** continue, the cliff gradually retreats ▪ As the cliff retreats, a gently sloping rock surface remains between the high-water mark and the low-water mark. This is called a **wave-cut platform**
Examples	▪ The best known cliffs in Ireland are the Cliffs of Moher in Co. Clare ▪ The highest cliffs in the country are at Slieve League in Co. Donegal

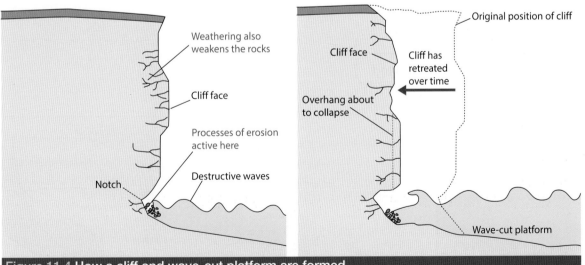

Figure 11.4 **How a cliff and wave-cut platform are formed**

Sea cave, sea arch, sea stack and blowhole

A number of landforms that are all linked together are also found on a cliff coastline. These are explained in table 11.3.

Table 11.3 Sea cave, sea arch, sea stack and blowhole			
	Description	**Formation**	**Examples**
Sea cave	An opening or hollow in the rock at the foot of a cliff	■ A weak spot in the rock, such as a crack (fault), will be attacked by the hydraulic action of the waves, compressed air and abrasion ■ The crack gets larger and develops into a small cave	■ Hook Head, Co. Wexford ■ Bridges of Ross, Co. Clare
Sea arch	A passage or tunnel that runs right through a headland	Either: ■ Where a cave is deepened and enlarged by erosion so that it cuts through to the other side of the headland or ■ Where two caves on opposite sides of a headland meet	
Sea stack	A pillar of rock that is cut off from the headland or cliff	■ When the waves erode the base of a sea arch, they widen it ■ Eventually the roof is unable to support itself and it collapses, leaving the former tip of the headland cut off as a sea stack ■ If the base of the sea stack is eroded, it will collapse to leave a **stump** of rock that is visible at low tide	
Blowhole	A passage that links the roof of a cave with the surface of the cliff top	■ Air is trapped and **compressed** in a cave by powerful storm waves. This builds up pressure and helps to loosen and shatter the rock at the back of the cave ■ The rock eventually **collapses**, forming a blowhole During stormy weather, sea spray may spurt out from the blowhole (see figure 11.5)	■ The Two Pistols, Co. Donegal ■ McSweeney's Gun, Co. Donegal

▶ Beach, sandspit and tombolo in Thailand

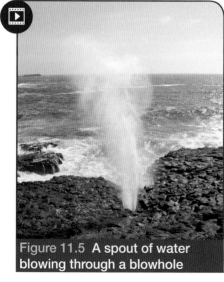

Figure 11.5 A spout of water blowing through a blowhole

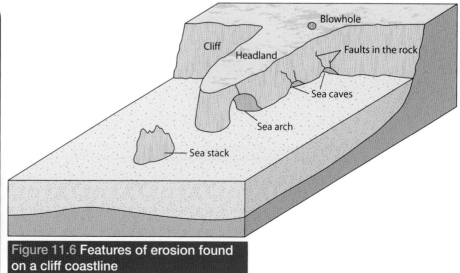

Figure 11.6 Features of erosion found on a cliff coastline

Learning
Activity

Curiosity

Figure 11.7 **Features of coastal erosion**

11.2 Examine the photograph at figure 11.7. Match each of the following landforms with one of the letters.

(i)   Notch

(ii) Sea cave

(iii) Sea arch

(iv) Stack

(v) Cliff

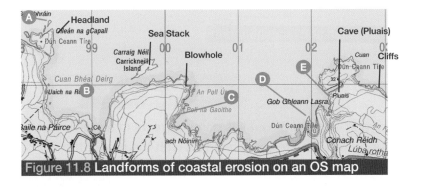

Figure 11.8 **Landforms of coastal erosion on an OS map**

Learning
Activity

Curiosity   Literacy

11.3   Examine the landforms labelled on the Ordnance Survey map at figure 11.8.

(a) Identify the landforms labelled A–E.

(b) Sketch figure 11.8 in your copy and label the landforms with the correct words.

(c) Explain how you identified the landforms at labels A–E.

Sea: the builder

Transportation

The sea's **load** includes stones, pebbles, sand and silt. The waves **transport** the load in two types of movement:

- Up the shore by the **swash** and back down the shore by the **backwash**. (See figures 11.1a and 11.1b on page 109.)

- Along the shore by **longshore drift**. This occurs when the waves approach the shore at an angle. (See figure 11.9 on the next page.)

2 The **swash** from the breaking waves moves material up the shore and deposits some of it there. Because of the direction of the waves, the material is also moved along the shore.

3 The **backwash** brings some of the material straight out, following the slope of the beach.

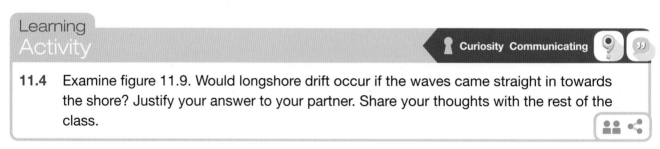

Direction of longshore drift

Path of sand particles

4 These processes are repeated over time and the material is gradually moved along the shore in a **zigzag** fashion. This movement is known as **longshore drift**.

Wave direction

1 The waves approach the shore at an **angle**.

→ Swash
→ Backwash

Figure 11.9 Waves move their load by swash, backwash and longshore drift

Learning Activity

Curiosity Communicating

11.4 Examine figure 11.9. Would longshore drift occur if the waves came straight in towards the shore? Justify your answer to your partner. Share your thoughts with the rest of the class.

Landforms of coastal deposition

Waves **deposit** their load when they lose some of their **energy** and can no longer transport such a large load. This may occur in **sheltered areas** like bays or where the shore **slopes very gently** out to sea.

A number of landforms are created as a result of **coastal deposition**. These are explained in table 11.4.

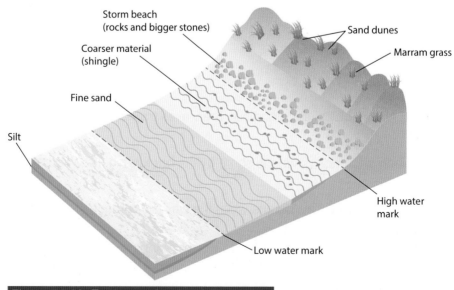

Storm beach (rocks and bigger stones)

Coarser material (shingle)

Fine sand

Silt

Sand dunes

Marram grass

High water mark

Low water mark

Figure 11.10 Features of coastal deposition

Table 11.4 Landforms of coastal deposition

	Description	Formation	Examples
Beach	A build-up of sand and shingle (small pebbles) deposited by **constructive waves** between low and high tide levels	▪ When waves break, the **swash** carries its load of both coarse and fine material up the shore and deposits it ▪ The **backwash** is weaker and it drags some of the finer material back towards the sea ▪ As a result, **finer** beach material is found **lower** down the beach, while **coarser** beach material is found at the **upper** beach ▪ In stormy weather, the swash is strong enough to hurl large stones and rocks up past the normal high tide level, where they remain to form a **storm beach**	▪ Greystones, Co. Wicklow ▪ Keel (Achill Island) ▪ Tramore, Co. Waterford
Sand dunes	Hills of sand that pile up on the shore, just beyond the high tide level	▪ Winds from over the sea **dry** the sand on the beach, making it lighter ▪ The wind blows the dry sand inland until it is **trapped** by a wall or vegetation ▪ The sand **piles up** to form low hills or dunes **Marram grass** is sometimes planted on the dunes. It has deep roots that help bind the sand particles together, preventing them from blowing further inland	▪ Inch, Co. Kerry ▪ Rosslare, Co. Wexford ▪ Tramore, Co. Waterford
Sand spit	A ridge of sand or shingle that is connected to the land at one end and extends across a bay	▪ A spit begins where there is a **change in the direction** of a coastline ▪ Longshore drift loses some of its energy and **deposits** material at a faster rate than it can be removed ▪ These deposits gradually **build up** above the level of the water ▪ As deposition continues, the spit **extends** further across the bay	▪ Tramore, Co. Waterford ▪ Inch, Co. Kerry ▪ Portmarnock, Co. Dublin
Lagoon	An area of water that has been cut off from the sea by a bank of sand	▪ If a sand spit continues to grow, it eventually reaches the far side of the bay to form a **sand bar**. Some of the bay is now sealed off from the sea ▪ A lake (**lagoon**) is formed ▪ Over time the lagoon begins to fill with silt and mud from rivers that may flow into it	▪ Our Lady's Island, Co. Wexford ▪ Lough Gill, Co. Kerry
Tombolo	A ridge of sand or shingle that leads from the mainland to a nearby island	When a **sand spit** grows **outwards** from the mainland, material is moved by longshore **drift** and is deposited in the sheltered waters between the mainland and the island	▪ Howth (Co. Dublin) was an island but was then connected to the mainland by the Sutton tombolo

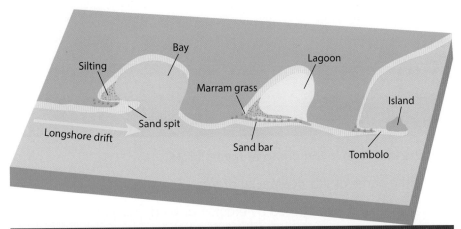

Figure 11.11 A sand spit grows across a bay. Its growth can also lead to the formation of a lagoon or a tombolo

Learning
Activity

Figure 11.12 Landforms of coastal deposition

11.5 Examine figure 11.12 and identify two landforms of coastal deposition. Check your answers with your partner and share with the rest of the class.

Learning
Activity

Figure 11.13 A sand spit growing across a bay

11.6 Examine figure 11.13. What evidence is there to suggest that longshore drift is occurring? Check your answer with your partner and share with the rest of the class.

Learning
Activity

Figure 11.14 A coastal landform

11.7 Look at the landform in the photo at figure 11.14.

    (a) State the name of this coastal landform.

    (b) State whether it was formed by erosion or by deposition.

Compare your answers with your partner's and share with the rest of the class.

Learning
Activity

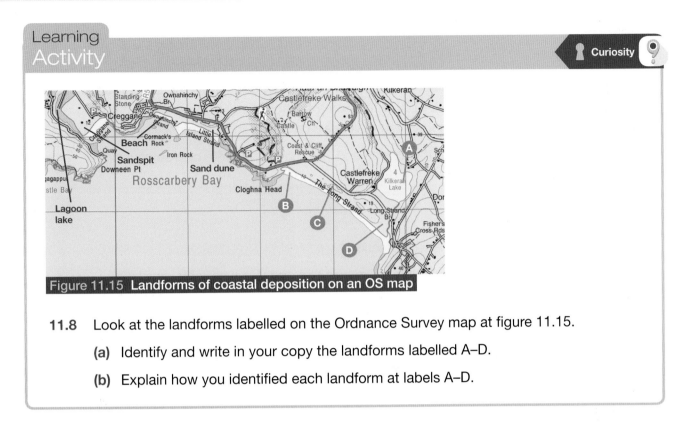

Figure 11.15 Landforms of coastal deposition on an OS map

11.8 Look at the landforms labelled on the Ordnance Survey map at figure 11.15.

(a) Identify and write in your copy the landforms labelled A–D.

(b) Explain how you identified each landform at labels A–D.

People and the sea

The sea plays an important role in a range of human activities. In turn, people interfere with the natural processes of the sea. In both situations, there are positive and negative effects.

The sea and economic activity

Table 11.5 How people use the sea		
Activity	**Positive effect**	**Negative effect**
Recreation and leisure	▪ The sea and beaches allow for a wide range of activities that include sailing, fishing and sunbathing ▪ Businesses in resort towns benefit when tourists come to stay	▪ Tourism can result in litter and pollution ▪ The sewerage systems of some tourist resorts are unable to cope with the increase in summer population ▪ Tourists can damage sand dunes while walking on them
Transport	▪ Bulky goods, including oil, ores and containers, can be transported quite cheaply over long distances ▪ Ferries transport people, cars and trucks	▪ Oil spillages, both from pipelines and tankers, can cause pollution. This can damage the coastal environment ▪ Spillages also lead to the destruction of fish and other sea creatures
Food supply	▪ The sea is an important source of food, both from fish caught in the wild and fish reared on fish farms ▪ Employment is provided in the fishing and processing sectors	▪ Overfishing, especially by super-trawlers, can lead to the depletion of fish stocks ▪ The cages of fish farms can be an eyesore when located in scenic areas Link 🔗 Chapter 25: pages 246–51

11.9 Imagine you write a travel blog. You are going to write a post on the coastal attractions of the Wild Atlantic Way (WAW). Concentrate on a section of the WAW of your choosing. Try to incorporate some of the terms you have learnt about in this chapter.

You may work with a partner if you wish and you may hand-write or type your post.

Coastal protection

There are two main approaches to coastal protection:

- **Hard engineering**, where physical structures are built to stop the waves in their tracks

- **Soft engineering**, where people work with nature in a more sustainable way of managing the coast.

Table 11.6 Coastal protection

	Sea wall	Rock armour	Groynes	Gabions
Description	A wall made of concrete built between the sea and the coastal town	Large boulders placed at the base of **soft cliffs** or in front of **sand dunes**	Low walls, often made of wood, that are built at right angles to the coast	Wire cages that are filled with small stones placed along beaches or sand dunes
Protection	They have a **curved top** to deflect the waves back out to sea. The sea may destroy these walls, especially during severe storms	The **power of the waves is reduced** as they hit the boulders	They **reduce longshore drift** by trapping sand. The sand accumulates and builds up the level of the beach	They break the power of the waves and help to slow down the rate of erosion
Examples	■ Bray, Co. Wicklow ■ Tramore, Co. Waterford ■ Galway	■ Tramore, Co. Waterford ■ Youghal, Co. Cork	■ Youghal, Co. Cork ■ Rosslare, Co. Wexford	■ Rosslare, Co. Wexford ■ Tramore, Co. Waterford ■ Lahinch, Co. Clare

Soft engineering has been used to protect sections of the coast at Rosslare:

- The beach has been nourished. Sand was dredged from the seabed offshore and pumped ashore.

- The sand dunes were restored. Marram grass was planted. Wooden fences were built to stop the sand blowing away and protect the marram grass from tourists.

Figure 11.16 Sea wall, rock armour and groynes on the English coast

🔑 **Curiosity Communicating**

11.10 Would you consider it important that coastal protection measures are made as attractive as possible, even if they cost more than unattractive ones that do the job? Justify your answer to your partner and share your thoughts with the rest of the class.

11.11 Will Ireland have to spend more on coastal protection measures in the future than it does now? Justify your answer to your partner and share your thoughts with the rest of the class.

Case study: Rosslare

Rosslare has two distinct settlements that lie just 8 km apart.

- **Rosslare Strand** has been a major holiday resort for nearly a century. It is situated along 8 km of safe, sandy beaches with Blue Flag status. The area enjoys the most hours of sunshine in Ireland and has a wide range of attractions for tourists.

- **Rosslare Harbour** is the site of Rosslare-Europort, a major ferry terminal. It has roll-on roll-off (ro-ro) passenger and freight services to Britain and France.

While both settlements make use of the sea and the coast, each has different needs. Sometimes, there is a conflict of interest in these needs.

GEO FACT

Nearly 3.5 km of the northern section of the Rosslare sand spit have been lost to coastal erosion.

Figure 11.17 **Beach at Rosslare Strand at risk of erosion by the sea. Rock armour protects part of it**

Figure 11.18 **Rosslare ferry terminal**

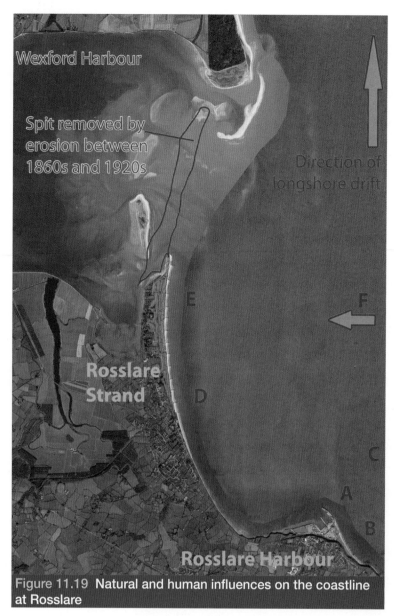

Figure 11.19 **Natural and human influences on the coastline at Rosslare**

A A **sea wall** was built at Rosslare Harbour, jutting out into the bay. It was built to provide shelter for the ferry terminal and to prevent silting in the harbour. Over the years it has been extended and new piles built.

B Some sand was trapped and a new beach began to develop ahead of the sea wall.

C The wall deflected longshore drift away from the coast. Most of the sand was deposited offshore in very deep water.

D The supply of sand to Rosslare Strand, to the north, was interrupted. Erosion of the beaches and sand dunes resulted. Parts of the golf course were flooded and some of the course was washed away.

E Expensive measures were taken to prevent further erosion. These included the use of groynes (wooden and stone), rock armour and gabions.

F **Beach nourishment** was also undertaken. Sand was dredged from the seabed about 6 km offshore and placed on the beach to build it up.

Learning
Activity

Curiosity Responsibility Reflecting

11.12 Read the extract opposite from the *Irish Independent*, which was written after very bad storms at the beginning of 2014.

(a) Imagine you are the editor of the newspaper for this piece, and write a headline to go with it.

(b) Imagine you are the picture editor for the newspaper for this piece, and search the internet for a suitable picture to accompany the article. Print this out at low resolution.

(c) Complete the activity summary sheet for this exercise in your Activity Book (page 70).

Learning Activity

Ireland 250 acres smaller after floods tear chunks off coastline
By Ralph Riegel

Ireland is 250 acres smaller – as the recent floods and storms tore large blocks off the country's coastline, with the repair bill now set to top €350m.

Environmental engineers and coastal erosion researchers estimate that in some areas, up to two metres have been washed away from vulnerable coastlines through a record succession of violent winter storms.

500 km of Ireland's coastline is at high risk and 1,600 km is at moderate erosion risk.

Ireland spends only €45m each year on flood defences but Minister Hayes said much more needs to be invested.

Mr Hayes said Ireland urgently needed to 'ramp up' spending to protect vulnerable areas such as Cork, acknowledged as Ireland's most flood-prone city.

In Clare, the clean-up focused on Lahinch where the promenade was virtually destroyed by giant waves in Superstorm Darwin.

Down the coast, Kerry County Council is facing repairs of €20m with Rossbeigh Strand and Fenit Island the worst hit by the storms.

Source: Adapted from *Irish Independent*, 10 March 2014

Reflecting on my learning

Reflecting Communicating Literacy

Write sentences using each of the following terms from this chapter. You may use more than one of the terms in your sentence if appropriate.

backwash	headland	sea cave
bay	hydraulic action	sea cliff
beach	lagoon	sea stack
blowhole	longshore drift	sea wall
compressed air	rock armour	storm beach
constructive waves	sand bar	swash
destructive waves	sand dunes	tombolo
gabion	sand spit	wave-cut platform
groyne	sea arch	

 PowerPoint summary

 Revision
Go to **www.edco.ie/geographynow** and try the interactive activities and quizzes.

Agents of erosion – glaciation

12

Go to **www.edco.ie/geographynow** and
try the interactive activities and quizzes.

Learning intentions

When you have completed this chapter you will be able to:

- Outline the causes and results of the Ice Age
- Analyse an impact of climate change on today's glaciers
- Explain how glaciers erode
- Explain how landforms are formed from glacial erosion
- Explain how landforms are formed from glacial deposition
- Explain how landforms are formed from meltwater deposition
- Identify glacial landforms on Ordnance Survey maps
- Identify glacial landforms in photographs
- Provide examples of where particular glacial landforms can be found in Ireland
- Describe the ways in which people interact with glacial processes.

Learning Outcomes

1.5 Explain how the processes of erosion, transportation and deposition shape our fluvial, marine and **glacial** landscapes

You are also working towards:

1.10 Investigate a range of physical processes active in a chosen location and the connections between them

Key terms

glaciation	arête	moraine
glacier	tarn	boulder clay
ice sheet	pyramidal peak	drumlin
Ice Age	U-shaped valley	erratic
plucking	ribbon lake	meltwater
abrasion	paternoster lakes	esker
striae	hanging valley	outwash plain
cirque	fiord	

Glaciation – the work of erosion

About two million years ago, the climate of many countries became much colder. There was only one season – winter – and all precipitation took the form of **snow**.

- Snow began to collect on colder **upland** areas.
- As more snow fell, the weight of the upper layers **compressed** the bottom layers into **ice**.
- Great rivers of ice, called **glaciers**, moved down from the uplands under the influence of gravity.
- While some glaciers melted, others joined together to cover lowland areas with **ice sheets**.
- Another **Ice Age** had begun.

During the Ice Age, up to **one third** of Earth's surface was covered with ice. Today, Greenland and Antarctica are still covered with ice sheets. Glaciers can be found in the higher parts of mountain ranges such as the Alps and Himalayas.

Ireland was covered by ice sheets on at least two occasions. The ice was up to 1,000 metres thick in places. The last of this ice melted just 10,000 years ago.

The results of **glaciation** are widespread over the Irish landscape.

DEFINITION

Ice Age

A period when large parts of several continents were covered by ice sheets.

GEO FACT

The ice sheets of the Arctic and Antarctic are now under threat from climate change.

Learning Activity

12.1 Read the extract and then answer the questions following it. Talk to your partner about your answers, and then discuss the questions in class.

Gigantic iceberg now floating free

For the last few months a large crack has been cutting across a vast chunk of ice in Antarctica. ESA's Sentinel-1 satellites have now seen the ice completely break away, making one of the biggest icebergs ever recorded.

The crack first appeared several years ago, but it did not grow by much to begin with. By January 2017 it had a total length of 175km.

This new gigantic iceberg is about 6000 sq km, and weighs more than a million million tonnes! It is difficult to predict what will happen to it next. It may stay floating in the area for many years. Or it may split apart into smaller icebergs that could drift north into warmer waters.

Source: European Space Agency (ESA) for kids website, 17 July 2017

(a) State how we know about this new iceberg.

(b) Ireland contributes a lot of money to the ESA, along with other countries. Do you think it is important that Ireland contributes to research in places like the Antarctic? Justify your answer.

(c) Would it be better if the iceberg stays floating in the Antarctic for many years, or if it moved into warmer waters? Justify your answer.

(d) Explain why it matters to us in Ireland that a large part of the glacier in the Antarctic has broken away.

> **GEO FACT**
>
> The iceberg contains about the same amount of water as Lake Ontario in North America.

Figure 12.1 The Franz Josef glacier in New Zealand. Identify the stream of meltwater flowing away from its snout (front)

How glaciers erode

As ice moves, it erodes the landscape by the processes of **plucking** and **abrasion**.

Plucking

As the ice moves, there is **friction** between it and the rock beneath it. This causes some of the ice to **melt**, and the water seeps into cracks in the rock. The meltwater freezes again and sticks to the glacier. As the glacier moves forward, it pulls or **plucks** chunks of rock away with it.

Abrasion

As the ice carries the plucked rocks away, they **scrape** or **scratch** the rock surface over which the glacier passes. This sandpaper effect wears down the rock. The scratches are called **striae**. They show us the direction in which the ice moved.

Landforms of glacial erosion

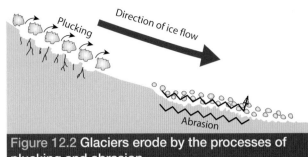
Figure 12.2 **Glaciers erode by the processes of plucking and abrasion**

Figure 12.3 **Scratches (striae) on the rock surface following abrasion by a glacier**

Most landforms of glacial erosion are found in **upland areas**. These landforms are summarised in table 12.1. In Ireland, these landforms were formed about 10,000 years ago.

Figure 12.4 **Cirques and arête in an upland area**

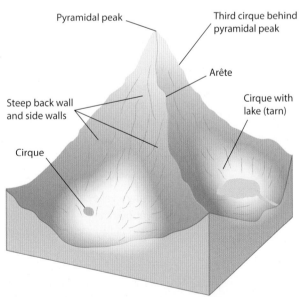
Figure 12.5 **Cirques, arêtes, tarn and pyramidal peak**

Table 12.1 Landforms of glacial erosion

Landform	Description	Formation	Examples
Cirque, or coom	A large hollow that is found high up in a mountain. It has three steep sides and may contain a lake. It was the **birthplace of a glacier**	- Snow collects in mountain hollows and is **compressed** to form ice - The ice **plucks** rocks from the sides of the hollow, causing the walls to become steep - These rocks are then used as a tool to deepen the hollow by **abrasion** - The ice builds up until it overflows the hollow and begins to flow downhill under its own weight - When the ice melts, a lake, called a **tarn**, is trapped in the cirque	- Coomshingaun, in the Comeragh Mountains (the largest cirque in Ireland and Britain) - Devil's Punchbowl, near Killarney - Lough Nahanagan, Co. Wicklow
Arête Pyramidal peak	A narrow, **steep-sided ridge** A pointed peak with several arêtes	- When two cirques develop side-by-side or back-to-back, the ground between them is gradually eroded backwards until just an arête remains - When three or more cirques form around a mountain, only a steep-sided peak, with several arêtes, remains as a result of erosion. This is called a **pyramidal peak**	- Coomshingaun, in the Comeragh Mountains - The upper slopes of Carrauntoohill, Co. Waterford, Macgillycuddy's Reeks in Co. Kerry, form a pyramidal peak
U-shaped valley	A wide, flat floor and steep sides	- When the glacier moves out of a cirque, it takes the easiest route down the mountainside. This is usually through a former river (V-shaped) valley. The glacier uses its load to reshape the river valley by **plucking** and **abrasion** - The glacier widens, deepens and straightens the V-shaped valley, changing it to a U-shaped valley - In doing this, it cuts the heads off the interlocking spurs, leaving them as **truncated spurs**	- Glendalough, Co. Wicklow - Doo Lough Valley, Co. Mayo - Black Valley, Co. Kerry
Ribbon lake	A long, narrow lake that occupies the floor of a glaciated valley If a river links a number of them, they are called **paternoster lakes** (or rosary bead lakes)	- A glacier scoops out hollows in soft rock on the valley floor, by **plucking** and removing large amounts of rock - When the glacier melts, the hollows fill with water to form lakes	On the valley floors at: - Gap of Dunloe, Co. Kerry - Black Valley, Co. Kerry
Hanging valley	A small tributary valley that hangs above the main glaciated valley	- Once occupied by a small glacier that was unable to erode as deeply as the main glacier - When the ice melted, the floor of the tributary valley was left high above the floor of the main valley - If a stream leaves the hanging valley, it drops into the main valley as a **waterfall**	- Polanass Waterfall, Glendalough, Co. Wicklow
Fiord	A long, narrow inlet that is very deep and has steep sides	- A once glaciated valley that ended as the glacier reached the coast - When the Ice Age ended, the glacier melted - This caused sea levels to rise, **drowning the glaciated valley** near the coast	- Killary Harbour, Co. Mayo

Curiosity

Learning Activity

12.2 Identify the glacial landform at each letter on the photograph at figure 12.6. Check your answers with your partner, and share with the rest of the class.

12.3 Explain to your partner why ribbon lakes might also be called paternoster lakes or rosary bead lakes. Look these up in a dictionary if you need to. Once you have agreed an explanation, share it with the rest of the class.

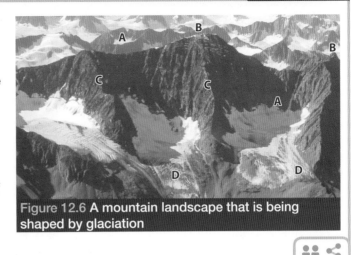

Figure 12.6 **A mountain landscape that is being shaped by glaciation**

Learning Activity

Curiosity

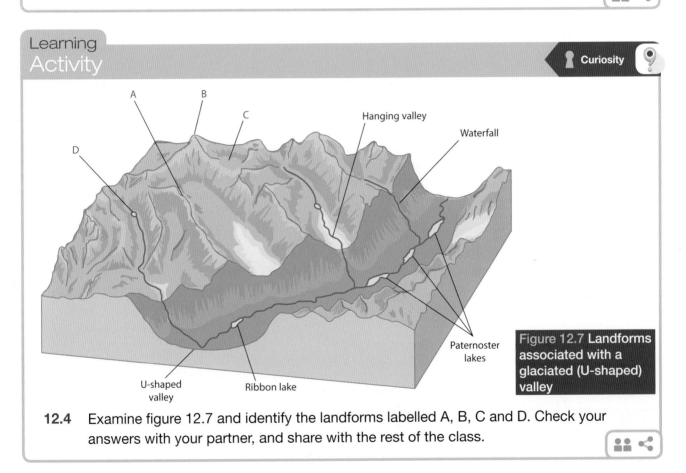

Hanging valley · Waterfall · Paternoster lakes · U-shaped valley · Ribbon lake

Figure 12.7 **Landforms associated with a glaciated (U-shaped) valley**

12.4 Examine figure 12.7 and identify the landforms labelled A, B, C and D. Check your answers with your partner, and share with the rest of the class.

Learning Activity

Curiosity Responsibility

12.5 Examine figure 12.8. Identify in which direction the glacier travelled: foreground towards background, or background towards foreground? Justify your answer to your partner, and share with the rest of the class.

12.6 Which country contains most of Europe's fiords? Research this question and compare your answer with your partner's. Share your findings with the rest of the class.

Figure 12.8 A fiord is a drowned glaciated valley

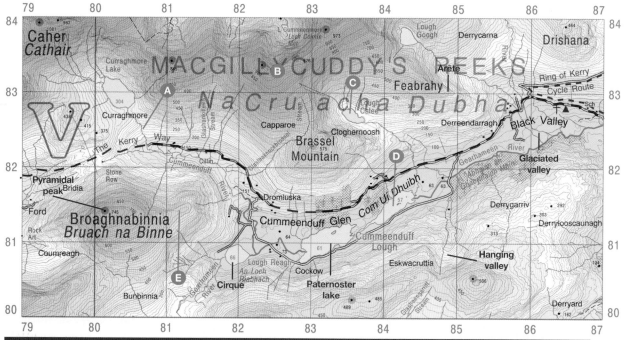

Figure 12.9 Landforms of glacial erosion on an OS map. Cummeenduff Glen is a U-shaped valley

Learning Activity

Curiosity

12.7 Look at the landforms labelled on the Ordnance Survey map at figure 12.9.

(a) Identify the landforms identified by labels A–E.

(b) Explain how you identified the landform at labels A–E.

Glaciation: the work of deposition

How glaciers transport their load

Glaciers are able to carry large amounts of eroded material. The term **moraine** describes the load of loose rock that is transported and later deposited by the glacier.

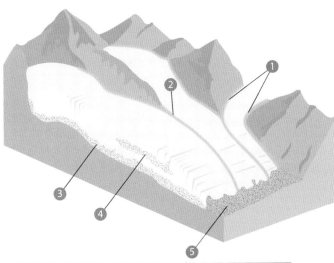

1 **Lateral moraines** are carried along the side of the glacier.

2 **Medial moraines** are formed when two lateral moraines join together.

3 **Ground moraines** are carried along beneath the glacier.

4 Some material is **carried inside** the glacier.

5 Some material is **pushed ahead** of the glacier.

Figure 12.10 **How glaciers transport their load**

Learning Activity

 Communicating Curiosity

12.8 Look at the photo at figure 12.11. Which type of moraines are shown in this photograph? Compare your thoughts with your partner's and justify your answer. Share your answers with the rest of the class.

Figure 12.11 **Moraines on a glacier**

Landforms of glacial deposition

Landforms of glacial deposition are usually found in **lowland areas**. Here the temperature is warmer and the ice begins to melt. It is unable to transport its load so it begins to **deposit** it. These landforms are summarised in table 12.2.

Table 12.2 **Landforms of glacial deposition**			
Landform	**Description**	**Formation**	**Examples**
Boulder clay plains	Lowland areas that have been covered by a layer of **boulder clay**. This is a mixture of boulders, stones and clay	▪ As the ice sheet melts, it loses some of its energy and begins to deposit its load on the lowland areas over which it passes	All the **fertile farming areas** of Ireland, including the Golden Vale (covering parts of Limerick, Tipperary and Cork), have a covering of boulder clay (see figure 12.13)
Drumlins	Small, oval-shaped hills that are made of **boulder clay** (see figures 12.14 and 12.15) Drumlins occur in groups, forming what is called a **basket-of-eggs landscape**	▪ The ice deposits some of its load of boulder clay ▪ As the remaining ice moves over the boulder clay, it **smooths** and **shapes** it into drumlins ▪ The movement of ice causes one end of a drumlin to be steep, while the other end has a gentle slope	The largest drumlin region in Ireland stretches from Clew Bay (Co. Mayo) through to Strangford Lough (Co. Down)
Moraine	The load of rock, stones and clay that was transported and later deposited on a valley floor by a glacier as it melted	When the glacier begins to melt, it deposits its load There are four main types, named according to where they were deposited (see figure 12.16): ▪ **Lateral moraine** – found along the sides of the valley ▪ **Medial moraine** – found along the middle of the valley ▪ **Ground moraine** – covers the floor of the valley ▪ **Terminal moraine** – marks the furthest point to which the glacier advanced	Glendalough, Co. Wicklow A line across the country from Clare to Wexford

Figure 12.12 Granite erratics deposited on a limestone surface. An erratic is a large boulder in an area where the rock type is different. As a result, it looks a little out of place in the landscape Erratics can tell us how far the ice travelled and the direction from which it came

Figure 12.13 The Golden Vale, with its boulder clay soils, is one of Ireland's main farming regions

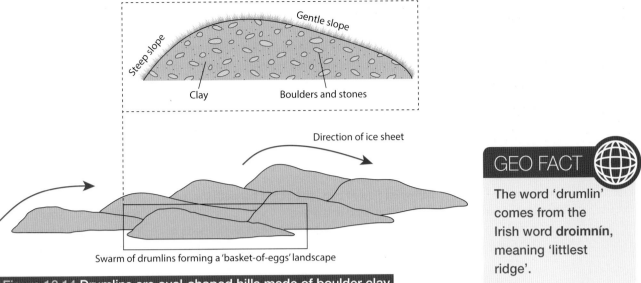

Steep slope

Gentle slope

Clay

Boulders and stones

Direction of ice sheet

Swarm of drumlins forming a 'basket-of-eggs' landscape

GEO FACT

The word 'drumlin' comes from the Irish word **droimnín**, meaning 'littlest ridge'.

Figure 12.14 Drumlins are oval-shaped hills made of boulder clay

Figure 12.15 Some drumlins, such as those at Clew Bay, Co. Mayo, have been **drowned** after the sea level rose and flooded the land between them

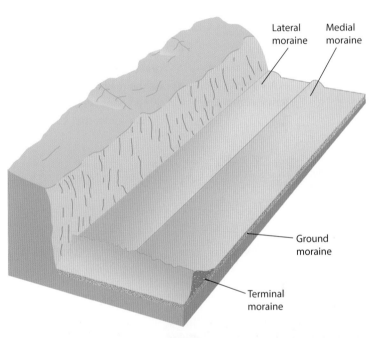

Lateral moraine

Medial moraine

Ground moraine

Terminal moraine

Figure 12.16 Moraines are named according to where they are deposited

Learning Activity

 Curiosity Responsibility Communicating

Conduct this research on your own. Check your answers with your partner and share them with the rest of the class.

12.9 Research approximately how far Connemara marble will have been transported before the glacier deposited it in the Burren.

12.10 Research which three counties the Golden Vale is in.

12.11 Research what agriculture is associated with the Golden Vale.

12.12 State the distance from Clew Bay to Strangford Lough, where drumlins can be found.

Landforms of meltwater deposition

Temperatures started to rise towards the end of the Ice Age and glaciers began to melt. Vast quantities of **meltwater** flowed away from them. This carried away the smaller particles (sand and gravel) and spread them over the landscape to form **eskers** and **outwash plains**. These are explained in table 12.3.

Table 12.3 Landforms of meltwater deposition			
Landform	**Description**	**Formation**	**Examples**
Esker	A long, narrow ridge made of **sand and gravel**	■ When the ice began to melt, huge streams of **meltwater** flowed through **tunnels beneath the ice**, transporting sand and gravel ■ Some of this material was **deposited** on the beds of the meltwater streams if the load got too great ■ As the water escaped from the tunnels, it **lost more of its energy** and deposited the remainder of its load ■ The deposited material built up to form eskers	The Esker Riada runs through the bogs of the Midlands, where it provides a dry foundation for the Dublin–Galway road
Outwash plain	A low, flat area made of sand and gravel deposits, found in front of a **terminal moraine**	■ When the ice sheet began to melt, huge quantities of meltwater **flowed** away from its front ■ The meltwater carried large amounts of **sand and gravel** with it ■ As the meltwater spread out, it **lost most of its energy** ■ It then **deposited** the heavier material first, followed by the lighter material	The Curragh of Kildare

Figure 12.17 Cross-section of an esker showing layers of sand and gravel

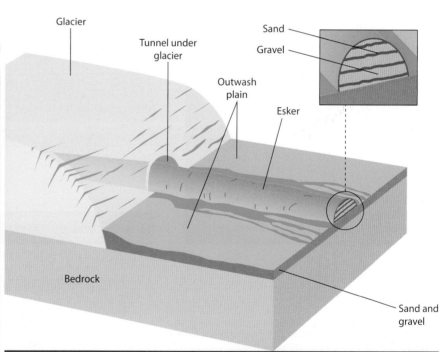

Figure 12.18 Eskers and outwash plains are formed from sand and gravel deposited by meltwater from glaciers

🔑 Curiosity 🔍

12.13 State the squares of the grid on figure 12.19 that contain an esker.

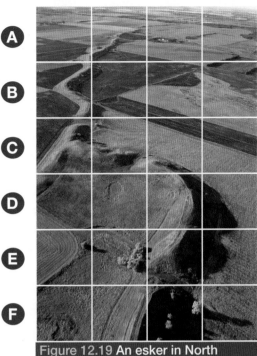

Figure 12.19 An esker in North Dakota

How people interact with and manage glacial processes

The effects of glaciation have had a huge influence on a range of human activities.

Hydroelectricity

Lough Nahanagan is cirque lake whose water is used as part of the ESB's pumped storage scheme at Turlough Hill. Here an artificial reservoir was built at the top of the hill.

Water is released from this reservoir and flows through a **penstock** (pipe) to four turbines buried in the mountain, generating electricity. The water then collects in the cirque.

During periods of low demand (night-time), the water is pumped back up to the reservoir from the cirque and the cycle repeats itself.

Agriculture

Large areas of Ireland have a thick covering of boulder clay.

This makes a fertile soil that is suitable for a variety of types of agriculture, including arable and dairy farming. The boulder clay landscape has a very gentle gradient that makes for good drainage. It also makes the use of machinery easier.

Erosion by glaciers removed much of the soil cover from parts of the landscape. Many of these areas now have a covering of blanket bog, while some areas are also badly drained. The result is that many of these upland areas are suitable only for sheep farming and forestry.

Figure 12.20 Aerial view of Lough Nahanagan (left) and the reservoir on the summit (right)

Figure 12.21 Boulder clay soils cover much of the lowlands of the south-east. They are fertile soils, used to support arable and pastoral farming

Tourism and leisure

Glaciation has created many beautiful landscapes with a variety of scenery and attractions throughout the country.

Many of the most scenic attractions are the result of glacial erosion. They include the area around Killarney, Connemara, Glenveagh National Park in Donegal, and the Wicklow Mountains.

Tourists bring many economic benefits to these areas. These include employment for local people in hotels and restaurants and as guides and instructors. There are also indirect jobs in building and maintenance. The extra income supports local services such as shops.

Figure 12.22 The valley of Glendalough is one of the most popular tourist attractions in the country. Its attractions include two lakes, hiking and climbing. It is also the site of an ancient monastic settlement, attracted there by the remote and peaceful setting

Learning Activity

Communicating Literacy Curiosity Responsibility Creativity

12.14 Work on your own or in small groups.

(a) Choose one of the areas in Ireland that we have mentioned in this chapter as an example of one or more glacial landforms, and research it as a tourist destination.

(b) Create a travel poster, booklet or automatically running slide display to persuade people to visit the area for a day-trip or holiday.

(c) Leave these around the classroom for everyone to look at, as instructed by your teacher.

Water supply

Large glacial lakes provide the water supply for urban areas. These lakes can also be used for recreational purposes, including boating and fishing.

Much of Dublin's water supply is stored in two valley reservoirs, commonly called the Blessington Lakes.

Sand and gravel

Eskers and lake-beds that are now exposed are valuable sources of sand and gravel for the building industry.

Some eskers have also been removed to provide road building materials.

Figure 12.23 Sand quarry and reservoir near Blessington, Co. Wicklow

Transport

Ireland's best-known esker is Esker Riada, which runs in an east–west direction across Ireland. The esker provided a dry foundation for much of the historic roadway, as well as for parts of today's M6, linking Dublin and Galway.

Glaciers cut valleys and gaps through mountainous regions. These openings made it easier to build roads through mountainous areas. These include the Gap of Dunloe, Co. Kerry, as well as Glenmalure and the Glen of the Downs in Co. Wicklow.

Figure 12.24 The Glen of the Downs in Co. Wicklow is a valley that was cut by floods of water from a melting glacier. Today, the N11 uses it to cut through the Wicklow Mountains

Learning Activity

 Curiosity Communicating

12.15 Suggest why eskers were used as a foundation for roads. Discuss your thoughts with your partner, and share your conclusions with the rest of the class.

12.16 Should eskers be protected and the removal of sand and gravel prohibited? Justify your answer to your partner, and share your thoughts with the rest of the class.

12.17 Examine figure 12.24 and, noting the shape of the valley, identify how we know it was formed by running water and not by a glacier. Discuss this with your partner and share with the rest of the class.

Reflecting on my learning

 Reflecting Communicating Literacy

Write sentences using each of the following terms from this chapter. You may use more than one of the terms in your sentence if appropriate.

abrasion	glaciation	paternoster lakes
arête	glacier	plucking
boulder clay	hanging valley	pyramidal peak
cirque	Ice Age	ribbon lake
drumlin	ice sheet	striae
erratic	meltwater	tarn
esker	moraine	U-shaped valley
fiord	outwash plain	

 PowerPoint summary

Revision
Go to **www.edco.ie/geographynow** and try the interactive activities and quizzes.

13

Go to **www.edco.ie/geographynow** and try the interactive activities and quizzes.

Learning intentions

When you have completed this chapter you will be able to:

- Explain what soil is and list its ingredients
- Describe how soils are formed
- Examine soil profiles
- Assess how leaching affects soil
- Relate soil and vegetation influences
- Assess the exploitation of soil around the world and in Ireland
- Consider the conservation of soil around the world and in Ireland.

1.4 Assess a soil type in a local area in relation to composition and vegetation

2.4 Assess the exploitation of water, fish stocks, forestry and soil as natural resources

Key terms

mineral matter

living organisms

humus

parent material

carbon sink

soil profile

soil horizon

bedrock

plant litter

topsoil

subsoil

soil texture

leaching

impermeable

hardpan

soil erosion

monoculture

desertification

overgrazing

overcropping

soil conservation

sustainable agricultural practices

DEFINITION

Sand is the largest particle found in soil. When you rub it, it feels rough. Sand is good for drainage, which means it lets water flow through it easily.

Silt is the medium-sized particle found in soil. Silt feels smooth when dry, and feels slippery when wet. Silt is better than sand or clay at holding nutrients.

Clay is the smallest particle found in soil. Clay feels sticky when wet and smooth when dry. It also turns hard as stone when dry.

Texture describes how a soil feels. It is influenced by the size and type of particles that make up the soil.

What is soil?

Soil is the thin layer of loose material on Earth's surface. It is one of the world's most important **natural resources**. Plants obtain their minerals from the soil, so **without soil there would be no food** for animals or people.

Soil has five main ingredients, both living and non-living. They are, with their approximate proportions:

- Mineral matter (45%)

- Air (25%)

- Water (25%)

- Humus (4%)

- Living organisms (1%).

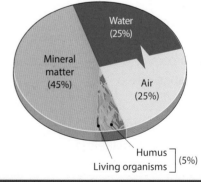

Figure 13.1 **The amount of water and air in soil varies, depending on the weather and how well the soil can hold water**

Link 🔗 **Science: Chemical World**

Mineral matter

Mineral matter is the **biggest ingredient** in soil. It is made up of **rock particles** that have been broken down by weathering and erosion. It includes **sand**, **silt** and **clay**.

Learning
Activity

Reflecting Communicating Co-operating

13.1 Work in pairs. One of you explain the term **weathering** to
your partner; the other explain the term **erosion** to your
partner. Help each other if you need reminding of what
these terms mean.

Link Chapters 7 and 8

Air

Air fills the spaces (or **pores**) between the mineral particles in the soil. Air contains **oxygen**
and **nitrogen**. These are vital for the growth of plants. Air also allows living organisms to
survive in the soil.

Water   Link Science: Biological World

Water helps to bind the soil particles together. Water is important for plant growth because
it contains **dissolved minerals**. Plants absorb these minerals through their roots.

Living organisms   Link Science: Biological World

Soil is home to creatures such as earthworms, woodlice and slugs. It is also
home to millions of **micro-organisms** – tiny creatures, too small to be seen by
the naked eye. They include bacteria and fungi.

When **worms** burrow through the soil, they mix it and also make it easier for
water and air to pass through. Micro-organisms help to break down dead
plants into humus.

GEO FACT

There are more
micro-organisms in
one handful of soil
than there are people
on Earth.

Humus

Organic matter is
composed of the
remains of dead
creatures and plants. It is
broken down and mixed
into the soil by the living
organisms.

As the organic matter
decays, it turns into a
dark brown or black
substance called
humus.

Humus provides
nutrients that make the
soil fertile. It also helps
to bind the soil particles
together.

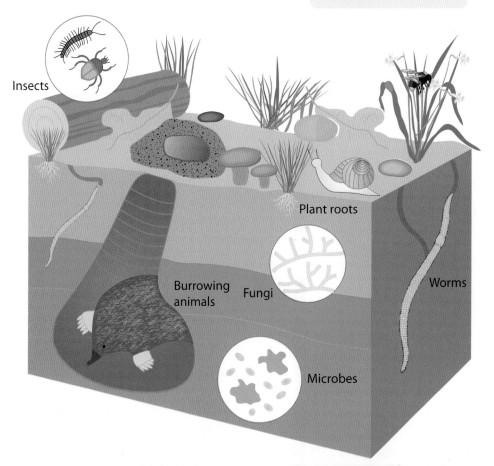

Figure 13.2 Living organisms help to make soil more fertile

How are soils formed?

A number of factors work together over a period of time to form soil. They are:

- Climate
- Parent material
- Vegetation
- Living organisms
- Landscape
- Time.

Climate

Temperature and rainfall influence the rate at which the parent rock is broken down by weathering. Hot climates experience **chemical weathering**, while cold climates experience **freeze-thaw**.

 Link Chapter 8: pages 73–74

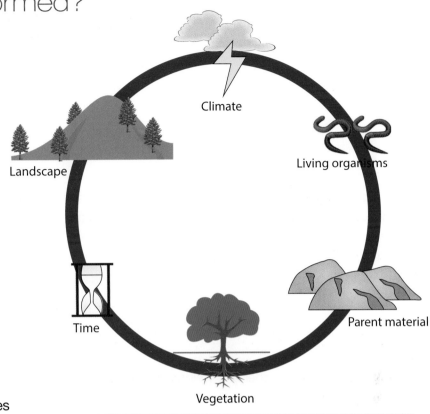

Figure 13.3 The factors that influence how soil is formed

Learning Activity — Reflecting Communicating Co-operating

13.2 Work in pairs. One of you explain the term **freeze-thaw** to your partner, and the other explain the term **chemical weathering** to your partner. Help each other if you need reminding of what these terms mean.

Parent material

The **type of rock** from which the soil is formed is called the **parent material**. This is what determines the type of soil in an area. For example, granite is slow to break down by weathering, while sandstone breaks down easily and forms soil quickly.

Soils that develop from limestone are more fertile than those that develop from granite or sandstone.

Vegetation

When vegetation dies, it is broken down and decays to add **humus** and **nutrients** to the soil. Deciduous vegetation provides more leaf fall than coniferous vegetation.

Learning Activity — Reflecting Communicating Co-operating

13.3 Work in pairs. One of you explain the term **deciduous** to your partner, and the other explain the term **coniferous** to your partner. Use a dictionary to look up these terms if you are not sure what they mean.  **Link** Chapter 24: pages 236–45

Living organisms

Micro-organisms such as **bacteria** and **fungi** help to break down the dead plant and animal life in the soil, turning it into humus.

As animals such as **earthworms** dig through the soil, they break it up and mix it, allowing more water and air to enter the soil. When these creatures die, their remains add nutrients to the soil.

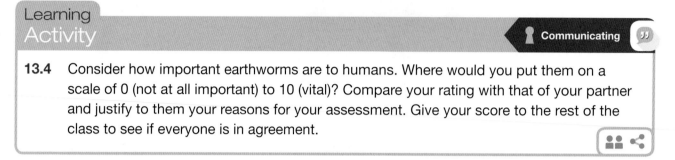

Learning
Activity

🔒 Communicating 💬

13.4 Consider how important earthworms are to humans. Where would you put them on a scale of 0 (not at all important) to 10 (vital)? Compare your rating with that of your partner and justify to them your reasons for your assessment. Give your score to the rest of the class to see if everyone is in agreement.

Landscape

Upland areas are cold and wet, so soils are often waterlogged. There is little plant and animal life, so there is less humus.

Lowland soils are generally deeper and well drained. They have more humus as there is plentiful plant and animal life.

Time

Time is one of the most important factors in soil formation. The longer a rock is exposed to the forces of **weathering**, the more it is broken down. It may take up to 400 years for 1 cm of soil to form.

Soil as a natural resource

Soil is an important natural resource. Healthy soil performs numerous functions.

- The most important function of soil is the **production of food** for both human and animal use. Soil stores nutrients and gradually releases them to plants and crops.

- **Clean water** is largely the result of water being filtered as it percolates through the soil and rock. In storing water, soil also assists in the control of flooding.

- Soil provides **raw materials** for industry, including:

    - Kaolin for the pottery industry

    - Sand for the construction industry

    - Soil bacteria for antibiotics.

- Soil is a **carbon sink**. Along with plants and the oceans, it absorbs and stores carbon dioxide from the atmosphere.

Soil is a **non-renewable resource**. It is formed at a rate very much slower than the rate at which it is being damaged. Today, one-third of the soil on Earth is either moderately or highly damaged. This is due to factors that include:

- The increased demand for food

- Poor farming practices.

The result is soil erosion, desertification, soil pollution and loss of soil fertility.

Learning Activity

Literacy Curiosity

13.5 Read the extract below. Then answer the questions following.

Third of Earth's soil is acutely degraded due to agriculture

By Jonathan Watts

A third of the planet's land is severely degraded and fertile soil is being lost at the rate of 24 billion tonnes a year, according to a new United Nations-backed study that calls for a shift away from the destructive aspects of agriculture today.

The alarming decline, which is forecast to continue as demand for food and productive land increases, will add to the risks of conflicts.

The Global Land Outlook is billed as the most comprehensive study of its type, mapping the interlinked impacts of urbanisation, climate change, erosion and forest loss. But the biggest factor is the expansion of industrial farming.

Heavy tilling, multiple harvests and abundant use of agrochemicals have increased yields at the expense of long-term sustainability. In the past 20 years, agricultural production has increased threefold and the amount of irrigated land has doubled.

> **DEFINITION**
>
> **Heavy tilling** involves the large-scale use of machinery in the farming of crops.

'Industrial agriculture is good at feeding populations but it is not sustainable. It's like an extractive industry,' says the UN.

The worst affected area is sub-Saharan Africa, but poor land management in Europe also accounts for an estimated 970m tonnes of soil loss from erosion each year with impacts not just on food production but biodiversity, carbon loss and disaster resilience. High levels of food consumption in wealthy countries such as the UK are also a major driver of soil degradation overseas.

Source: Adapted from the *Guardian*, 12 September 2017

(a) Answer these questions with a partner.

   (i) Suggest why the risk of conflict (wars) becomes greater when land suitable for farming becomes more scarce, as predicted in the second paragraph.

   (ii) Identify from the article five activities that together cause soil degradation and loss.

   (iii) Paragraph three states that the biggest impact on soil loss is industrial farming. Identify the three things stated in the article that are part of industrial farming.

   (iv) Explain how industrial farming is like an extractive industry.

   Link Chapter 22: pages 218–225

   (v) Explain how high food consumption in countries such as the UK and Ireland impact on the soils overseas.

(b) Share your thoughts on the questions above with the rest of your class.

Communicating Co-operating Curiosity Responsibility

13.6 'Safeguarding the soil with laws is the primary way of protecting people, plants, and animals. Without healthy, alive soil, there is no future. Healthy, alive soil protects us from environmental disasters, from climate change, from poisons all around.' So says People4Soil, a European citizens' initiative.

Walking debate: People4Soil set up an online petition to persuade the European parliament to make laws to protect soil. If you were eighteen and therefore old enough to sign this petition, would you do so?

(a) Consider your reasons for deciding whether or not to join in asking for laws to be made to protect soil. When your teacher says to, move to the sign that reflects how you feel: Sign, Not sure, Not sign.

(b) Each person should give a justification to the class for why they have chosen their position. If their reason makes you change your mind about your first thoughts, move to join the other group.

Does the majority of your class think there should be laws, or should not be laws, or are they undecided?

Soil profiles

If you dig down into the ground as far as the **bedrock**, you will find a number of different layers. Each layer is called a **horizon**. The layers can be seen along road cuttings and other areas where the soil is exposed.

Apart from the surface layer of **plant litter**, there are usually three horizons in a soil profile. They differ from one another in colour, content and texture.

DEFINITION

Bedrock

The hard layer of rock that lies beneath looser rocks and soil.

Plant litter

Dead plant material, such as leaves and twigs, that has fallen to the ground.

GEO FACT

Soil texture refers to the feel of a soil: the size and type of particles that make it up.

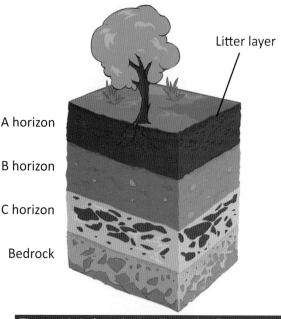

Litter layer

A horizon

B horizon

C horizon

Bedrock

Figure 13.4 A typical soil profile. Compare with the photograph at figure 13.5

A horizon

The upper layer of soil is called the **topsoil**. It is usually darker than lower layers as it has a high humus content. It is **loose and crumbly**. Most of the organisms live in this layer. It is generally the most **fertile** layer of soil.

B horizon

Found beneath the A horizon, this is called the **subsoil**. It is usually lighter in colour because it has less humus. It has more **stones** than the A horizon because it is closer to the parent material and is protected from weathering.

C horizon

The C horizon consists of partially weathered **parent material**. It is made up of large and small rock particles. It lies directly on top of the solid bedrock.

Figure 13.5 **A soil profile**

Learning
Activity 🔑 Curiosity Literacy

13.7 Examine the soil profile in the photo at figure 13.5. Answer the following questions in your copy.

(a) Name the horizons that you can identify.

(b) Describe the plant litter.

Leaching

In wet climates, such as in Ireland, water soaks down through the soil. As it does so, it washes minerals, humus and nutrients down into the B horizon. This process is known as **leaching**.

Leaching can cause the A horizon to lose its fertility because it washes the nutrients down beyond the reach of plant roots.

Learning
Activity 🔑 Curiosity Communicating
Co-operating

13.8 Consider what leaching means to farmers. Why would it be a problem? Discuss your thoughts with your partner and then share them with the rest of the class to see what conclusion everyone has come to.

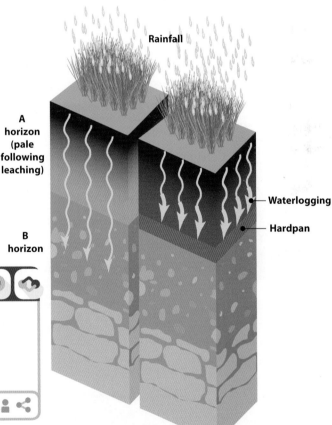

Rainfall

A horizon (pale following leaching)

B horizon

Waterlogging

Hardpan

Figure 13.6 **Leaching (left) and hardpan (right)**

Hardpan

If leaching is very severe, minerals such as clay and iron oxide (rust) build up at the bottom of the A horizon. They cement together to form a crust called **hardpan**.

Since hardpan is **impermeable**, it causes the soil above it to become **waterlogged**.

DEFINITION

Impermeable
Rocks that do not let water soak through them are described as impermeable.

Figure 13.7 The upper layer of this soil profile has a very pale colour because the nutrients have been leached from it. Note the layer of hardpan, formed by a crust of iron oxide (rust)

Natural vegetation and soil

Soil conditions can influence vegetation; vegetation, in turn, can influence soil conditions.

Table 13.1 **How soil influences vegetation**	
Drainage	**Sandy** soils are free-draining and can support a wide range of vegetation.
	Clay soils become waterlogged and support a limited range of vegetation.
Nutrients	**Fertile** soils contain a wide range of nutrients, including nitrogen and calcium, and can support a wide range of vegetation.
	Infertile soils can support only a limited range of vegetation.
Depth	**Deep** soils support vegetation with long roots such as deciduous forests.
	Shallow soils are limited in the vegetation that they can support (e.g. conifers).

Table 13.2 **How vegetation influences soil**	
Plant litter	**Deciduous** trees provide lots of plant litter to form humus and brown earth soils.
	Coniferous trees provide little plant litter (mostly needles), leading to the formation of relatively infertile soil.
Soil erosion	**Roots** bind soil particles together, thus slowing down or preventing soil erosion.
	Loss of vegetation cover results in soil being eroded by surface water.
Leaching	**Vegetation** can absorb surface water, thus reducing the amount of leaching.
	Without vegetation, the water moves downward in the soil, leaching nutrients.

Learning Activity

Curiosity Communicating

Figure 13.8 Soil and vegetation in a lowland landscape

Figure 13.9 Soil and vegetation in an upland landscape

13.9 Examine figures 13.8 and 13.9 with your partner and identify two ways in which soil conditions and vegetation have influenced one another.

The sustainable exploitation of soil

Healthy soil is essential. It:

- Produces crops used to feed humans and animals
- Grows fibres and trees
- Stores and filters groundwater
- Stores vast quantities of carbon
- Supports innumerable organisms
- Provides bacteria from which antibiotics can be developed.

Soil is a **non-renewable** resource and is increasingly under pressure.

Learning Activity

Curiosity Communicating

13.10 Earlier in the chapter we discussed how soil is made. Why, then, do we consider it to be a non-renewable resource? Discuss this with your partner and share with the rest of the class.

Soil erosion

Soil erosion is the washing away or blowing away of the upper part of the soil cover.

Undisturbed by humans, soil is usually covered by a canopy of grasses, shrubs and trees. The canopy protects the soil when the rain falls or the wind blows.

GEO FACT

Half of the topsoil on Earth has been lost in the last 150 years.

When the plant cover is disturbed by cultivation, grazing, deforestation, burning or bulldozing, the soil is exposed to erosion by wind and water. The slow rate of natural erosion is greatly speeded up. Soil is lost at a rate much faster than new soil can be created.

Loss of fertility

Agriculture practices, many on an industrial scale, damage and degrade soil quality.

Pesticides and other **chemicals** used on crop plants have helped farmers to increase yields. However, the **overuse** of some of these chemicals changes the nature of the soil and interferes with the micro-organism population.

GEO FACT

Most of the eroded soil ends up in the oceans, rivers or reservoirs, increasing the risk of flooding as well as water pollution from fertilisers and pesticides.

Monoculture is the continuous production of one type of crop year after year on the same area of land. **Chemical fertilisers** are used to replace the nutrients absorbed from the soil. Plants are more open to disease, requiring the increased use of **pesticides**.

Desertification

Soil can be damaged if it is overused; it can lose its nutrients and become infertile. This means vegetation and crops can't grow. The area can become like a desert. This spread of desert conditions is known as **desertification**.

The areas that are most affected by desertification are those at the edge of existing deserts.

Nowhere is desertification more severe than in the **Sahel**, a region at the southern edge of the Sahara Desert.

Desertification in the Sahel

Desertification in the Sahel results from a combination of **climate change** and **human activities**.

Learning
Activity   Curiosity Responsibility

13.11 With the aid of an atlas or other reference, identify the countries marked A to D on figure 13.10 that make up part of the Sahel.

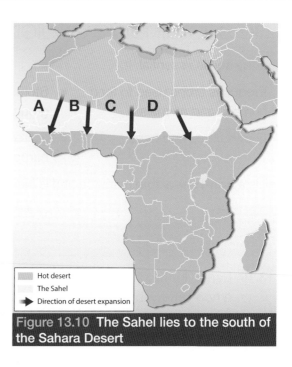

Hot desert
The Sahel
Direction of desert expansion

Figure 13.10 **The Sahel lies to the south of the Sahara Desert**

Climate change The climate of the Sahel has changed over the last thirty years.

- Rainfall in the region has become unreliable. Rains may come late or may not come at all.

- Higher temperatures lead to increased evaporation and less condensation.

As a result, several **droughts** have occurred.

Human factors The countries of the Sahel have a high birth rate, leading to **rapid population growth** and an **increased demand for food**. This placed increased pressure on the land:

- People keep large herds of cattle and goats, leading to **overgrazing** of the land. Overgrazing is caused by grazing too many animals on a piece of land for too long, so it is unable to recover its vegetation.

- **Overcropping** occurs when land is continuously cultivated, as many farmers change from grazing to growing food crops. The soil does not get time to recover the nutrients that have been taken out by other crops. Without fertilisers, the soil soon loses its nutrients and the crops fail.

- People need wood for shelter and cooking. This leads to **deforestation** as people travel from place to place in search of trees and even shrubs. Their roots no longer anchor the soil and soil erosion is speeded up.

Results of desertification

Desertification has had very serious results for the people of the Sahel:

- Vast areas of land are now **unable to support agriculture**.

- Hundreds of thousands of people have **died** because of **famine**, for example in the 1980s.

- Millions of people have been forced to **migrate** in search of food or aid. Many of these people still live in **refugee camps**.

- Many people have moved into urban areas, leading to the growth of **slums**.

- Millions of **animals have died**.

Figure 13.11 **The Sahel region**

Solutions to desertification

Desertification can be stopped – or even reversed – if there is good management of soil. Most solutions to desertification in the Sahel are carried out at a local level rather than in the region as a whole.

Figure 13.12 Young trees in a nursery in the Sahel prior to being planted as part of a shelter belt

 Learning Activity — Curiosity Responsibility Communicating Creativity

13.12 Investigate solutions to desertification. List three ways and combine them with your partner's list. Share your list with another pair of students, and combine your lists.

13.13 In your group of four, research 'The Great Green Wall'. Create a slide presentation, including images. Present this to the rest of the class.

Soil erosion is a world-wide problem

There are very few countries in the world in which soil erosion is not a problem. For example:

- China and India are losing soil at a rate thirty to forty times faster than the natural replacement rate.

- The United States is losing soil ten times faster than it is being replaced.

At these rates, and with current practices and population growth, much of the world's topsoil could be gone **within a few decades**.

Soil degradation has now affected about **one-third** of global land area. The UN estimates that about another one per cent of the global land area is degraded each year.

 Learning Activity — Curiosity Communicating Literacy

13.14 EU legislation protects our air and our water as their quality is so important for our health. Currently, there is no EU directive to protect our soil. Do you think there should be laws to protect the exploitation of Ireland's soil? Discuss your thoughts with your partner. Share and continue the discussion with the rest of the class.

Soil conservation

Soil conservation is the prevention of soil loss from erosion or reduced fertility. It is best done by using **sustainable agricultural practices**. Some of these practices are explained in table 13.3.

DEFINITION

Sustainable agriculture

How we meet our need for food, fibres and wood in the present without impeding the ability of future generations to meet their needs.

Table 13.3 Sustainable agricultural practices

Practice	What it is	How it works	Where it is used
Crop rotation	Growing, for example, a cereal crop and a root crop in the same field on consecutive years	It increases the **yield** and the **fertility** of the soil because the nutrients used by one of the crops are replaced by the different crop in the next year	Beneficial in all crop farming areas
Contour ploughing	Sloping land is ploughed along the contours rather than up and down the slope	The furrows will be level and can hold rain, preventing run-off and reducing soil erosion	Effective in the large cotton fields and tobacco fields of the southern states of the USA
Terrace farming	**Terracing** is a method of creating flat areas on hillsides. Mud or stone walls are built and the space behind them is filled with soil	When it rains, instead of washing away the soil, the soil stays in place. Nutrients are retained or carried down to the next level	Popular in Asia for planting rice
Windbreaks	Rows of tall trees that are planted close together around the farmland	Evergreen trees are best as they provide year-round protection. Trees and hedges slow down surface run-off and keep nutrients in the soil	Effective when combined with **strip farming**, where different crops, such as cereals and root crops, are grown in long strips in the same field

Figure 13.13 Windbreaks protecting soil from wind erosion and vines from wind damage in New Zealand

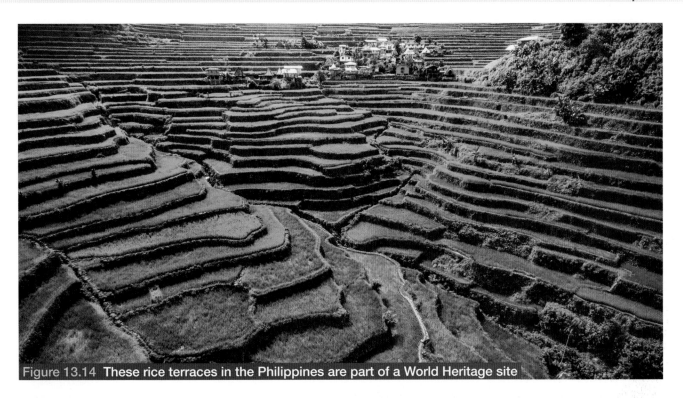

Figure 13.14 These rice terraces in the Philippines are part of a World Heritage site

Learning Activity

Communicating Co-operating Responsibility Creativity

13.15 Farmers add fertiliser to their fields to improve the quality of the soil. Gardeners can add compost – a natural fertiliser – to their gardens. In small groups:

(a) Research how to make compost.

(b) Research the benefits of composting – to the soil and to the environment.

(c) Present your findings to the rest of the class in a series of posters. Make sure each member of your group creates or contributes to one of the posters.

Reflecting on my learning

Reflecting Communicating Literacy

Write sentences using each of the following terms from this chapter. You may use more than one of the terms in your sentence if appropriate.

bedrock	mineral matter	soil horizon
carbon sink	monoculture	soil profile
desertification	overcropping	soil texture
hardpan	overgrazing	subsoil
humus	parent material	sustainable agricultural practices
impermeable	plant litter	topsoil
leaching	soil conservation	
living organisms	soil erosion	

 Revision
Go to **www.edco.ie/geographynow** and try the interactive activities and quizzes.

 **PowerPoint summary**

Soils of Ireland

14

 Go to **www.edco.ie/geographynow** and try the interactive activities and quizzes.

Learning intentions

When you have completed this chapter you will be able to:

- State the four main types of soil in Ireland
- Identify different soil types from their descriptions
- Summarise the characteristics of different soil types
- Identify farming activities suited to these soils
- Assess the soil type in your local area.

Key terms

brown earth soils   peaty soils

podzol soils   gley soils

Soils of Ireland

There are four main soil types in Ireland:

- Brown earth soils
- Peaty soils
- Podzol soils
- Gley soils.

These are summarised in table 14.1.

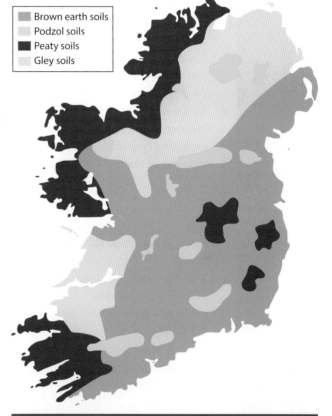

Brown earth soils
Podzol soils
Peaty soils
Gley soils

Figure 14.1 This map shows the general locations of the main soil types in Ireland

Learning Activity

 Curiosity Responsibility

14.1 Looking at figure 14.1 and using an atlas or other reference source, identify:

(a) Two counties with brown earth soils.

(b) Two counties with podzol soils.

(c) The most common soil type in Ireland.

(d) The main soil type in your county.

(e) One soil type common in lowland areas.

Table 14.1 Main soil types in Ireland

Soil type	Relief, drainage, climate and vegetation	Soil characteristics	Human response
Brown earth soils	■ Found in low-lying areas, where the climate is less extreme ■ Developed on the **boulder clays** deposited after the last ice age ■ Developed in areas that were formerly covered by **deciduous forest**	■ A plentiful supply of plant litter decayed to form **humus**, giving the soil its **dark brown** colour ■ Due to mixing by organisms, the A and B horizons **blend into** one another ■ Brown earth soils are **well drained** ■ There is **very little leaching**	■ The most **fertile** soils in Ireland ■ Suited to a wide range of farming activities, including **arable** and **pastoral** ■ Due to its lowland location, much brown earth land is lost to settlement, transport and industry **DEFINITION** **Pastoral farming** Livestock farming (e.g. dairy or sheep), rather than growing crops.
Podzol soils	■ Found in both upland and lowland areas, mainly in areas that were covered by **coniferous forest** ■ Developed in a **cold, wet** and **poorly drained** environment ■ As a result, plant litter decayed very slowly producing only **small amounts of humus**	■ The soil is **acidic** because of the pine needles ■ Heavy rainfall causes **leaching**, and **hardpan** may develop. This gives the A horizon a greyish colour ■ Podzols are very heavy soils and, as a result, are **badly drained**	■ Lacking in nutrients and **relatively infertile** ■ Limited use for agriculture. ■ Mainly used for rough grazing and forestry ■ Fertility can be improved by the addition of **lime** (crushed limestone) and **fertiliser**
Gley soils	■ Associated with areas where the **drainage is poor** ■ These include areas with **impermeable bedrock** and **clay soils**, such as floodplains ■ Many of these areas are flat, where the water is unable to drain away	■ Since they have a lot of clay, **waterlogging** is common. As a result, there is very **little oxygen** in the pores ■ There is very little bacterial action so **humus builds up** on the surface ■ Leaching and hardpan are problems	■ **Limited agricultural** potential ■ Mainly used for pastoral farming (**sheep grazing**) and **forestry** ■ Fertility can be improved by **deep ploughing** and the addition of **fertiliser**
Peaty soils	■ Found in uplands (**blanket bog**) and lowlands (**raised bog**) ■ Especially common in areas with **high rainfall** ■ Associated with badly drained lowlands	■ Very **dark** in colour and have a spongy texture ■ Apart from water, peat soils contain solid organic matter that decays slowly ■ The **partly decayed solids** include roots, stems, leaves and seeds	■ An **acidic soil** that has few nutrients and is not naturally very fertile ■ When drained, it is great for growing root crops and salads. (Think **compost**!) ■ Harvested as a **non-renewable** source of fuel

GEO FACT

Peat (or turf) consists of partially decayed organic matter and is used as fuel and garden compost.

Figure 14.2 Brown earth soil covers much of the Irish landscape. It is a fertile soil that suits both arable and pastoral farming

Figure 14.3 The A horizon, or topsoil, has a dark brown colour and is rich in humus. The B horizon is the subsoil

Figure 14.4 Podzol soils were formed in areas associated with coniferous forests. It is a relatively infertile soil

Figure 14.5 Podzol soils are heavily leached. Minerals are washed downwards and the A horizon is left with a greyish tinge

Figure 14.6 Gley soils develop in areas where the drainage is very poor. As a result, they become waterlogged

Figure 14.7 Drainage channels are dug to help drain gley soils and make them suitable for pastoral farming

Figure 14.8 Peat soils are spongy and retain water. They are easily waterlogged

Figure 14.9 Peat consists of a variety of slowly decaying organic matter

Learning Activity

Communicating Co-operating

14.2 Read the extract and, with your partner, answer the questions following.

Ireland's Peatlands

Loss of peatland is caused by habitat change and exploitation (e.g. through drainage and peat extraction), non-native plants, nutrient pollution and climate change. In addition to their biodiversity value, peatlands are also very important carbon sinks, and act like large sponges to help protect us from flooding. When bogs are drained and harvested, they can no longer perform these functions. Indeed, drained and degraded bogs go from being carbon sinks to very large carbon sources. It has been estimated that the annual emissions from Ireland's degraded peatlands are roughly equal to Ireland's annual transport emissions from cars. The only way to reverse this trend is to block drains and restore our peatlands. This will have benefits in terms of nature conservation and climate change as well as easing and preventing flooding.

Source: Adapted from An Taisce website

DEFINITION

Biodiversity

Short for biological diversity, which is the variety of plant and animal life found in a location.

Questions

(a) Identify from the extract three environmental benefits of peatlands.

(b) Describe how people make a living from peatlands.

(c) State the comparison given for the amount of carbon emissions from bogs that have been harvested and damaged.

GEO FACT

Bord na Móna will cease harvesting and processing peat by 2030. Instead, it will produce energy through sustainable means such as biomass, solar, wind and waste-to-energy.

Learning Activity

Communicating Co-operating Curiosity Responsibility

14.3 **Walking debate:** Do you think Ireland should reduce the amount of harvesting of peatlands?

(a) Think about how peatlands benefit and harm people and wildlife. When your teacher says to, move to the sign that reflects how you feel: Agree, Not sure, Disagree.

(b) Each person should give to the class a justification for why they have chosen their position. If your classmate's reason makes you change your mind about your first thoughts, move to join their group. You can move as often as you like until everyone has decided on their position on this subject.

Learning Activity

Curiosity Co-operating

14.4 Peaty soils are found along the western part of the country (see figure 14.1). Suggest why this is so. (Hint: Examine a physical map of Ireland.) Discuss your thoughts with your partner. Share your conclusions with the rest of the class.

Learning
Activity

Responsibility Curiosity

14.5 The maps in this book have given a very broad view of the types of soil in Ireland. Use Teagasc's interactive soil map (do a web search on the term "Teagasc soil map") to find the precise soil type:

(a) Where you live. **(b)** Where your school is.

Check with others in your class that you have found the right area and soil type.

Farming

Farming is considered a primary economic activity.  **Link** Chapter 22: pages 218–225

Learning
Activity

Reflecting Literacy

Work with a partner for these questions.

14.6 What do we mean by 'primary economic activity'?

(a) Write a definition of primary economic activity in your copy.

(b) Show your partner your definition and ask them whether they consider it an accurate description.

14.7 You and your partner take one question each from (a) and (b) below and tell your partner your thoughts:

(a) Is a farmer with land made up of podzol soil more likely to plant forestry or rear cattle? Justify your answer.

(b) Is a farmer with land made up of brown earth soil more likely to have a dairy farm or forestry for harvesting? Justify your answer.

Land use capability in Ireland

Soil type is the main influence on land use in Ireland. However, land use is also governed by altitude, slope and drainage. As a result of all of these factors, there are wide variations in the capability of the land from east to west. The most capable soils are found to the east of the country, with the most limited soils found along the west.

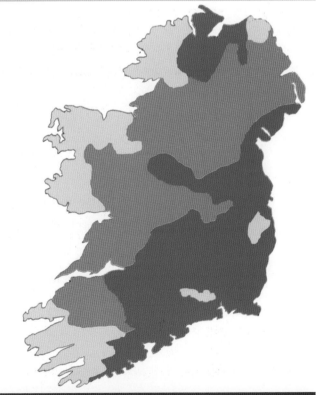

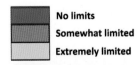

No limits
Somewhat limited
Extremely limited

Figure 14.10 General view of the impact of soil type, altitude and drainage on agriculture in Ireland

Learning
Activity

 Curiosity

14.8 Examine the map of Ireland in figure 14.10.

(a) Identify which soil type provides the greatest land use capability.

(b) Identify which soil provides the most limited land use capability.

Check your answers with your partner and share with the rest of the class.

14.9 Would you say this map is very accurate? Justify your answer to your partner and discuss with the rest of the class.

Reflecting on my learning

Reflecting Communicating Literacy

Write sentences using each of the following terms from this chapter. You may use more than one of the terms in your sentence if appropriate.

brown earth soils

peaty soils

gley soils

podzol soils

PowerPoint summary

Revision
Go to **www.edco.ie/geographynow** and try the interactive activities and quizzes.

Section

2

Exploring How We Interact with the Physical World

The restless atmosphere

15

 Go to **www.edco.ie/geographynow** and try the interactive activities and quizzes.

Learning intentions

When you have completed this chapter you will be able to:

- Describe Earth's atmosphere
- Explain why the atmosphere is important for life on Earth
- Describe the natural greenhouse effect
- Identify Ireland's latitudes
- Explain why we have seasons
- Compare summer in the northern hemisphere with winter in the northern hemisphere.

1.6 Classify global climates and analyse the factors that influence the climate in Ireland

Key terms

atmosphere

troposphere

ozone layer

solar energy

natural greenhouse effect

latitude

axis

seasons

The atmosphere

A blanket of air, which we call the atmosphere, surrounds Earth. The atmosphere is made up of various gases, including **nitrogen** and **oxygen**.

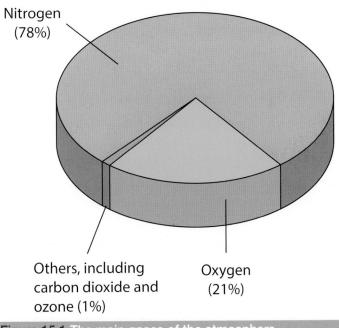

Nitrogen
(78%)

Others, including
carbon dioxide and
ozone (1%)

Oxygen
(21%)

Figure 15.1 The main gases of the atmosphere

Why the atmosphere is important

Without the atmosphere, there would be no life on Earth. The atmosphere:

- Provides us with the air we breathe

- Absorbs heat from the sun by day

- Retains heat at night

- Protects us from harmful rays from the sun.

The layers of the atmosphere

There are **four** layers to the atmosphere. The most important of these is the troposphere. The troposphere:

- Is the layer closest to Earth
- Is about 12 km thick
- Contains over 75% of Earth's gases
- Contains about 99% of the atmosphere's water vapour
- Is the layer where weather forms.

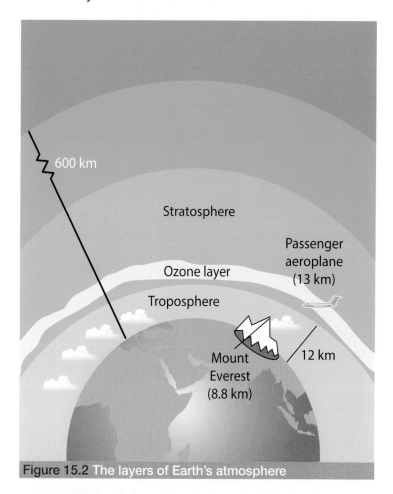

Figure 15.2 **The layers of Earth's atmosphere**

GEO FACT

The stratosphere is the layer of atmosphere above the troposphere and is about 50km high.

The ozone layer is part of the stratosphere.

DEFINITION

The ozone layer

This absorbs the sun's harmful ultraviolet (UV) rays, and prevents most of them from reaching the ground.

Learning Activity

Creativity

15.1 Create a poster to explain why the atmosphere is important to life on Earth.

The heat machine

The **sun** is a huge mass of burning gases that give off solar energy. This energy provides **heat** and **light** to the atmosphere and to Earth's surface. It also influences our climate and weather.

Incoming energy is not evenly distributed. It varies at different locations across the globe and at different times of the year.

 Link Science: Space

GEO FACT

Snow-covered areas and ice caps reflect much of the solar energy that reaches them.

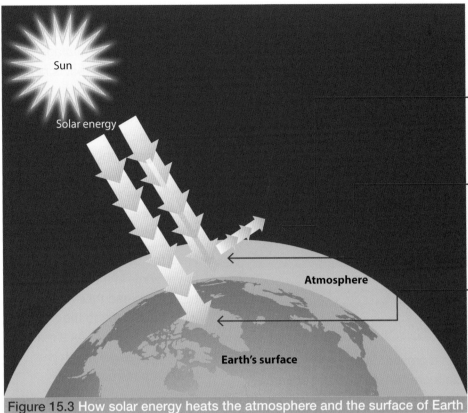

About 25% of solar energy is reflected by clouds and dust in the atmosphere, as well as by the ozone layer.

About 25% of solar energy is absorbed by the atmosphere and the dust and water vapour that it contains.

Just half of the solar energy gets through the atmosphere and reaches the surface of Earth, where it is absorbed by the land and oceans.

Figure 15.3 How solar energy heats the atmosphere and the surface of Earth

The natural greenhouse effect

Link Science: Space

We have seen how solar energy is absorbed by gases in the atmosphere. The gases act like the glass of a greenhouse, letting heat in but preventing much of it from escaping. This is nature's way of keeping Earth warm. It is called the natural greenhouse effect.

Without it, temperatures would be below freezing point and life as we know it probably wouldn't exist.

Uneven heating of Earth

The surface of Earth is unevenly heated by the incoming solar energy. The amount received at any place on Earth's surface depends on the latitude of that place and the angle of the sun's rays.

Latitude and heat

Places that are near to the **equator** (low latitudes) are much warmer than places that are near to the **poles** (high latitudes). This is due to:

- The angle of the sun in the sky
- The curve of Earth's surface
- The layer of atmosphere that surrounds Earth.

> **DEFINITION**
>
> **Latitude**
>
> The distance north or south of the equator of a place on Earth's surface. It is measured as an angle, in degrees.

Learning

Activity

Curiosity

15.2 Use an atlas to find the following latitudes. Check your answer with your partner's, and share with the whole class.

(a) The latitudes between which Ireland lies.

(b) The latitude nearest where you are.

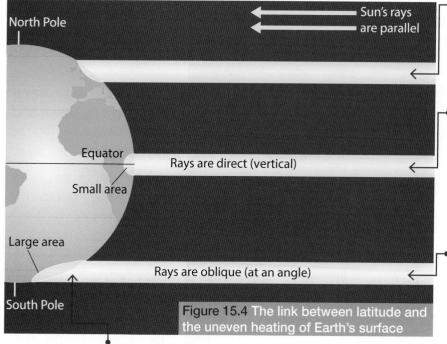

North Pole

Sun's rays are parallel

Equator

Rays are direct (vertical)

Small area

Large area

Rays are oblique (at an angle)

South Pole

Figure 15.4 **The link between latitude and the uneven heating of Earth's surface**

The sun's rays pass through a greater depth of atmosphere near the poles, so they lose more heat than at the equator.

- Ireland's position is in the mid-latitudes. As a result, it has a moderate average temperature, one that is neither very hot nor very cold.

- At or near the equator, the sun is at a high angle in the sky. It shines straight downwards so its rays have less ground to cover. As a result, the ground warms up rapidly and becomes very hot.

- Near the poles, the sun is at a lower angle in the sky. Its rays have to spread their heat over a large area due to the curve of Earth's surface. As a result, these places get much less heat than the equator.

Seasons and the sun

It takes Earth a full year to make one complete **orbit** around the sun. Since Earth's **axis** is slightly tilted, it orbits the sun at a slant. This means that different areas of Earth point towards or away from the sun at different times of the year. This causes the different **seasons**.

GEO FACT

Earth spins on its **axis** once every 24 hours, giving us day and night (light and dark).

DEFINITION

Axis

The axis of Earth is an imaginary line linking the North Pole and South Pole.

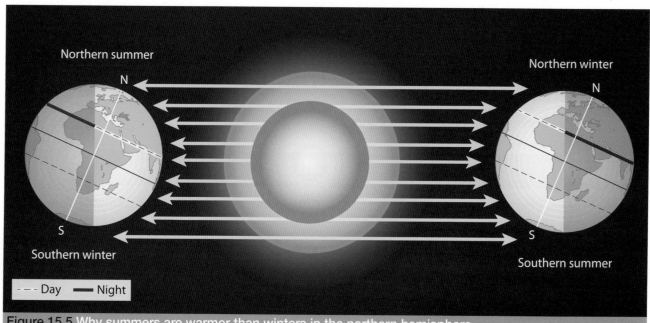

Northern summer

N

Northern winter

N

Southern winter

S

Southern summer

S

--- Day — Night

Figure 15.5 **Why summers are warmer than winters in the northern hemisphere**

Learning Activity

Curiosity

15.3 Interpret figure 15.5 to explain why summers are warmer than winters in the northern hemisphere: create a table in your copy using phrases (i) to (vi) (see right) under the following headings:

- Summer in the northern hemisphere
- Winter in the northern hemisphere.

Check your table with your partner's, and share with the rest of the class.

Statements for your table:

(i) The northern hemisphere is tilted towards the sun.

(ii) The northern hemisphere is tilted away from the sun.

(iii) Days are short, while nights are long.

(iv) Days are long, while nights are short.

(v) It receives much more solar energy, so its weather is warmer.

(vi) It receives much less solar energy, so its weather is colder.

Energy transfer

Because of the uneven heating of Earth's surface, there are energy differences across the globe, with:

- A **surplus** of energy at the tropics
- A **deficit** of energy at polar regions.

Some of this difference is balanced out as energy is transferred between the regions by **winds** and **ocean currents**.

Link 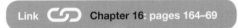 **Chapter 16**: pages 164–69

Reflecting on my learning

Reflecting Communicating Literacy

Write sentences using each of the following terms from this chapter. You may use more than one of the terms in your sentence if appropriate.

atmosphere	natural greenhouse effect	solar energy
axis	ozone layer	troposphere
latitude	seasons	

 PowerPoint summary

 Revision
Go to **www.edco.ie/geographynow** and try the interactive activities and quizzes.

Section

2 Wind and ocean currents

16

Go to **www.edco.ie/geographynow** and try the interactive activities and quizzes.

Learning intentions

When you have completed this chapter you will be able to:

- Describe how winds form
- Identify the prevailing wind for Ireland
- Name and describe the global winds
- Explain what ocean currents are
- Describe the impact of currents on climate
- Illustrate how ocean currents affect Ireland.

164

Key terms

wind

atmospheric pressure

low pressure

high pressure

prevailing wind

wind pattern

wind belt

Coriolis effect

the doldrums

trade winds

westerlies

polar winds

ocean current

warm current

cold current

Gulf Stream

North Atlantic Drift

The moving atmosphere

The atmosphere is not a calm place. Its lower layer is always in motion. This moving air is called wind. The faster the air moves, the more wind there is. And, as the winds move around the globe, they **transfer heat**.

How winds form

Winds form because the sun heats different parts of Earth unequally. Places closer to the equator get much more heat than places near the poles (see figure 15.4, page 162).

- When air is **heated**, it expands and becomes **lighter**. It rises and creates an area of low atmospheric pressure (LP).

- When air is **cooled**, it becomes **heavier** and descends. It presses down on Earth's surface and creates an area of high atmospheric pressure (HP).

- Air moves **from high** pressure areas **to low** pressure areas. This is wind.

> **DEFINITION**
>
> **Atmospheric pressure**
>
> The weight of the air pressing down on Earth's surface.

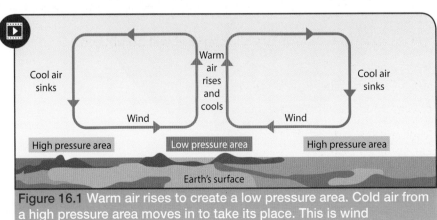

Figure 16.1 Warm air rises to create a low pressure area. Cold air from a high pressure area moves in to take its place. This is wind

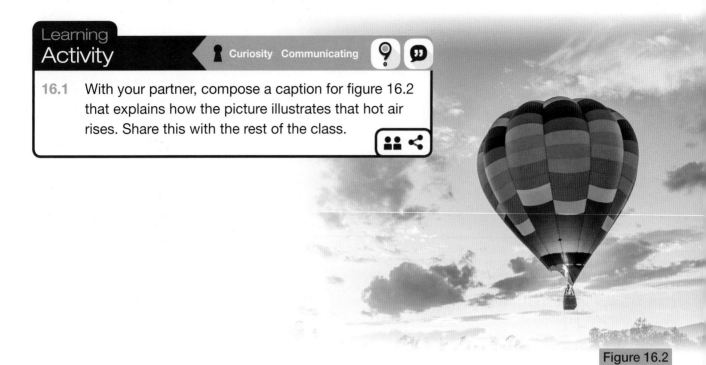

Learning Activity

Curiosity   Communicating

16.1   With your partner, compose a caption for figure 16.2 that explains how the picture illustrates that hot air rises. Share this with the rest of the class.

Figure 16.2

Some facts about winds

- Winds are named after the direction **from which they blow**.

- Winds are deflected to their right in the northern hemisphere and to their left in the southern hemisphere by the Coriolis effect.

- The wind that is most frequent in an area is called the prevailing wind.

- Winds that blow from the equator towards the poles are **warm winds**.

- Winds that blow from the poles towards the equator are **cold winds**.

GEO FACT

If heat were not transferred around the globe, Ireland would be frozen over all year round.

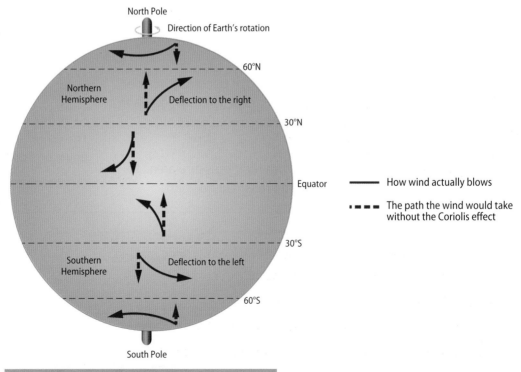

Figure 16.3 The Coriolis effect deflects winds

Learning
Activity
 Curiosity Responsibility

16.2 Research which wind is the prevailing wind for most of Ireland. Note in your Activity Book (page 97) where you found this information.

Check your answer with your partner's and share with the rest of the class.

Global winds

A combination of unequal heating of the atmosphere and the Coriolis effect gives us the global patterns that we have today. These are explained in figure 16.4 and table 16.1.

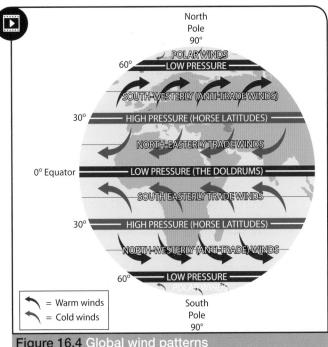

= Warm winds
= Cold winds

Figure 16.4 Global wind patterns

Table 16.1 Global winds

Trade winds	The westerlies	The polar easterlies
Movements of air towards the equator: • From the **north-east** in the **northern hemisphere** • From the **south-east** in the **southern hemisphere** They were called trade winds because they were used by captains of sailing ships to cross the oceans	Movements of air from about latitude 30° towards latitude 60°. They are deflected by the Coriolis effect to blow: • From the **south-west** in the **northern hemisphere** • From the **north-west** in the **southern hemisphere**	Movements of air outwards from the high pressure areas at the poles The winds are **dry** and **very cold**

DEFINITION

The doldrums

This is an area close to the equator (see figure 16.4) that has very **calm weather**. Winds are very light or have died out entirely.

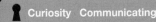

Learning
Activity
 Curiosity Communicating

16.3 Examine figure 16.4. Consider your answers to these questions on your own. Check your answers with your partner, and then share with the rest of the class.

(a) The wind patterns shown are called **wind belts**. Suggest why they are called **belts**.

(b) State how many wind belts there are.

(c) What is the name of the area of low pressure that divides the belts in the northern hemisphere from those in the southern hemisphere?

(d) What are the areas called where the westerlies meet the trade winds?

(e) Identify the wind belt that affects Ireland most frequently.

(f) State the direction of the winds you identified in part (e).

(g) Are the winds that affect Ireland most frequently warm or cold winds?

What are ocean currents?

The water of the ocean surface moves in regular patterns called surface ocean currents. These currents are like giant rivers that flow slowly through the oceans. As they do so, they transfer heat.

The movement of ocean currents results from:

- **Unequal heating of the oceans: Solar heating** causes the ocean water to heat and expand. Near the equator the water is about 8 cm higher than in the middle latitudes. This causes a very slight slope and water wants to flow down the slope. By the time it reaches the poles, it is cold and heavy so it sinks.

- **The prevailing winds:** As the winds blow over the surface of the oceans, there is **friction** between the water and the wind. This causes some of the water to be dragged along, roughly following the global wind pattern. For example, the south-westerly winds help to drag the **North Atlantic Drift** towards Ireland.

- **The rotation of Earth:** As Earth rotates on its axis from west to east, it causes the currents of the northern hemisphere to move to the right. As a result, a **clockwise pattern** has developed in the currents of the North Atlantic.

Effects of ocean currents

The most important effect of ocean currents is their impact on **climate**. They transfer heat around the globe.

Currents that flow from the equator towards higher latitudes bring warm water and are called warm currents. Currents that flow from the direction of the poles bring cold water and are called cold currents.

Ocean currents and Ireland

The Gulf Stream is a warm current that begins in the Gulf of Mexico and flows in a north-easterly direction towards the North Atlantic Ocean. It continues across the ocean, and is known as the North Atlantic Drift. It flows in a north-easterly direction past the coast of Western Europe.

The North Atlantic Drift influences Ireland by:

- Raising the temperature of our coastal waters by about 8°C. This keeps them **ice-free** all year round.

- Transferring some heat to the air. The prevailing south-westerly winds that blow over Ireland are much **warmer** than they would otherwise be. This warm air is also able to hold more moisture, bringing us **more rainfall**.

Figure 16.5 Satellite image showing the Gulf Stream and North Atlantic Drift

---

Learning Activity Curiosity Creativity

16.4 Create a poster or series of drawings to explain how ocean currents affect Ireland. Label your drawing(s) using names, arrows and compass points. Put your posters around the wall for the rest of the class to look at.

Figure 16.6 Due to the warming influence of the North Atlantic Drift, icebergs melt before they reach our waters. This is in contrast to the colder waters off the coast of Canada and the north-east USA, where icebergs are common

Reflecting on my learning

Reflecting Communicating Literacy

Write sentences using each of the following terms from this chapter. You may use more than one of the terms in your sentence if appropriate.

atmospheric pressure	North Atlantic Drift	warm current
cold current	ocean current	westerlies
Coriolis effect	polar winds	wind
Gulf Stream	prevailing wind	wind belt
high pressure	the doldrums	wind pattern
low pressure	trade winds	

 PowerPoint summary

 Revision
Go to **www.edco.ie/geographynow** and try the interactive activities and quizzes.

Water in the atmosphere

17

Go to **www.edco.ie/geographynow** and try the interactive activities and quizzes.

Learning intentions

When you have completed this chapter you will be able to:

- Identify the main cloud formations
- Identify different types of precipitation.

Key terms

water cycle

evaporation

condensation

precipitation

clouds

cirrus

cumulus

stratus

relief rainfall

rain shadow

cyclonic rainfall

convectional rainfall

Water

Water is a renewable **natural resource**, vital for the survival of life on the planet. Less than 3% of Earth's water is fresh water; the remainder is salt water.

The water cycle

The **water cycle** is Earth's way of recycling water. It describes the journey water takes as it constantly passes between the atmosphere, the oceans and the land.

Link ⊂⊃ **Science: Biological World**

GEO FACT

If water were not a renewable resource, Earth would run out of fresh water in a month.

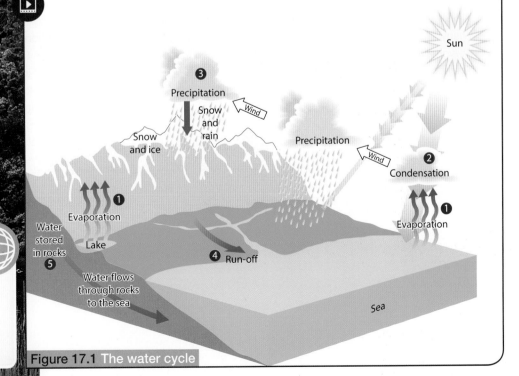

Figure 17.1 The water cycle

1   **Evaporation** Energy from the sun causes sea water and fresh water to evaporate. This changes it from a liquid to a gas (water vapour) in the atmosphere.

2   **Condensation** The water vapour is so light that it rises into the atmosphere. As it rises, it cools and **condenses** into tiny water droplets to form **clouds**.

3   **Precipitation** The droplets join up and become heavier. Eventually the water falls and returns to Earth (**precipitates**) in the form of rain, snow, sleet or hail.

4   **Run-off** Some precipitation evaporates immediately. More of it soaks into the ground. The rest of the water finds its way back to the sea by rivers and streams. This is known as surface **run-off**.

5   **Underground water** The bulk of the water soaks into the ground, where it is held in the soil or in pores (tiny holes) in the rocks. From there it can return to the sea or people can drill wells for a water supply.

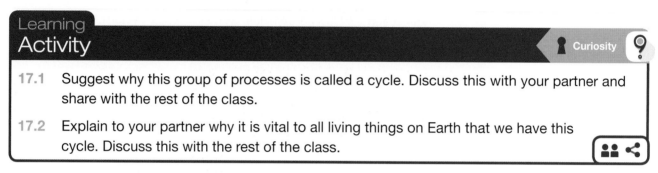

Learning
Activity
Curiosity

17.1   Suggest why this group of processes is called a cycle. Discuss this with your partner and share with the rest of the class.

17.2   Explain to your partner why it is vital to all living things on Earth that we have this cycle. Discuss this with the rest of the class.

Clouds

The atmosphere contains moisture in the form of **water vapour**. When the water vapour condenses, it forms tiny water droplets or ice crystals. These are so small and light that they can float in the air. When billions of them come together they become a visible cloud.

Clouds are grouped according to their **shape** and the **height** at which they occur. The darker the colour of the cloud, the more likely it is that precipitation is about to occur. There are three main types of cloud, as described in table 17.1.

Table 17.1 Main types of cloud

Cirrus	Cumulus	Stratus
▪ Wispy, like a lock of hair ▪ At high altitude ▪ They consist of tiny ice crystals ▪ Associated with good weather	▪ Fluffy or woolly in appearance ▪ At medium altitude ▪ Known as fine weather clouds ▪ Can bring rain if they darken in colour	▪ Form layers and can block out the sky ▪ At low altitude, and are grey in colour ▪ Bring continual drizzle and light rain ▪ Called fog if they reach ground level

Learning
Activity

Curiosity

17.3 Look at the three photos (a), (b) and (c). Match each one with a type of cloud described in table 17.1.

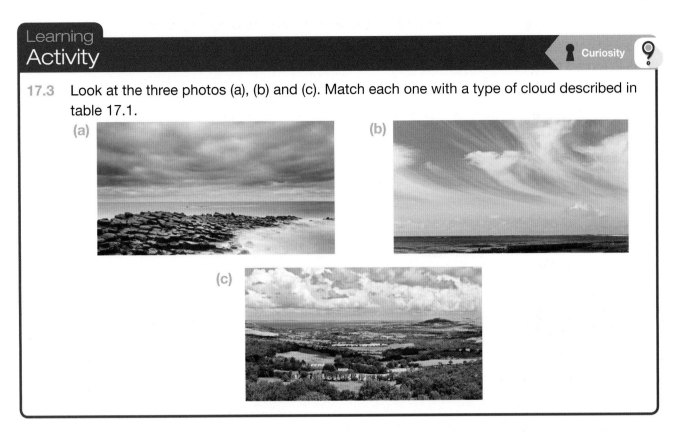

Precipitation

When cloud particles become too heavy to remain suspended in the air, they fall to Earth as precipitation. Precipitation occurs in a variety of forms: rain, hail, sleet or snow.

Rainfall is by far the most common form of precipitation. There are three types of rainfall:

- Relief rainfall
- Cyclonic (frontal) rainfall
- Convectional rainfall.

Relief rainfall

Relief rainfall occurs when a large body of air (called an air mass, as we will see in the next chapter) is forced to rise over a **mountain range**.

- Warm, **moist air** blows in from over the sea.
- If it meets a coastal **mountain range**, it is forced to rise.
- This causes the air to **cool** and **condensation** occurs.
- Clouds form and eventually **rain falls** on the **windward** side of the mountain.
- The air that descends on the sheltered (**leeward**) side of the mountain has very little moisture left. Condensation ceases and a **rain shadow** is created.

Ireland receives relief rainfall throughout the year; most of it falls in the mountainous areas of the west coast.

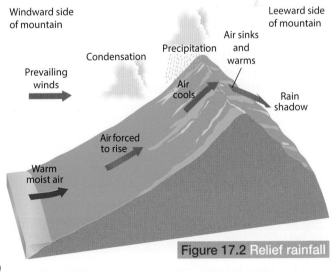

Figure 17.2 Relief rainfall

DEFINITION

Rain shadow

A dry area on the sheltered (leeward) side of a mountain.

Cyclonic (frontal) rainfall

Cyclonic (frontal) rainfall occurs when an **air mass is forced to rise** at a front (where two air masses meet).

- Cold, polar air and warm, moist tropical air masses meet at a **front**.
- The light, warm air mass rides up over the cold, heavy air mass.
- This causes the warm air to **cool** and **condensation** occurs.
- Clouds form and eventually **rain falls**.
- Rain is light at first, but eventually becomes heavier.

Fronts develop over the Atlantic and, when they move in, they bring changeable weather to Ireland. Rainfall is most frequent during winter.

Convectional rainfall

Convectional rain occurs when the atmosphere close to the ground is heated, causing moisture-laden air to rise.

- Earth's surface is heated by **solar energy**.
- The land warms the air above it and moisture is **evaporated**.
- This warm, moist air then rises and **cools**.
- **Condensation** occurs and clouds form.
- Heavy **showers** follow. They are sometimes accompanied by thunder.

Convectional rainfall occurs each afternoon in equatorial regions. It also occurs in Ireland, but only in summer during hot and sunny afternoons.

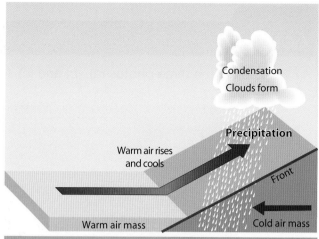

Figure 17.3 Cyclonic (frontal) rainfall

GEO FACT

The west of Ireland receives over 2,000 mm of rainfall annually, while parts of the east and Midlands receive as little as 800 mm.

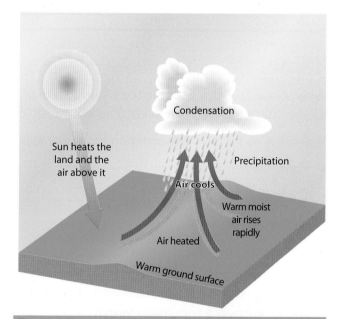

Figure 17.4 Convectional rainfall

GEO FACT

A sun shower is a form of convectional rainfall.

Learning Activity

 Curiosity Reflecting Communicating

17.4 How recently has there been precipitation where you are? What type of precipitation was this? Check your answer with your partner and share with the rest of the class.

Learning Activity

17.5 Examine the photo.

(a) State the type of rain that is falling.

(b) Justify your answer to (a).

Reflecting on my learning

Reflecting Communicating Literacy

Write sentences using each of the following terms from this chapter. You may use more than one of the terms in your sentence if appropriate.

cirrus

clouds

condensation

convectional rainfall

cumulus

cyclonic rainfall

evaporation

precipitation

rain shadow

relief rainfall

stratus

water cycle

 PowerPoint summary

 Revision
Go to **www.edco.ie/geographynow** and try the interactive activities and quizzes.

Gathering and recording weather data

 Go to **www.edco.ie/geographynow** and try the interactive activities and quizzes.

Learning intentions

When you have completed this chapter you will be able to:

- Define the term weather
- Describe how air masses influence the weather
- Explain what a front is and how it is shown on a weather map
- Distinguish between depressions and anticyclones
- Consider the instruments used in collecting data for weather forecasting
- Monitor local weather over a period
- Present a weather forecast, using maps and images.

Key terms

weather

air mass

front

cold front

warm front

depression

isobar

warm sector

cold sector

anticyclone

meteorology

synoptic chart

weather station

Stevenson screen

temperature

atmospheric pressure

relative humidity

wind speed/direction

precipitation

sunshine

Air masses and weather systems

Air masses are large bodies of air that have similar temperature, pressure and moisture throughout. They can be thousands of kilometres across.

Air masses move around and **influence the weather** that a country experiences.

- **Maritime** air masses tend to bring rain.

- **Continental** air masses tend to be dry.

- **Polar** and **Arctic** air masses are cold.

- **Tropical** air masses are warm.

DEFINITION

Weather

The word used to describe the state of the atmosphere at any particular time and place.

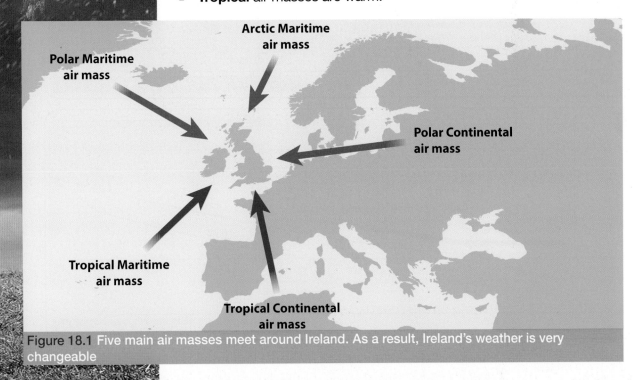

Figure 18.1 Five main air masses meet around Ireland. As a result, Ireland's weather is very changeable

Fronts

When two air masses meet, they do not mix very well because of the differences between them. The boundary area between two air masses is called a front. Fronts can be **cold** or **warm**, as explained in table 18.1.

Table 18.1 Fronts	
Cold front	**Warm front**
Occurs when a cold air mass pushes in and replaces a warm air mass <ul><li>The warm air mass is lighter so it is forced to rise rapidly into the atmosphere</li><li>As the **warm air rises**, it cools and condensation takes place. Masses of cloud develop. **Heavy rain** falls along the front</li></ul>	Occurs when a warm air mass approaches a cold air mass <ul><li>The warm air is lighter so it rises up over the cold air</li><li>As the warm air rises, it cools and condenses to form dark, rain-bearing clouds. **Periods of rain** soon follow</li></ul>
Shown on a weather map by a solid blue line with triangular teeth:	Shown on a weather map by a solid red line with semicircles:

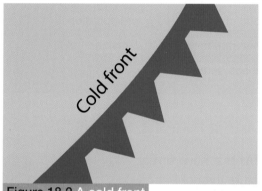

Figure 18.2 A cold front

Figure 18.3 A warm front

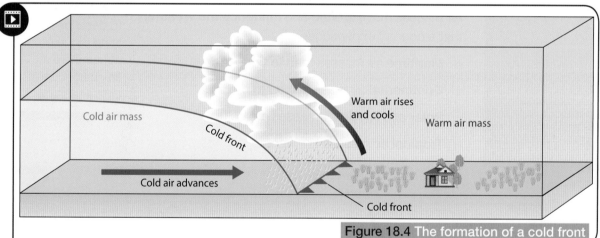

Figure 18.4 The formation of a cold front

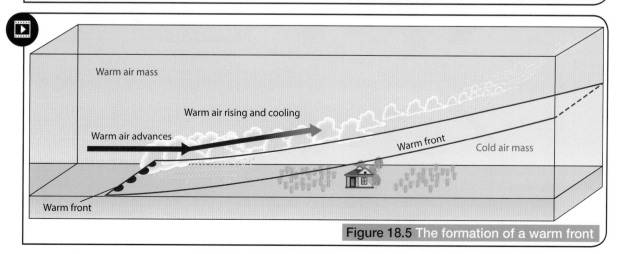

Figure 18.5 The formation of a warm front

Learning Activity

Curiosity Communicating

18.1 Consider answers to the following questions and discuss them with your partner. Share with the rest of the class.

(a) Will the triangles/semicircles be facing in the direction of or away from the direction the front is moving? Justify your answer.

(b) Will a cold front have warmer temperatures in front of it, or behind it?

(c) Will a warm front have warmer temperatures in front of it, or behind it?

Depressions (low pressure)

Depressions are areas of **low pressure** that produce **unsettled** conditions. These conditions include rainy, cloudy and windy weather.

Depressions can measure up to 2,000 km across and tend to have an oval shape. Pressure is lowest in the centre. The depressions that affect Ireland develop in the mid-Atlantic and move eastwards.

- Depressions develop when a warm tropical air mass meets a cold polar air mass, creating **warm and cold fronts**.

At the **cold front**, the cold air mass moves faster and is heavier than the warm air. It cuts in beneath it, thus forcing the warm air upwards.

At the **warm front**, the warm air is being pushed forward. As it is lighter than the cold air ahead of it, it is forced upwards.

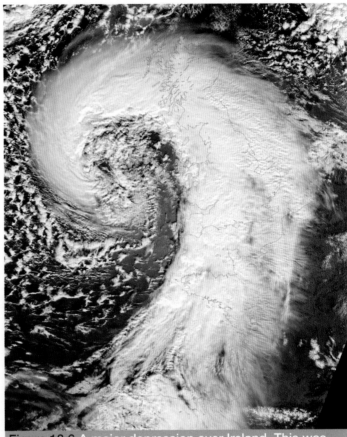

Figure 18.6 A major depression over Ireland. This was Storm Darwin as it hit the country in February 2014

- The depression is formed where these two fronts meet. Here the warm air is rising upwards and out of the cold air's way. This creates an area of **low pressure**.

DEFINITION

Isobars

Lines drawn on a weather map connecting places of equal atmospheric pressure, measured in **millibars**.

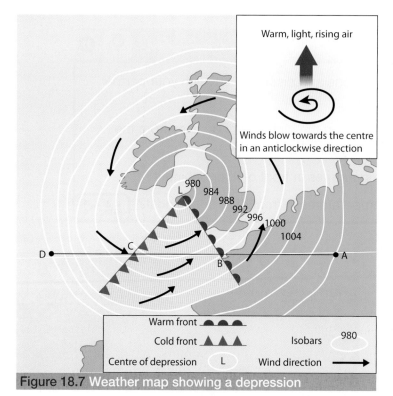

Warm, light, rising air

Winds blow towards the centre in an anticlockwise direction

980
984
988
992
996
1000
1004

L

D

C

B

A

Warm front ●●●

Cold front ▲▲▲

Isobars 980

Centre of depression L

Wind direction ⟶

Figure 18.7 **Weather map showing a depression**

Learning
Activity

Curiosity

18.2 Examine figure 18.7. Answer the following questions. Check your answers with your partner and share them with the rest of the class.

(a) What do the white lines on the weather map indicate?

(b) What do the numbers on the white lines measure?

(c) What is the atmospheric pressure at L?

(d) What is the atmospheric pressure at D?

18.3 When isobars on a weather chart are close together, will it be a windy day or a calm day? Justify your answer.

Depressions bring very unsettled weather, with wet, cloudy and windy conditions. These conditions change quite rapidly as the depression passes. Figure 18.8 is a profile of the depression depicted in figure 18.7 (the letters D–A match in both pictures).

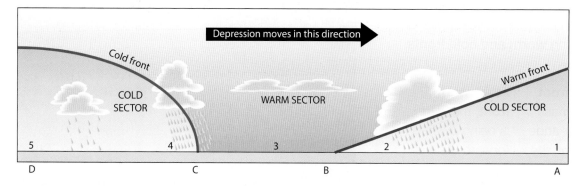

Depression moves in this direction

Cold front

COLD SECTOR

WARM SECTOR

Warm front

COLD SECTOR

5   4   3   2   1

D   C   B   A

5	4	3	2	1
Clouds thin out	Thick, low cloud	Thin cloud with breaks	Cloud thickens	Very little cloud
Sky clears	Continuous rainfall	Drizzle or dry	Heavy rainfall	Dry but may drizzle
Squally winds	Strong winds	Winds drop	Wind speed increases	Light winds

Figure 18.8 **Profile across a depression (between A and D in figure 18.7), showing the general weather conditions that occur. Read both diagrams from right to left (i.e. from A to D and from 1 to 5)**

Anticyclones (high pressure)

An anticyclone is an air mass with **high pressure** at the centre. It is also known as **a high**. Since an anticyclone consists of a single air mass, there are no fronts.

Anticyclones appear on weather charts as a series of closed isobars of 1000 millibars and above.

Anticyclones are usually slow-moving features.

Anticyclone weather conditions will be:

- The weather conditions include **clear, cloudless skies**. This is because the descending air is warmed and condensation is unlikely to occur.

- Winds, if any, are very light and blow in a clockwise direction in the northern hemisphere.

- In **summer**, the clear skies bring **hot, sunny weather**.

- In **winter**, the clear skies bring low temperatures. The lack of cloud cover means that nights are **cold and frosty**.

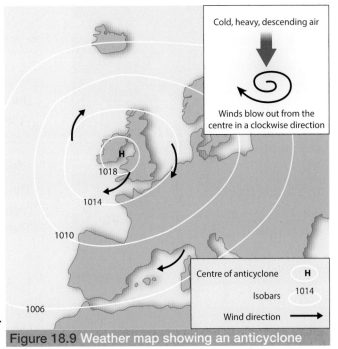

Figure 18.9 Weather map showing an anticyclone

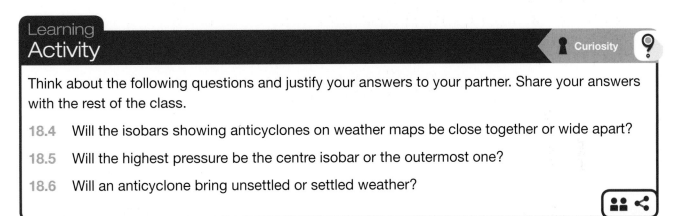

Learning Activity — Curiosity

Think about the following questions and justify your answers to your partner. Share your answers with the rest of the class.

18.4 Will the isobars showing anticyclones on weather maps be close together or wide apart?

18.5 Will the highest pressure be the centre isobar or the outermost one?

18.6 Will an anticyclone bring unsettled or settled weather?

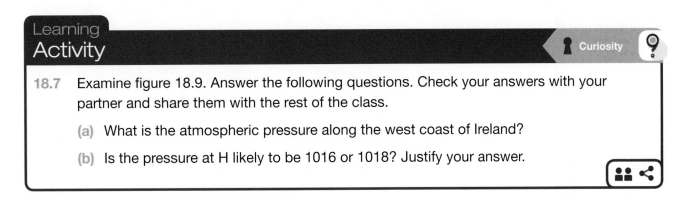

Learning Activity — Curiosity

18.7 Examine figure 18.9. Answer the following questions. Check your answers with your partner and share them with the rest of the class.

(a) What is the atmospheric pressure along the west coast of Ireland?

(b) Is the pressure at H likely to be 1016 or 1018? Justify your answer.

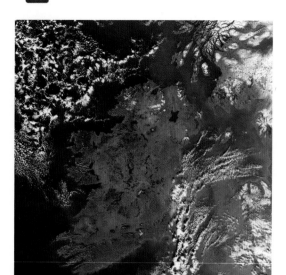

Figure 18.10 Clear skies over Ireland as an anticyclone (area of high pressure) is centred on the country

GEO FACT

The proper name for a weather map is **synoptic chart**.

GEO FACT

Anticyclones cover large areas that can be thousands of kilometres across.

Weather

Weather is the word used to describe the **state of the atmosphere at any particular time and place**. Weather conditions can change every day and can vary over short distances.

Elements of weather

The study of weather is called meteorology. It involves measuring the elements of weather at least once a day. These elements include:

- Temperature
- Atmospheric pressure
- Relative humidity
- Wind speed and direction
- Precipitation
- Sunshine.

Weather forecasts

A weather forecast predicts what the weather will be for a particular place. Meteorologists prepare weather forecasts. They study information that is collected from a number of sources. These sources include weather stations, satellites, radar stations, gas rigs and shipping.

The importance of weather forecasts

We are all interested in the weather forecast for our local area. The upcoming weather will influence what we wear and the activities that we undertake. It may even affect our mood.

Some occupations require very accurate weather forecasts, e.g. farming, fishing, tourism, air traffic and sport.

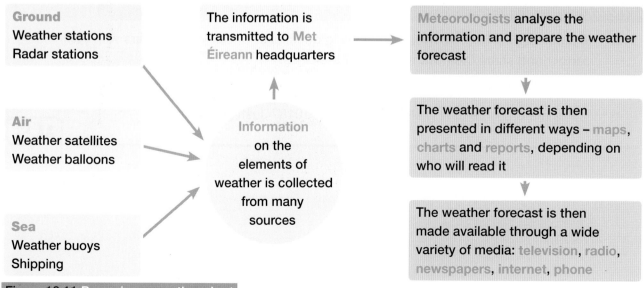

Figure 18.11 **Preparing a weather chart**

Curiosity

Learning Activity

18.8 One of you explain to your partner why a farmer and a trawler worker would each need an accurate weather forecast.

The other explain to your partner why an airline pilot and a tourist would each need an accurate weather forecast.

The weather station

A **weather station** is a place where information about the elements of weather is gathered and recorded using many different instruments. **Met Éireann** gathers data from twenty-five land-based weather stations.

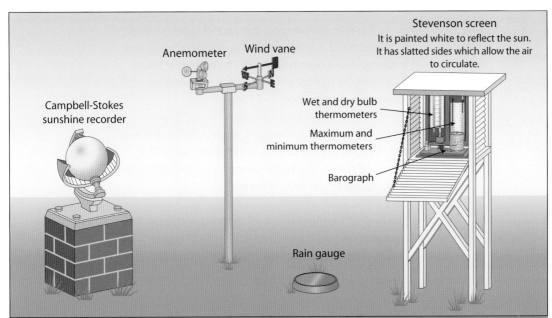

Figure 18.12 The weather instruments found in a typical land-based weather station. The Stevenson screen does not measure any element of weather. It is a home for some instruments

Measuring weather

We will now examine how each element of weather is measured. In doing this, we will look at the following:

- The **element** that is being measured
- The **instrument** used to measure it
- The **unit** of measurement
- **How it is shown** on a weather (synoptic) chart.

Figure 18.13 Taking readings at a Stevenson screen

Measuring temperature

What it is	The degree of hotness or coldness of the atmosphere
Why we measure it	To help us make decisions on activities and taking precautions for particularly warm or particularly cold conditions
Measuring instrument	Thermometer
Unit of measurement	degrees Celsius/Centigrade (°C)
How it is shown on a weather chart	Isotherms – lines join places of equal temperature (see figure 18.15)

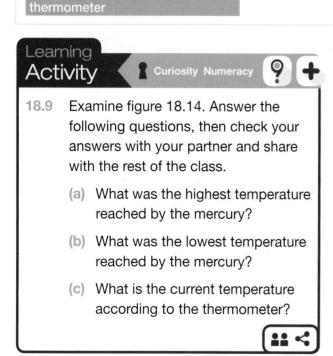

- To reset the thermometer, press the **reset button**. This releases a magnet and the needles drop onto the mercury to start the cycle again.

- When the temperature rose, the alcohol in the left-hand tube expanded. It pushed down on the mercury so that it rose up in the right-hand tube. The bottom of the pin marks the highest point reached by the mercury (**maximum temperature**).

- When the temperature dropped, the alcohol contracted and dragged the mercury up the left-hand tube. The bottom of the pin marks the lowest point reached by the mercury (**minimum temperature**).

- The level of the mercury shows the **temperature at the present time**.

Figure 18.14 Maximum-minimum thermometer

Learning Activity

Curiosity Numeracy

18.9 Examine figure 18.14. Answer the following questions, then check your answers with your partner and share with the rest of the class.

(a) What was the highest temperature reached by the mercury?

(b) What was the lowest temperature reached by the mercury?

(c) What is the current temperature according to the thermometer?

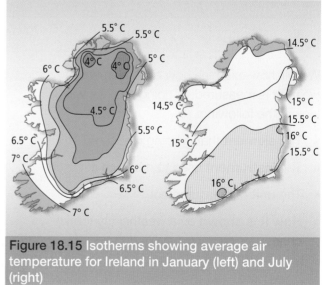

Figure 18.15 Isotherms showing average air temperature for Ireland in January (left) and July (right)

Learning Activity

 Curiosity Numeracy

18.10 Examine figure 18.15. Answer the following questions. Check your answers with your partner and share with the rest of the class.

(a) Identify which province has the highest temperatures in January.

(b) Calculate the difference between the maximum and minimum temperatures in July.

Calculating mean (or average) annual temperature and temperature range

Table 18.2 Temperature table

Months	Jan	Feb	Mar	Apr	May	Jun	Jul	Aug	Sep	Oct	Nov	Dec
Mean monthly temperature (°C)	10	13	16	18	20	23	25	27	22	16	14	12

Calculations

Mean temperature = $\dfrac{\text{Sum of monthly temperatures}}{\text{Number of months}}$ = $\dfrac{216}{12}$ = 18°C

Temperature range = Maximum temperature – Minimum temperature = 27°C – 10°C = 17°C

Learning Activity

 Curiosity Numeracy

18.11 Calculate the following. Check your answers with your partner and share with the rest of the class.

(a) Calculate the mean (average) monthly temperature and the temperature range for:

(i) The first three months of the year

(ii) The last four months of the year.

(b) If the maximum temperature was 16°C and the minimum temperature was –2°C, what would be the temperature range? Justify your answer.

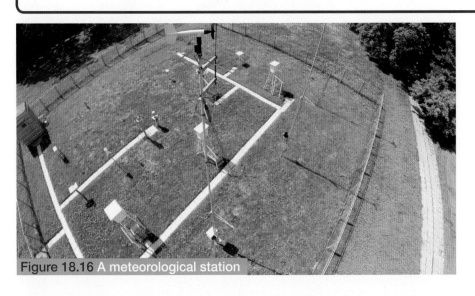

Figure 18.16 A meteorological station

Measuring atmospheric pressure	
What it is	The **weight of the atmosphere** as it presses down on Earth
Why we measure it	Changing/different pressures indicate different or changing weather conditions
Measuring instrument	Barometer. A barograph is a barometer that is connected to a chart to record the atmospheric pressure
Unit of measurement	millibars (mb) or hectopascals
How it is shown on a weather chart	Isobars – lines that join places of equal atmospheric pressure

The end of the pointer has an inked nib that records the pressure on the graph paper.	A drum slowly rotates, with a page of graph paper attached.	The movement of the drum is transferred to a pointer by a series of levers.	The corrugated drum is flexible. When the pressure of the air increases, the drum is pushed down slightly. When the pressure of the air decreases, the drum rises slightly.

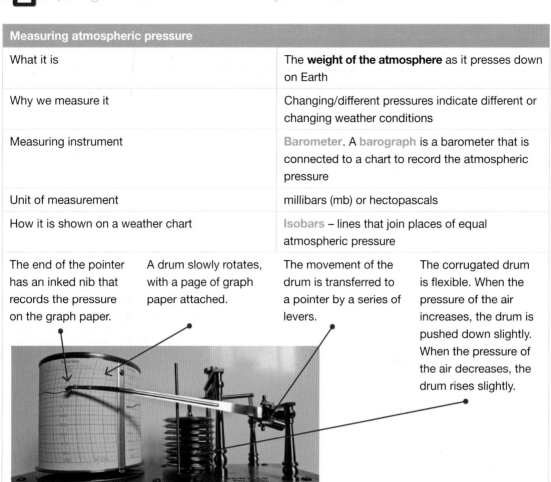

Figure 18.17 Atmospheric pressure is measured and recorded on a barograph

Weather (synoptic) charts provide information on **elements of weather** that include air pressure, rainfall, sunshine, wind and temperature. The information is shown using symbols.

The most common type of weather chart is the one that shows **atmospheric pressure** (see figure 18.18).

These charts show the atmospheric pressure pattern using **isobars** (lines of equal pressure) and indicate areas of high pressure (H) and low pressure (L), along with the associated **fronts** (see figures 18.2 and 18.3, page 178).

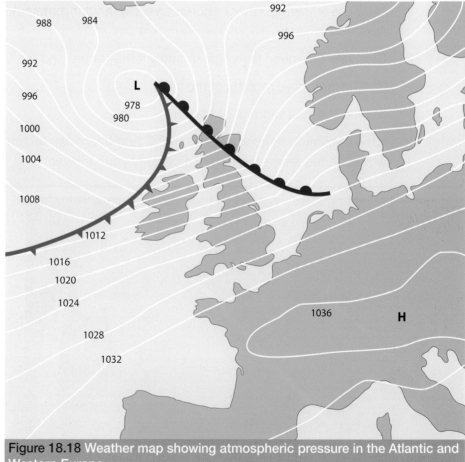

Figure 18.18 Weather map showing atmospheric pressure in the Atlantic and Western Europe

Learning
Activity
  Curiosity

18.12 Examine figure 18.18 and answer these questions. Check your **answers** with your partner and share with the class.

(a) Which letter, L or H, represents a low pressure centre?

(b) Which area, L or H, has very little wind?

(c) Describe briefly the weather conditions that are approaching the **west** coast of Ireland. Hint: refer to figure 18.7, page 180.

Measuring relative humidity	
What it is	The amount of water vapour in the air compared to the amount it would contain if it were **saturated**
Why we measure it	The amount of water vapour in the air can influence precipitation and temperature
Measuring instrument	Hygrometer. **The most common type uses wet and dry bulb thermometers**
Unit of measurement	Expressed as a **percentage**. If the air has all the moisture that it can hold at a given temperature, the relative humidity is 100%. If it has half the moisture that it can hold, the relative humidity is 50%

The difference in temperature between the dry bulb and the wet bulb is used to calculate the relative humidity of the air using a special table.

When both temperatures are the same, the air has the maximum amount of moisture that it can hold. As the difference between the two temperatures increases, relative humidity decreases and the air is drier.

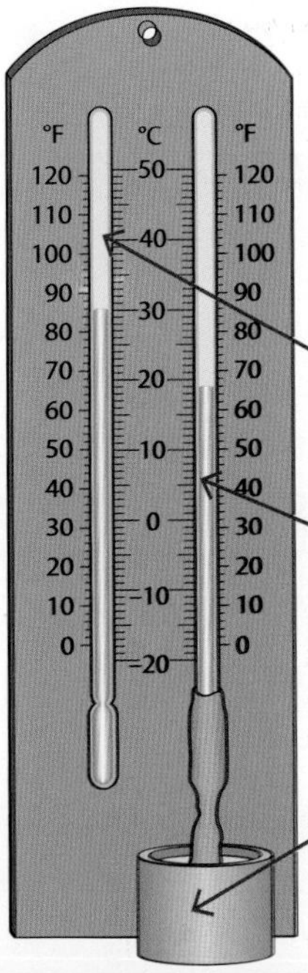

The **dry bulb thermometer** measures the temperature of the air.

The **wet bulb thermometer** gives the temperature of the saturated air.

Muslin bag dipped in water keeps the thermometer wet.

Figure 18.19 Wet and dry bulb thermometers are used to measure relative humidity

 DEFINITION

Saturated
Full of water; saturated air holds the maximum amount of water vapour possible.

Measuring wind speed and direction

What it is	The lower layer of the atmosphere is always in motion. This moving air is called **wind**. See chapter 16
Why we measure it	Wind speed affects weather forecasting as well as many professions
Measuring instrument	**Anemometer**. The direction of the wind is indicated by a wind vane
Unit of measurement	kilometres per hour (kph)
How it is shown on a weather chart	Wind direction is described by the direction **from which** the wind is blowing (see pages 166–67)

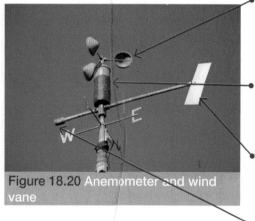

Figure 18.20 Anemometer and wind vane

The three **cups** spin in the wind. They rotate more quickly when the wind is strong.

The speed of the wind is read from a **dial** on a meter.

The **fin** is large and is blown forward by the wind.

The head of the arrow points towards the **direction from which** the wind blows. (Wind direction is named by the direction from which it blows.)

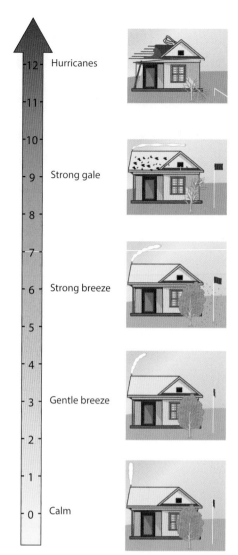

Figure 18.21 The Beaufort scale

The **Beaufort scale** was devised to estimate wind speed by describing its effects on the landscape. The scale ranges from 0 (calm conditions where smoke rises vertically) to 12 (hurricanes with widespread damage).

GEO FACT

The Beaufort scale was named after the Irishman who devised it.

Figure 18.22 A windy day. What measurement do you think this would be on the Beaufort scale?

Measuring precipitation	
What it is	Moisture that results from the condensation of water vapour in the atmosphere returns to Earth as precipitation. It occurs in a variety of forms, including rain, hail, sleet and snow
Why we measure it	To help us make decisions for a wide range of activities, including agriculture, transport and tourism
Measuring instrument	Rain gauge
Unit of measurement	millimetres (mm)
How it is shown on a weather chart	Isohyets – lines that join places of equal precipitation

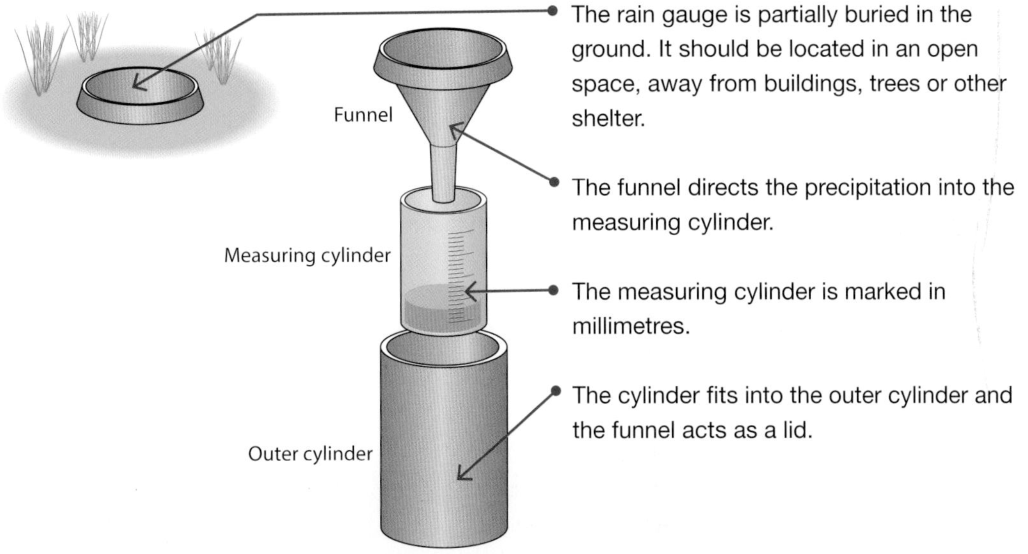

Funnel

Measuring cylinder

Outer cylinder

The rain gauge is partially buried in the ground. It should be located in an open space, away from buildings, trees or other shelter.

The funnel directs the precipitation into the measuring cylinder.

The measuring cylinder is marked in millimetres.

The cylinder fits into the outer cylinder and the funnel acts as a lid.

Figure 18.23 Rain gauge

Figure 18.24 A rain gauge in the ground

Measuring sunshine	
What it is	Direct sunlight unbroken by clouds
Why we measure it	To indicate the amount of solar energy reaching Earth, as well as for issues such as tourism
Measuring instrument	Campbell-Stokes sunshine recorder
Unit of measurement	hours per day
How it is shown on a weather chart	**Isohels** – lines that join places of equal sunshine

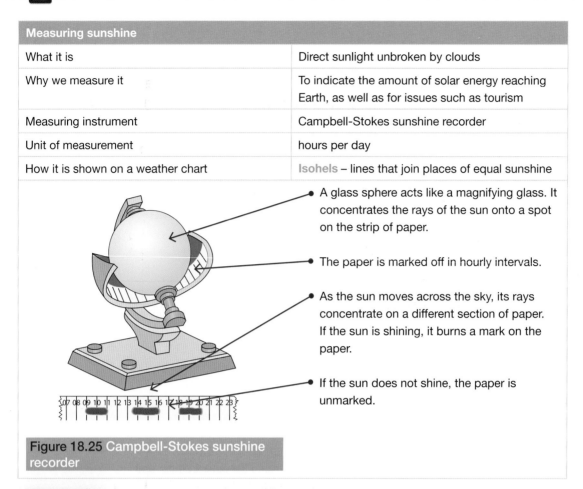

A glass sphere acts like a magnifying glass. It concentrates the rays of the sun onto a spot on the strip of paper.

The paper is marked off in hourly intervals.

As the sun moves across the sky, its rays concentrate on a different section of paper. If the sun is shining, it burns a mark on the paper.

If the sun does not shine, the paper is unmarked.

Figure 18.25 Campbell-Stokes sunshine recorder

Learning Activity

Curiosity Numeracy

18.13 Examine figure 18.25. Answer this question and check your answer with your partner, then share with the rest of the class.

State for how many hours the sun shone on the strip of paper.

Learning Activity

Curiosity Responsibility Creativity

18.14 All the instruments we have described in this chapter have electronic versions. Research pictures of these on the internet, and create a poster to let people know what they look like and, briefly, how they work. You may work with a partner, if you wish.

Learning Activity

Curiosity Communicating Creativity Co-operating

18.15 Work in small groups. Using the internet or newspaper, look up the weather for the next five days in your area. Prepare a weather forecast to present as a group to the rest of your class. This can be by a slide show or talk. Use images where appropriate. Make sure you use the terminology you have learned in your course.

Other weather charts

Met Éireann is the Irish weather (meteorological) service.

Apart from providing detailed weather forecasts, Met Éireann also publishes maps each day giving information of the weather conditions at midday and the expected conditions overnight and for the following day. The elements that are shown are:

- Isobars
- Rainfall
- Cloud cover
- Temperature.

Learning Activity

Curiosity Responsibility

18.16 (a) Go to **www.met.ie/forecasts/atlantic-charts.asp** (or find the page by typing into a search engine "Met Eireann Atlantic charts"). Examine the maps for today and answer the following questions in your copy.

    (i) What is the atmospheric pressure at Ireland?

    (ii) What type of front lies to the west of Ireland?

    (iii) Is Ireland affected by rainfall?

    (iv) Identify any link between the rainfall and cloud cover maps.

    (v) Identify any link between isobars and rainfall maps.

    (vi) Describe two ways in which the charts for tomorrow's weather are different from those for today.

  (b) Compare your answers with your partner's and share with the rest of the class.

Learning Activity

Curiosity Responsibility

18.17 Search on the internet for "Weather alarm Europe". Are there any weather warnings for today in:

  (a) Ireland?　　　　　　　　　　　(b) The rest of Europe?

Reflecting on my learning

Reflecting Communicating Literacy

Write sentences using each of the following terms from this chapter. You may use more than one of the terms in your sentence if appropriate.

air mass	isobar	temperature
anticyclone	meteorology	warm front
atmospheric pressure	precipitation	warm sector
cold front	relative humidity	weather
cold sector	Stevenson screen	weather station
depression	sunshine	wind speed/direction
front	synoptic chart	

 PowerPoint summary

 Revision
Go to **www.edco.ie/geographynow** and try the interactive activities and quizzes.

19

 Go to **www.edco.ie/geographynow** and try the interactive activities and quizzes.

Learning intentions

When you have completed this chapter you will be able to:

- Explain what a hurricane is
- Describe the formation of a hurricane
- Analyse a recent hurricane
- Assess the impacts of a hurricane.

Key terms

hurricane   cyclone   tropical storm

typhoon   eye   storm surge

Hurricanes

Hurricanes are the most powerful storms that occur in Earth's atmosphere.

To be classed as a hurricane, the storm must have **continuous wind speeds of over 120 kph**. That is just for a category 1 hurricane! A category 5 hurricane has continuous wind speeds of over 250 km/hr.

GEO FACT

Hurricanes, typhoons and cyclones are all the same type of weather event. Different names are used in different places.

Some facts about hurricanes

- Hurricanes can form only over warm, tropical waters near the equator.

- The winds in a hurricane blow in a large spiral around a centre known as the eye. The eye is generally 30 to 50 kilometres wide.

- The winds may extend outward on either side of the eye for 500 kilometres.

- The winds blow in an **anti-clockwise** direction in the northern hemisphere due to the Coriolis effect.

- The hurricane season in the Atlantic lasts from **June to November**, with the peak months being August and September.

- As a hurricane nears land, it can bring **torrential rains**, **high winds** and **storm surges**.

Figure 19.1 Weather map symbol for a hurricane

How hurricanes form

Hurricanes form only over warm ocean waters near the equator. The water temperature must be at least 26°C and the air must be moist (high humidity). The stages of formation are shown in figure 19.2.

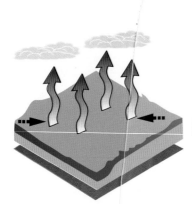  

- Warm, moist air over the ocean rises upward from near the surface. This creates an area of unusually low air pressure.

- Air from surrounding areas pushes in to take the place of the warm, rising air. It too becomes warmer and rises.

- As the warm, moist air rises, it cools, condenses and forms clouds.

- All this movement of air creates wind.

- A column of low pressure develops at the centre and the winds blow around it.

- As the weather system develops, it begins to **spin** because of the Coriolis effect.

- As the storm spins faster and faster, the **eye** of the storm develops at its centre. This is a calm area of very low pressure.

- The most violent winds occur in the area surrounding the eye.

- Tropical storms usually weaken when they hit land, because they are no longer being fed by the energy from the warm ocean waters.

Figure 19.2 The stages in the development of a tropical storm and hurricane

Figure 19.3 Hurricane Ophelia over Ireland. Note the eye in the centre and how the cloud swirls as the hurricane moves in an anti-clockwise direction

DEFINITION

Storm surge

The rise in seawater level during a storm. The seawater is pushed towards the shore by the force of the winds that swirl around the hurricane.

Hurricane Ophelia

Most hurricanes that form in the Atlantic are pushed westwards towards the Gulf of Mexico and the Caribbean by the trade winds.

However, the hurricane that developed there in early October 2017 took an entirely different track. It headed in a north-easterly direction towards Ireland and Britain.

This was Hurricane Ophelia and it made landfall in Ireland on Monday 16 October as the most powerful storm ever to hit the whole country.

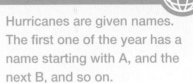

GEO FACT

Hurricanes are given names. The first one of the year has a name starting with A, and the next B, and so on.

The path of Hurricane Ophelia

- Ophelia started out in the mid-Atlantic where, this year, the ocean temperatures were warmer than usual.

- It began as a tropical storm but gathered strength as it travelled. Instead of crossing the Atlantic toward the hurricane-ravaged Caribbean, it went in a north-easterly direction towards Ireland.

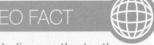

GEO FACT

Ophelia was the tenth Atlantic storm in a row to reach hurricane status, a new record.

- Ophelia briefly became a Category 3 hurricane on the Saturday. In doing so, it became the strongest hurricane ever observed so far east in the Atlantic Ocean.

- It gradually weakened to a Category 1 hurricane on Sunday.

- The waters off the southwest coast of Ireland are too cool to support a hurricane so that by the time it hit Ireland on Monday, Ophelia had further weakened to a tropical storm.

- As the centre of the storm lost its wind speed, it grew in area, with the winds spreading out to cover more territory.

- Ophelia tracked directly over Ireland on Monday, bringing wind gusts of greater than 120 kilometres per hour.

- Met Éireann had issued its highest possible 'status red' warning, covering the whole country ahead of Ophelia's arrival.

- The storm continued across Scotland before dying out over southern Scandinavia on Wednesday.

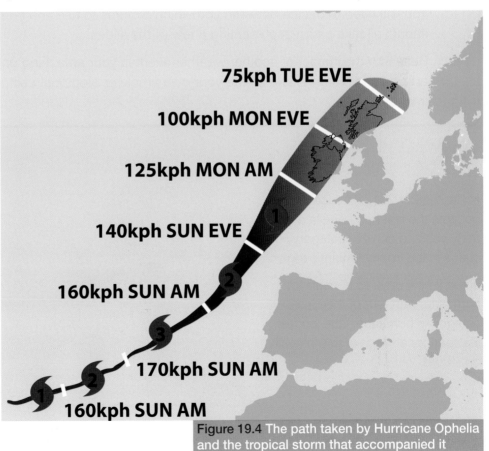

Figure 19.4 The path taken by Hurricane Ophelia and the tropical storm that accompanied it

Figure 19.5 Twenty-seven mature trees along the Marina in Cork were felled by Storm Ophelia

The impact of Ophelia was felt throughout the country. There was major damage to property, large-scale flooding, power cuts and widespread disruption to transport, much of the latter as a result of fallen trees.

Learning Activity

Communicating Co-operating Responsibility Creativity

19.1 In small groups, find pictures on the internet that show the impacts of Hurricane Ophelia on the areas it affected. Put these into a slide show and present it to the rest of the class, commenting on each picture.

You will need to decide between you which pictures to use and how to caption them. You should all take a turn at presenting a few of the slides.

19.2 Research the impact of another weather event in your area. Find online or newspaper articles and pictures, and create your own article or blog post using the information and images.

Hurricane Irma

In September 2017, Hurricane Irma became the first hurricane in almost thirty years to achieve category 5 status in the tropical Atlantic region.

It spent nine days as a major hurricane, with four of them as a category 5 hurricane – the longest life span for a storm of this intensity on record.

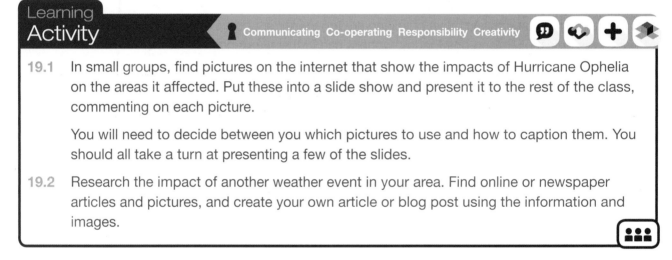

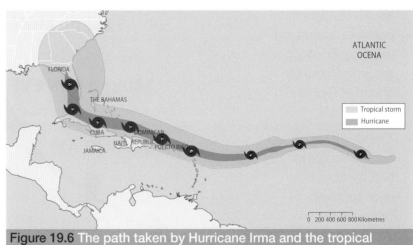

Figure 19.6 The path taken by Hurricane Irma and the tropical storm that accompanied it

Learning Activity

🔑 Curiosity Responsibility

19.3 Research Hurricane Irma. Write the answers to the following in your copy.

(a) What wind speed (in kmh) must be reached for a storm to be classified as a hurricane?

(b) What wind speed (in kmh) must be reached for a hurricane to be classified as category 5?

(c) Identify three impacts of the hurricane on the island of Puerto Rico.

(d) Identify three impacts of the hurricane on the state of Florida.

(e) Investigate why the impact of the hurricane on Puerto Rico was more severe than the impact it had on Florida.

(f) Note your source(s) for your answers to questions (a) to (e).

Reflecting on my learning

🔑 Reflecting Communicating Literacy

Write sentences using each of the following terms from this chapter. You may use more than one of the terms in your sentence if appropriate.

cyclone	hurricane	tropical storm
eye	storm surge	typhoon

 PowerPoint summary

 Revision
Go to **www.edco.ie/geographynow** and try the interactive activities and quizzes.

The greenhouse effect and climate change

20

Go to **www.edco.ie/geographynow** and try the interactive activities and quizzes.

Learning intentions

When you have completed this chapter you will be able to:

- Differentiate between the natural greenhouse effect and the enhanced greenhouse effect
- Describe how the greenhouse gases affect global warming
- Identify any effects of global warming in your area
- Itemise the ways in which global warming can be reduced
- Take steps to reduce your own carbon footprint.

Key terms

- natural greenhouse effect
- global warming
- climate change
- greenhouse gases
- carbon dioxide
- methane
- nitrous oxide
- fossil fuels

The greenhouse effect

Some of the gases in the atmosphere trap solar energy. Known as greenhouse gases, they include carbon dioxide, methane, nitrous oxide and water vapour.

This process, called the natural greenhouse effect, maintains Earth at a temperature that is warm enough to support life. Greenhouse gases are natural gases and have always been in the atmosphere. So, the natural greenhouse effect has always been there!

Enhanced greenhouse effect

The problem we now face is that **human activities** – especially burning fossil fuels (particularly for transport and industry), agriculture practices and land clearing – have released huge quantities of greenhouse gases into the atmosphere. This means that the atmosphere can now trap much more heat. This is known as the enhanced greenhouse effect.

The main effects of this are global warming and climate change.

Global warming

Over the years there was a balance between the incoming energy and the outgoing energy. As a result, Earth's temperatures remained more or less constant.

Earth is now warmer than it has been for thousands of years. Scientists believe that global temperatures will continue to rise. The heating up of planet Earth is called global warming.

GEO FACT

2015, 2016 and 2017 have been Earth's three hottest years on record.

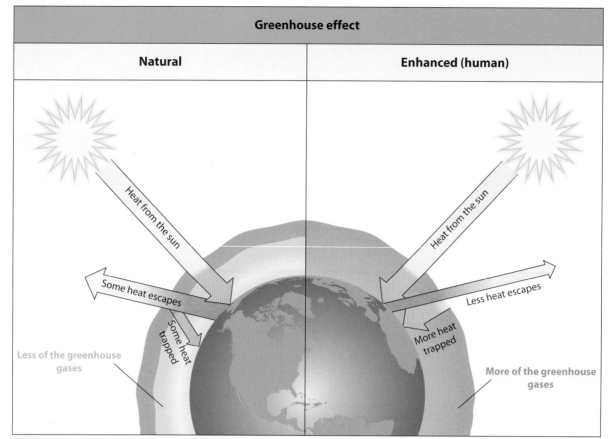

Figure 20.1 The natural and enhanced (human) greenhouse effect

Global warming

Global warming refers to the **long-term trend of increasing average global temperature**. The temperature of Earth is increasing at nearly twice the rate it was 50 years ago.

Causes of global warming

Global warming is thought to be due to an **increased greenhouse effect**. The volume of greenhouse gases in the atmosphere has increased enormously in recent years. They trap more heat and so the world's temperatures are gradually increasing.

Most of the increase in greenhouse gases is as a direct result of **human activity**.

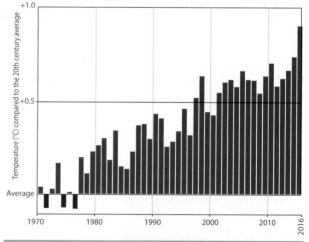

Figure 20.2 Average global temperature is rising steadily

Table 20.1 Greenhouse gases		
Carbon dioxide	**Methane**	**Nitrous oxide**
The most common of the greenhouse gases	A very powerful greenhouse gas, one unit of which can trap thirty times as much heat as a unit of carbon dioxide	Even more potent than methane
▪ **Burning of fossil fuels** such as coal, oil and natural gas; these fuels are used in transport, generating electricity, industry and homes ▪ **Deforestation**, especially in tropical rainforests	▪ **Agriculture**, mainly through cattle farming and rice growing ▪ By-product of the **extraction and use of fossil fuels** ▪ Decay of organic waste in **landfill sites**	▪ **Agriculture**, especially the use of nitrogen **fertilisers** ▪ **Industry**, especially the production of **nylon**

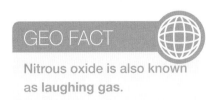

Nitrous oxide is also known as laughing gas.

  Reflecting **Communicating**

20.1   Class discussion: we can all take small steps to reducing our contribution to greenhouse gases. As a class, discuss the ways we can do this. One person will write these as bullet points on the board.

Effects of global warming

The effects of global warming are becoming increasingly easy to see:

- **A steady increase in global temperatures:** 16 of the 17 warmest years on record have occurred since 2000.

- **A rise in sea levels:** Ice caps and sea ice are melting. Ocean waters are expanding as they heat up. There is an increased risk of flooding in low-lying coastal areas, floodplains, deltas and coral islands.

- **Changes in agriculture:** Some regions, such as France and Ireland, will be able to produce more food; other regions, such as the south of Spain and south of Italy, will have reduced yields.

Learning
Activity **Curiosity** **Communicating**

20.2   Is there any evidence of the effects of global warming in your local area? Discuss this with your partner and then share your thoughts with the rest of the class.

Climate change and its effects

Climate change means a major long-term change in aspects of climate that result from the increasing average global temperature. These include changes in temperature, rainfall and wind. The changes result in extreme and unpredictable weather.

- **Heat waves** would lead to major health problems and an increase in forest fires.

- **Tropical storms and hurricanes** are already becoming more frequent and more intense, leading to loss of life and damage to property.

- **Increased precipitation** patterns: wetter conditions are leading to more frequent and more severe flooding.

- **Increased drought and desertification**. This is already leading to a decline in agriculture and will result in famine.

- **Local conflicts** (wars) and **mass migration** have also resulted from climate change due to competition for scarce resources.

GEO FACT

Lake Chad, which spans the countries of Chad, Nigeria, Niger and Cameroon and borders the Sahara desert, has got smaller by a huge 95% since 1963. About half of the shrinkage has been caused by climate change, and the other half by high demand for agricultural water.

Solutions to climate change

The Paris climate conference, held in December 2015, resulted in the first ever global agreement in the fight against climate change. The main aim of the agreement is to ensure that average global temperatures increase by not more than 2°C above pre-industrial levels. The agreement also requires that, by 2050, man-made emissions should be reduced to levels that can be absorbed by our forests and oceans.

There are many ways in which the impact of climate change can be reduced:

- **Clean energy** Reduce dependence on fossil fuels. Use cleaner and renewable energy sources such as solar, wind, wave and hydro power.

- **Change transport policy** Increase vehicle efficiency by changing from fossil fuels to battery and electric power. Encourage and develop efficient public transport systems to reduce dependence on cars.

- **Reduce deforestation** This should be accompanied by reafforestation (replanting trees), especially in tropical regions.

- **Reduce, reuse and recycle** This reduces the need for goods, as well as the energy and resources used in their manufacture.

- **Use energy-efficient appliances** These include lights, fridges and heaters.

> **GEO FACT**
>
> Between them, China and the USA are responsible for more than 40% of global emissions of carbon dioxide into the atmosphere.

Learning Activity

Curiosity Responsibility Communicating Co-operating

20.3 In small groups, research and present (by a slide presentation, podcast, poster or talk) ways in which we can reduce our carbon footprint in our daily lives.

(a) Find out what is meant by **carbon footprint**. Write a definition of this.

(b) Individually, research ways we can reduce our carbon footprint in our daily lives. (You started thinking about this in activity 20.1.) Make a note of where you found your information.

(c) Using a placemat template, each of you write down an idea for reducing our carbon footprint. Keep circulating the placemat until you run out of ideas.

(d) Nominate a chairperson to project manage your presentation. Between you create your presentation or write a script for your podcast or talk. Use images where appropriate.

(e) Present your findings to the rest of the class.

> **GEO FACT**
>
> In 2015, global temperatures reached 1°C above pre-industrial levels for the first time.

Climate change and Ireland

The **Environmental Protection Agency (EPA)** is an independent body that is responsible for protecting and improving the environment as a valuable asset for the people of the Republic of Ireland.

Environmental Protection Agency
An Ghníomhaireacht um Chaomhnú Comhshaoil

One of its roles is to monitor changes in environmental trends and to detect early warning signs of neglect or deterioration in the environment.

What impact will climate change have for Ireland?

The EPA's Climate Change Research Programme carries out relevant and up-to-date studies on climate change in Ireland. Analysis of the meteorological records shows that Ireland's climate is changing in line with global patterns.

Figure 20.3 Flooding in Ireland will get worse as climate change continues

Indicators of climate change

- Mean temperature increase by 0.06°C per decade between 1890 and 2010.

- During the period 1980–2010, it increased by 0.14°C per decade.

- Eight of the ten warmest years in Ireland have occurred since 1990.

- A reduction in the number of frost days and shortening of frost season length.

- An increase in annual rainfall in northern and western areas with decreases or small increases in the south and east.

These changes are reflected in Ireland's natural environment with an increase in the growing season.

Future impacts

Climate change impacts are projected to increase in the coming decades and during the rest of this century. The scale and extent of these impacts is uncertain.

Learning Activity

Curiosity Responsibility Communicating

20.4 (a) Research the predicted adverse impacts of climate change on Ireland. (Hint: In your search engine, type "Ireland climate change predictions".)

(b) Create an information poster listing the predictions, including suitable images.

Reflecting on my learning

Reflecting Communicating Literacy

Write sentences using each of the following terms from this chapter. You may use more than one of the terms in your sentence if appropriate.

- carbon dioxide
- greenhouse gases
- nitrous oxide
- climate change
- methane
- fossil fuels
- natural greenhouse effect

 PowerPoint summary

 Revision
Go to **www.edco.ie/geographynow** and try the interactive activities and quizzes.

Global climates

21

Go to **www.edco.ie/geographynow** and try the interactive activities and quizzes.

Learning intentions

When you have completed this chapter you will be able to:

- Explain what we mean by climate
- Describe the world's climates and the factors that influence them
- Describe the factors that influence local climates
- Assess whether your area has a local climate
- Name and locate the world's climates
- Interpret climographs
- Classify the characteristics of various climates
- Classify images to describe Ireland's climate
- Consider climate as a factor in tourism.

Learning Outcomes

1.6 Classify global climates and analyse the factors that influence the climate in Ireland

You are also working towards

2.9 Assess the interrelationships between the physical world, tourism and transport

Key terms

climate

latitude

temperate climate

continental effect

local climate

aspect

altitude

hot climate

cold climates

equatorial climate

hot desert climate

savanna climate

climograph

cool temperate oceanic climate

moderate climate

warm temperate oceanic climate

Mediterranean climate

continental climate

tundra climate

boreal climate

Introducing climate

Climate is the average condition of the weather over a long period of time – usually thirty-five years – across a large area of the world's surface.

Factors that influence world climates

There are several different climates across the world, each with its own characteristics of **temperature** and **precipitation**. The climate experienced in any part of the world is influenced by a number of factors. These factors also apply to the climate experienced in Ireland. They are:

- Latitude
- Distance from the sea
- Prevailing winds and air masses
- Ocean currents.

Latitude

The **latitude** of a place is its **distance north or south of the equator**. Latitude is measured in **degrees**.

Link Chapter 15: pages 161–62

- Areas near the equator receive more sunlight than anywhere else on Earth. The sun is high in the sky and its rays are concentrated on a smaller area of Earth's surface, giving greater heat.

■ Away from the equator, the sun's rays are more slanted. Its heat is spread over a wider area, so it is cooler.

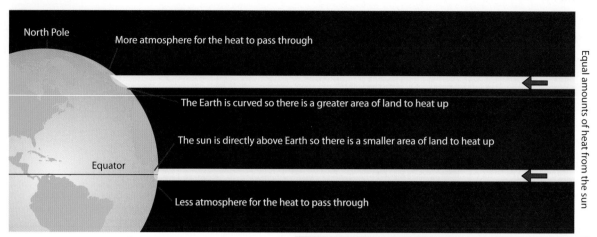

Figure 21.1 How latitude influences temperature

Distance from the sea

The sea takes longer to warm than land does during summer. It takes much longer to cool during winter.

The sea moderates our climate.

■ **Coastal areas** have cooler summers and milder winters than inland areas. Temperatures are more even throughout the year, giving a **small temperature range**. This is known as a temperate climate.

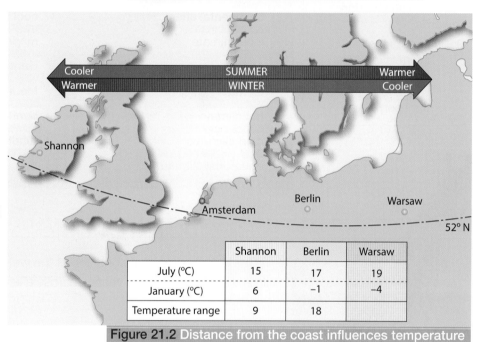

	Shannon	Berlin	Warsaw
July (°C)	15	17	19
January (°C)	6	−1	−4
Temperature range	9	18	

Figure 21.2 Distance from the coast influences temperature

■ The **interiors of continents** are too far from the sea to be influenced by it. These areas have hot summers and cold winters, giving them a **large temperature range**. This is called the continental effect.

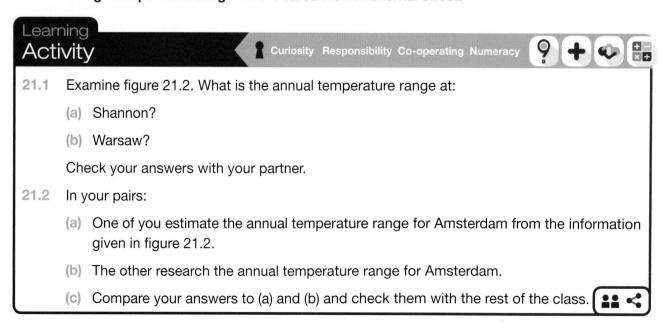

Learning Activity

Curiosity Responsibility Co-operating Numeracy

21.1 Examine figure 21.2. What is the annual temperature range at:

(a) Shannon?

(b) Warsaw?

Check your answers with your partner.

21.2 In your pairs:

(a) One of you estimate the annual temperature range for Amsterdam from the information given in figure 21.2.

(b) The other research the annual temperature range for Amsterdam.

(c) Compare your answers to (a) and (b) and check them with the rest of the class.

Air masses and winds

Link · Chapter 18: page 177

Ireland comes under the influence of **five air masses**. These air masses are moved along by winds. As they move towards Ireland, each of them brings the weather conditions of the region over which it formed.

The air masses are classified as:

- Maritime or continental, depending on whether they form over sea or land
- Arctic, polar or tropical, depending on the latitude at which they formed.

Air Mass: Polar Maritime
Source: Greenland Arctic Sea
Air: Wet and cold
Brings: Cold, showery, unstable
weather conditions

Air Mass: Arctic Maritime
Source: Arctic
Air: Wet and cold
Brings: Wintry showers, some
snow and frosty nights

Air Mass: Polar Continental
Source: Central Europe
Air: Very cold in winter
Hot in summer
Brings: Snow in winter
Dry summers

Air Mass: Tropical Maritime
Source: Atlantic
Air: Warm and moist
Brings: Cloud, rain and
mild weather.

Air Mass: Tropical Continental
Source: North Africa
Air: Hot and dry
Brings: Hot dry weather with
occasional thunderstorms

Figure 21.3 Five air masses influence Ireland and each one brings its own weather conditions

Learning Activity

 Curiosity

21.3 Which air mass would you say is affecting the weather in Ireland today? Justify your answer.

Ocean currents

See 'Ocean currents and Ireland', chapter 16, page 168.

Factors that influence local climates

Sometimes a small area can experience a climate that is different from that of the whole region. This is known as a local climate. Local climates are influenced by:

- Aspect
- Altitude.

Aspect

Aspect refers to the **direction a slope faces** in relation to the sun's rays. Due to Ireland's position in the **northern hemisphere**:

- **South-facing slopes are warmer** because the sun's rays strike the ground at a more direct angle. These slopes are also influenced by **warm, southerly winds**.

- **North-facing slopes are colder** because they do not get the direct rays of the sun and may be in the shade. These slopes may also be in the path of **cold, northerly winds**.

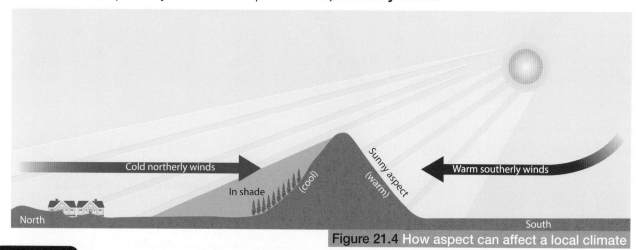

Cold northerly winds
In shade
(cool)
Sunny aspect (warm)
Warm southerly winds
North
South

Figure 21.4 How aspect can affect a local climate

Learning Activity Curiosity

21.4   Does aspect affect the area where your school is situated? Explain your answer.

21.5   Where in your county is aspect likely to affect the local climate? Refer to a local map (an OS map or one on the internet) and explain your answer with reference to that.

Altitude

Altitude refers to **height above sea level**. The higher the place is above sea level the colder it is. This is because, as altitude increases, air becomes thinner and is less able to absorb and hold heat. Temperatures drop by about 1°C for every 100-metre increase in altitude.

Upland areas:

- Are **more exposed to wind** than sheltered lowland areas, which reduces temperatures even further
- Receive **more precipitation** because, as the air is cooled, it can hold less water vapour.
- Receive **snow** if the temperature goes below freezing point.

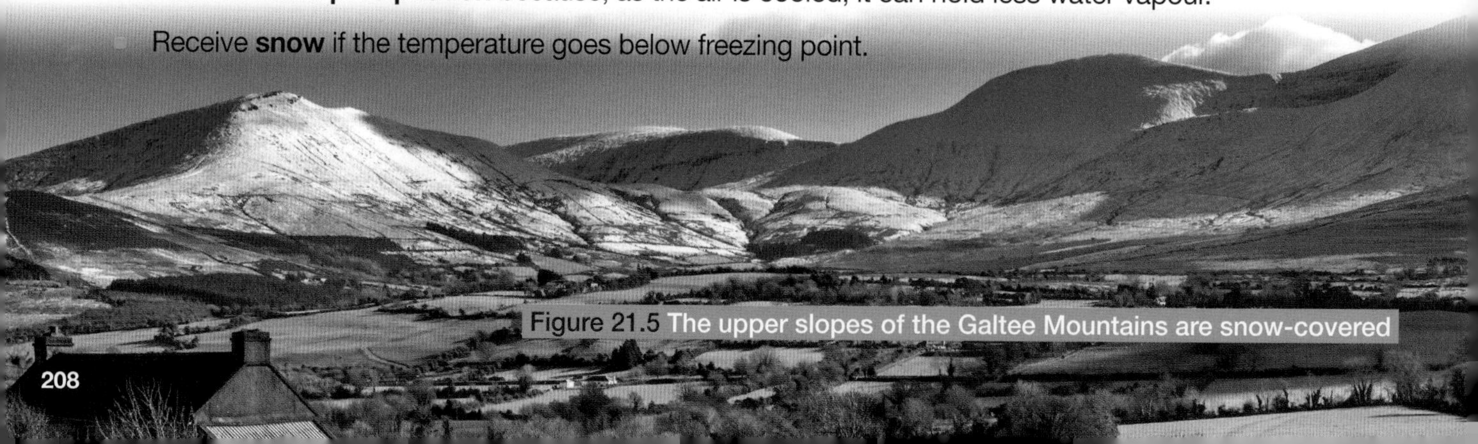

Figure 21.5 The upper slopes of the Galtee Mountains are snow-covered

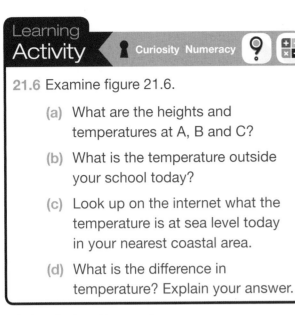

21.6 Examine figure 21.6.

(a) What are the heights and temperatures at A, B and C?

(b) What is the temperature outside your school today?

(c) Look up on the internet what the temperature is at sea level today in your nearest coastal area.

(d) What is the difference in temperature? Explain your answer.

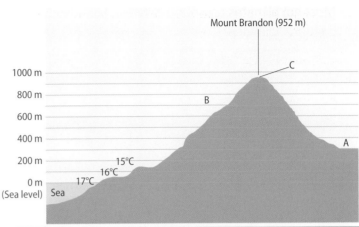

Figure 21.6 Example of temperature decrease at Mount Brandon in Kerry, when the temperature at sea level is 17°C

World climates

Earth can be divided into different climatic zones. Each of these has its own **temperature** and **rainfall pattern**. In turn, climate controls the natural vegetation cover of each region.

There are three broad climate zones:

- Hot climates
- Temperate climates
- Cold climates.

GEO FACT

Most of the world's people inhabit regions with a temperate climate because they are the most comfortable regions to live in.

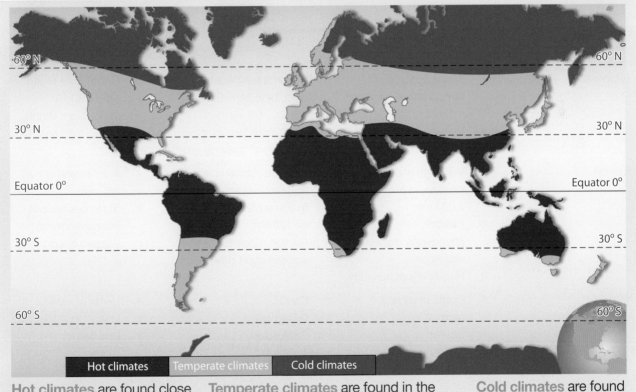

Hot climates | Temperate climates | Cold climates

Hot climates are found close to the equator. They include:

- Equatorial climate
- Hot desert climate
- Savanna climate.

Temperate climates are found in the mid-latitudes. They include:

- Cool temperate oceanic climate
- Warm temperate oceanic climate (also called Mediterranean climate)
- Continental climate.

Cold climates are found close to the poles. They include:

- Tundra climate
- Boreal climate.

Figure 21.7 There are three broad climate zones: hot, temperate and cold

Hot climates of the world

Most hot climates are found between latitudes 30° N and 30° S. They include hot desert, equatorial and savanna climates.

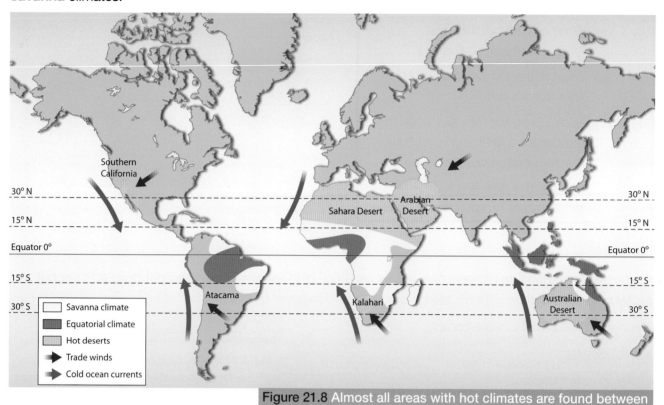

Figure 21.8 Almost all areas with hot climates are found between 30° N and 30° S

Table 21.1 Characteristics of equatorial and savanna climates

	Equatorial climate	Hot desert climate	Savanna climate
Temperature	■ Average daytime temperatures are high – at about 27°C ■ Very low temperature range	■ Daytime temperatures are high, between 30°C and 50°C ■ Night-time temperatures can be close to freezing point	■ Hot all year round (25°C–30°C) ■ Winters are slightly cooler than summers
Rainfall	■ Very high annual rainfall – in excess of 2,000 mm ■ Rainfall (thunderstorms) every afternoon ■ High levels of humidity	■ Average rainfall is less than 250 mm per annum ■ In some places, it is as low as 100 mm ■ Rainfall tends to come in sudden short downpours	■ Annual total is over 800 mm ■ Summers are wet (monsoon rains) ■ Winters are dry
Wildlife	■ Exotic birds (e.g. parrots) ■ Snakes ■ Monkeys ■ Butterflies	■ Camel ■ Desert fox ■ Rattlesnake ■ Tarantula ■ Vulture	■ Herds of cattle ■ Lion ■ Cheetah ■ Giraffe
Natural vegetation	■ Tropical rainforest ■ Hardwoods including ebony and rosewood	■ Desert vegetation includes cactus, palm and yucca ■ Plants have adapted to survive in drought conditions	■ Scattered trees ■ Grassland (green or brown, depending on the season)

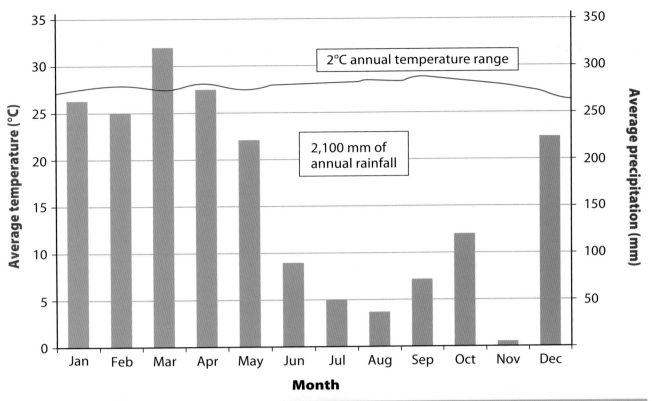

Figure 21.9 Climograph for Manaus in the Amazon rainforest

DEFINITION

Climograph

A graphical representation of a location's temperature and precipitation over a year.

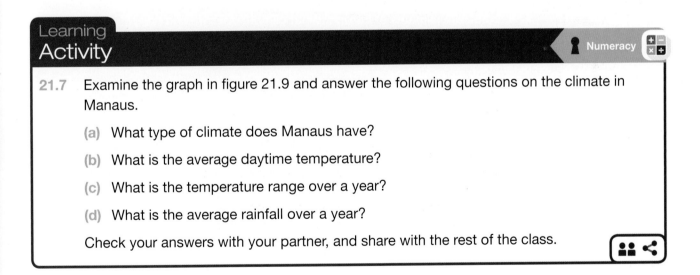

Learning
Activity

🔑 Numeracy

21.7 Examine the graph in figure 21.9 and answer the following questions on the climate in Manaus.

(a) What type of climate does Manaus have?

(b) What is the average daytime temperature?

(c) What is the temperature range over a year?

(d) What is the average rainfall over a year?

Check your answers with your partner, and share with the rest of the class.

Temperate climates of the world

Most temperate climates are found in the **mid-latitudes**. They include cool temperate oceanic, warm temperate (also known as Mediterranean) and temperate continental climates.

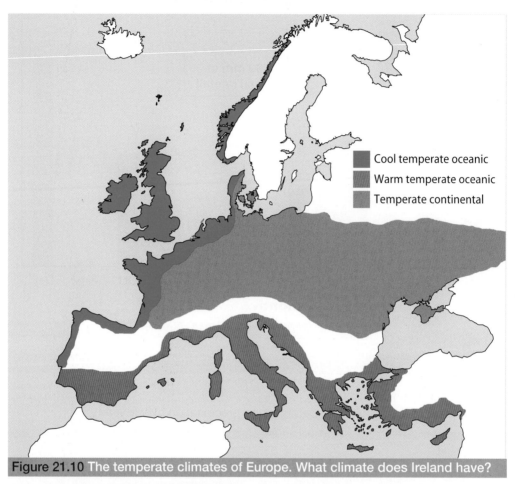

Cool temperate oceanic

Warm temperate oceanic

Temperate continental

Figure 21.10 The temperate climates of Europe. What climate does Ireland have?

Table 21.2 Characteristics of temperate climates

	Cool temperate oceanic	Warm temperate oceanic	Temperate continental
Temperature	▪ Summers are warm, with temperatures averaging 15°C to 17°C ▪ Winters are mild, with temperatures averaging 4°C to 6°C ▪ Annual temperature range is about 11°C	▪ Summers are hot with temperatures averaging 30°C ▪ Winters are mild with temperatures averaging between 10°C and 15°C	▪ Hot summers, with average temperatures of about 20°C ▪ Winters are cold, with the average temperature below freezing point (0°C)
Rainfall	▪ Rainfall throughout the year, with a winter maximum ▪ Annual total varies between 800 mm and 2,000 mm, reducing from west to east ▪ It is a moderate climate, neither too hot nor too cold	▪ Summers are generally dry, with some drought ▪ Winters are moist, with rainfall amounts between 400 mm and 700 mm	▪ Precipitation throughout the year, decreasing as distance from sea increases ▪ Rainfall maximum occurs in summer ▪ Ground can be snow-covered for several months in winter
Wildlife	▪ Deer, fox, badger ▪ Robin, blackbird ▪ Ladybird, grasshopper	▪ Wolf, boar, deer ▪ Flamingo, puffin ▪ Toad	▪ Sheep, camel ▪ Vulture, kestrel
Natural vegetation	▪ Deciduous forest ▪ Oak, ash, elm ▪ Most now cut down	▪ Evergreen woodland ▪ Trees include cork oak, cedar and olive	▪ Grassland (e.g. Steppes)

Ireland and its cool temperate oceanic climate

Figure 21.11 Ireland's climate

Learning
Activity
Curiosity

21.8 The following are captions for the photos in figure 21.11. Match the caption to the photos labelled A–F.

(i) Most of the natural vegetation has been removed to make way for agriculture and settlement

(ii) Ireland's natural vegetation is deciduous forest. Species include oak, ash and elm

(iii) All of these factors have enabled settlements to develop in Ireland over a long period of time

(iv) Ireland's native wildlife includes the hare, red squirrel and red deer, seen here in Killarney National Park

(v) Winters in Ireland are mild. Rainfall is highest in upland areas

(vi) Summers in Ireland are warm. The sunniest part of the country is the south-east. Some rain also falls

DEFINITION

Deciduous

A tree that sheds its leaves annually.

Climograph for Kinsale, Co. Cork.

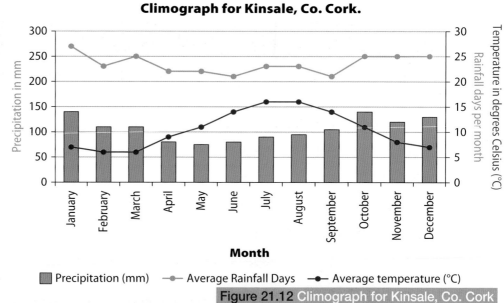

Figure **21.12** Climograph for Kinsale, Co. Cork

Learning Activity

Numeracy

21.9 Examine figure 21.12. Answer the following questions. Check your answers with your partner's.

(a) (i) What is the highest temperature?

   (ii) Which month has the highest temperature?

(b) (i) What is the lowest temperature?

   (ii) Which month has the lowest temperature?

(c) What is the temperature range?

(d) In how many months does precipitation exceed 100 mm?

(e) Which month has the most rainfall days?

(f) If you were to draw a precipitation line graph, would it match the line for 'rainfall days per month'? Explain your answer with reference to the two lines.

Tourism in a warm temperate climate

Warm temperate oceanic climate is also known as **Mediterranean climate** because the area surrounding the Mediterranean Sea is the largest region that experiences this climate.

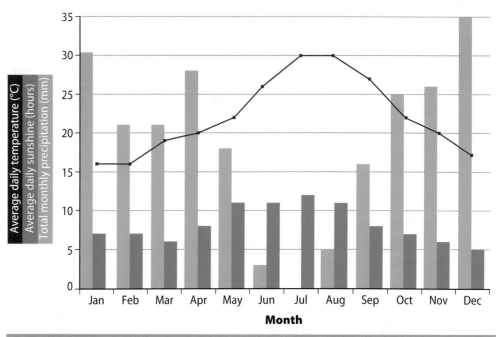

Figure **21.13** Temperature, sunshine and precipitation chart of a Mediterranean (warm temperate) climate

Learning
Activity   Numeracy

21.10 Examine figure 21.13 and answer the following questions. Check your answers with your partner's.

(a) What is the highest temperature?

(b) What is the lowest temperature?

(c) What is the temperature range?

(d) In how many months does precipitation exceed 30 mm?

(e) Which month experiences total drought?

(f) Describe the line for average daily temperature, using the terms: constant, slightly, sharply, gradually.

Figure 21.14 Sunbeds and parasols on a beach in Greece

Tourism in the Mediterranean

The hot, dry, sunny weather of the Mediterranean climate is very attractive to holidaymakers. As a result, **tourism** is the most important industry in many coastal areas, including the Costa del Sol, the French Riviera and Majorca.

 Link   Chapter 38: pages 362–73

GEO FACT

The Costa del Sol receives almost 3,000 hours of sunshine each year.

Learning
Activity   Curiosity Responsibility Communicating Literacy

21.11 Compare a beach holiday in the Mediterranean with one in Ireland.

(a) Find on the internet a picture of a Mediterranean beach resort and a picture of an Irish beach resort.

(b) On two separate sheets, or by placing them side by side on one sheet, compare the two scenes. (This can be in the form of a table with headings, or by describing them in paragraphs.)

Cold climates of the world

The cold climates of the world are found mainly in the northern hemisphere because, apart from Antarctica, there is no matching land mass in the southern hemisphere.

GEO FACT

The word **tundra** means 'without trees'.

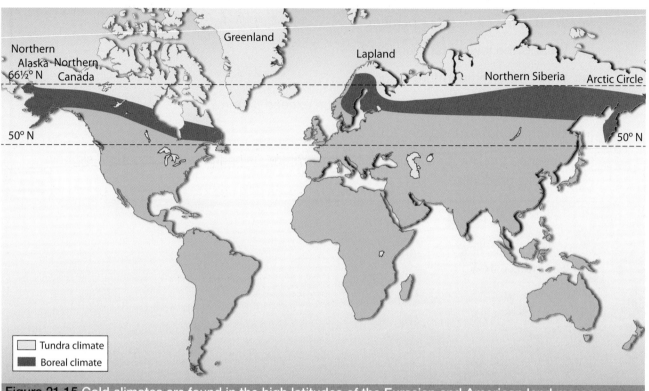

Figure 21.15 Cold climates are found in the high latitudes of the Eurasian and American land masses

Table 21.3 Characteristics of cold climates

	Boreal climate	Tundra climate
Temperature	▪ Summers are short and have long hours of daylight ▪ Coastal areas are cool (about 10°C). Inland areas are warmer (about 15°C) ▪ Winters are cold and have long hours of darkness ▪ Temperatures can reach as low as –25°C	▪ Summers are short and cool, with temperatures averaging about 5°C ▪ Winters are long and cold, with temperatures dropping to –35°C ▪ There is a large annual temperature range
Precipitation	▪ Precipitation is generally less than 400 mm per annum ▪ Maximum precipitation occurs in summer ▪ Winter precipitation is mainly in the form of snow	▪ Precipitation is low, usually less than 250 mm per annum ▪ Snow is the main form of precipitation
Wildlife	▪ The brown bear survives the winter by hibernating, while the musk ox has a double layer of fur ▪ Most animals and birds migrate south for the winter	▪ Animal and birdlife can survive in the region during the summer ▪ Most animals and birds migrate south for the winter
Vegetation	▪ Evergreen forest called taiga ▪ Most trees are coniferous ▪ Tree species include pine, spruce and fir	▪ Plants are low lying and sparse ▪ Tree species include dwarf shrubs, mosses and lichens

DEFINITION

Hibernating

Animals passing all or part of the winter in a deep sleep.

Coniferous

Trees that bear cones.

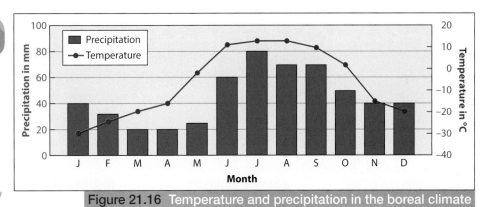

Figure 21.16 Temperature and precipitation in the boreal climate

Learning Activity

 Curiosity

21.12 In small groups, think about tourism in cold climates. Research the types of tourism that you would find in:

(a) A boreal climate.

(b) A tundra climate.

(c) Discuss the advantages of tourism to these areas.

(d) Discuss the disadvantages of tourism to these areas.

(e) Nominate a spokesperson to share your group's thoughts with the rest of the class.

Link 🔗 **Chapter 38: pages 362–73**

Reflecting on my learning

 Reflecting Communicating Literacy

Write sentences using each of the following terms from this chapter. You may use more than one of the terms in your sentence if appropriate.

altitude	continental effect	Mediterranean climate
aspect	cool temperate oceanic climate	moderate climate
boreal climate	equatorial climate	savanna climate
climate	hot climate	temperate climate
climograph	hot desert climate	tundra climate
cold climates	latitude	warm temperate oceanic climate
continental climate	local climate	

 PowerPoint summary

Revision
Go to **www.edco.ie/geographynow** and try the interactive activities and quizzes.

 Go to **www.edco.ie/geographynow** and try the interactive activities and quizzes.

Learning intentions

When you have completed this chapter you will be able to:

- Name some of Earth's natural resources and what they are used for
- Provide a definition for the term 'natural resource'
- Outline the ways in which natural resources can be extracted
- Explain how extracting natural resources is a primary economic activity
- Outline how quarrying takes place
- Describe the impacts of quarrying
- Assess the benefits and disadvantages of extracting natural gas.

Key terms

natural resources

mining

quarrying

natural gas

Natural resources from rocks

Earth's natural resources include:

- **Metal ores:** iron ore, copper, lead and zinc

- **Precious metals and stones:** gold, silver and diamonds

- **Building materials:** stone, sand and gravel

- **Energy sources:** uranium, oil, natural gas and coal.

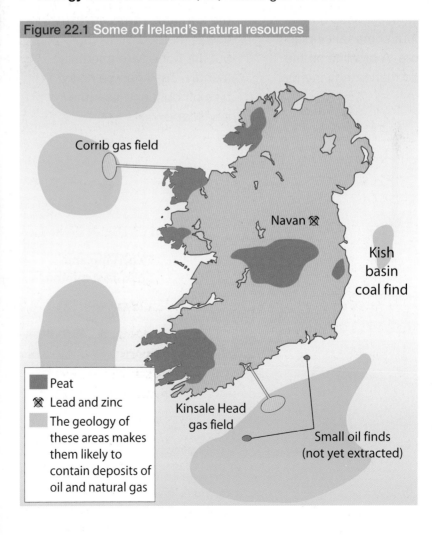

Figure 22.1 Some of Ireland's natural resources

Corrib gas field

Navan ✗

Kish basin coal find

Kinsale Head gas field

Small oil finds (not yet extracted)

■ Peat
✗ Lead and zinc
☐ The geology of these areas makes them likely to contain deposits of oil and natural gas

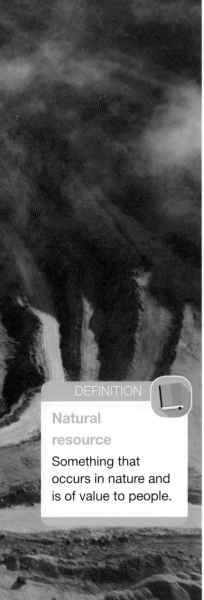

DEFINITION

Natural resource

Something that occurs in nature and is of value to people.

Extracting Earth's natural resources

Minerals from Earth's crust are exploited for use in **industry**, **agriculture** and **transport**. They are removed by one of three methods:

DEFINITION

Exploit

Use for business or industry.

- **Drilling** involves boring through rock to reach an underground source.

- **Quarrying** involves the removal or extraction of minerals from the surface of Earth. It can result in the removal of a hillside or the creation of a large hole in the landscape. On a very large scale, this process is known as **open cast** (or open pit) (see figure 22.2.)

- **Mining** involves underground working where the minerals are accessed via a series of tunnels.

These activities are called primary sectors of the economy because they are making direct use of natural resources. Another primary sector in some areas is **agriculture**, which also makes use of natural resources. The type of primary activity that takes place in an area is linked to its natural resources.

Link 🔗 **Chapter 26: page 252–58**

Drilling is used to extract oil or gas from an **underground** source. Most drilling takes place on land, but some takes place offshore. A pipeline on the seabed then brings the fuel ashore.

Quarrying and open-cast mining are used where the resource is **on or close to the surface**. These are a cheap method of mining but are not environmentally friendly. They can be noisy, give off dust and scar the landscape.

Shaft mining is used where the resource lies in seams **deep beneath the surface**. It is reached by constructing shafts down to the seams. Shaft mining is used to extract lead and zinc ores from the mines in Navan.

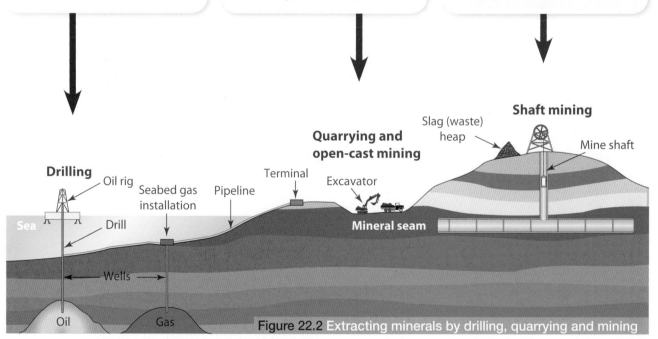

Figure 22.2 Extracting minerals by drilling, quarrying and mining

Quarrying

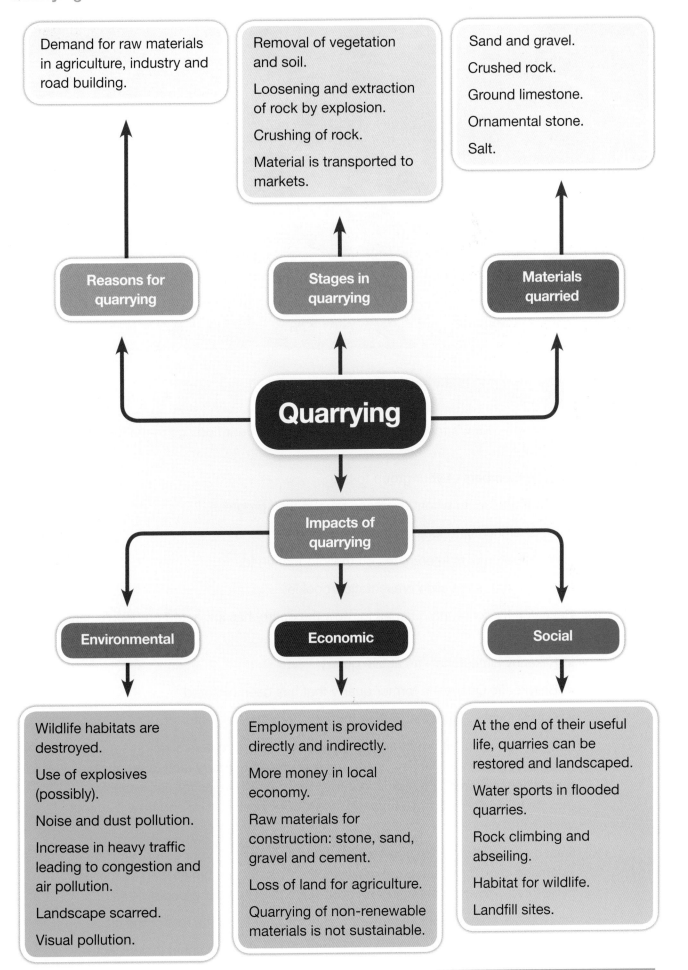

Demand for raw materials in agriculture, industry and road building.

Removal of vegetation and soil.

Loosening and extraction of rock by explosion.

Crushing of rock.

Material is transported to markets.

Sand and gravel.

Crushed rock.

Ground limestone.

Ornamental stone.

Salt.

Reasons for quarrying

Stages in quarrying

Materials quarried

Quarrying

Impacts of quarrying

Environmental

Economic

Social

Wildlife habitats are destroyed.

Use of explosives (possibly).

Noise and dust pollution.

Increase in heavy traffic leading to congestion and air pollution.

Landscape scarred.

Visual pollution.

Employment is provided directly and indirectly.

More money in local economy.

Raw materials for construction: stone, sand, gravel and cement.

Loss of land for agriculture.

Quarrying of non-renewable materials is not sustainable.

At the end of their useful life, quarries can be restored and landscaped.

Water sports in flooded quarries.

Rock climbing and abseiling.

Habitat for wildlife.

Landfill sites.

Figure 22.3 An analysis of quarrying

Figure 22.4 Building materials are extracted by quarrying

Learning Activity

Co-operating Responsibility Communicating Literacy Creativity

22.1 In small groups, you will research quarries and present your findings to the rest of the class.

(a) Choose members of your group to be:

(i) Chairperson, to whom everyone reports their progress

(ii) Researcher(s), to look up the information

(iii) Note taker(s), to keep notes on the information found

(iv) Creator(s) of the slide presentation/booklet.

(b) Research the following quarries for how the quarry has impacted on people, land and wildlife:

- Kilkenny Limestone – an active quarry

- Ballykeeffe Quarry – a former quarry that has been restored

- Calary Quarry – a former quarry that has not yet been restored.

(c) Using pictures and information you have discovered, create a slide presentation or booklet giving an overview of the three stages of a quarry (active, awaiting restoration, restored). Provide about four slides/short pages for each quarry. Include brief information on **how** the landscape is being used and **how** it affects wildlife and people at each stage.

(d) Based on the information you have found, discuss within your group: (i) whether quarrying should be restricted, or (ii) whether it is acceptable as long as the land is restored. Provide a summing-up slide/page to state your group's views.

(e) As a group, present your slide presentation or booklet to the rest of the class.

(f) Complete your individual 'group presentation' assessment sheet in your Activity Book (page 129).

Learning Activity

Communicating Co-operating Responsibility Curiosity

22.2 Imagine a quarry is about to open at a site near your school.

Your class divides into five groups, with each group being given one of the following roles:

- An environmentalist

- A retired person living nearby

- A member of the local planning authority

- A young person who has recently left school

- The land owner where the quarry is located.

(a) Choose one member of your group to act as your spokesperson.

(b) Help this person identify three points that the person in the given role might make. Remember, these may not be things that you personally would agree with, but that the person whose role you are taking might think about.

Use a placemat template that your teacher will show you – each member of the group will think about the points your role person might make; pass the placemat around the group for you each to write your point in your space. Keep passing this around until you can't think of any more points.

Then decide between you which are the three most relevant points. One person should rewrite these in the middle.

(c) Your spokesperson will then present your three points to the rest of the class.

(d) Vote for which person's (that is, the role of environmentalist, etc.) point of view you most agree with. (Even if you are the spokesperson, you can choose a different role to vote for.)

Natural gas

Natural gas is a fossil fuel. It originates from the remains of plants and animals that lived many millions of years ago. These organisms were buried and exposed to extreme heat underneath thousands of metres of soil and rock. Heat and pressure transformed the once-living organisms into natural gas.

Some facts about natural gas

(a) Natural gas is an **abundant** source of energy, supplying more than a fifth of the world's energy needs. Natural gas is now **cheaper** than almost any other fuel.

(b) Natural gas is a relatively **clean fossil fuel**. It emits less than half the carbon dioxide of coal when it is burned. For this reason, it is regarded as a good bridging fuel between other fossil fuels (coal and oil) and renewable energy (wind and solar).

(c) Being a fossil fuel, natural gas is **not renewable** and supplies will deplete eventually. Gas is **not a sustainable** answer to energy demands.

(d) Natural gas consists almost entirely of methane and large gas leaks create **environmental problems**. Methane is a very powerful greenhouse gas, although it doesn't stay as long in the atmosphere as carbon dioxide.

(e) Natural gas has a **wide range of uses** in residential, commercial and industrial settings. It is used to generate electricity and provide heat in houses, offices and shops. It is also used in the manufacture of plastics and fertilisers. It can even be used to power vehicles.

(f) Natural gas is **transported** under water through big pipelines as well as over land by massive liquefied natural gas (LNG) tankers.

(g) Natural gas is a **major employer**, both directly and indirectly. Areas of employment include exploration, production, distribution and rig construction.

> **GEO FACT**
>
> When natural gas is cooled to –160°C, it changes from a gas to a liquid, taking up just 1/600th of its original volume.

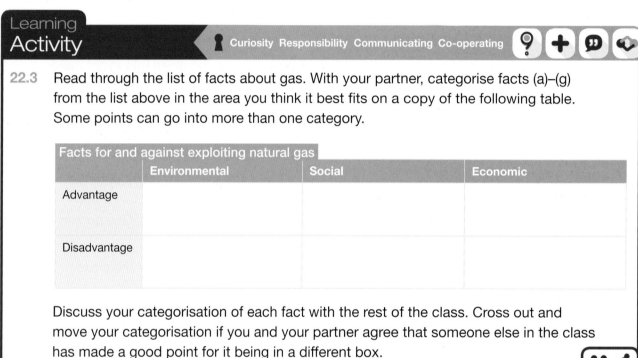

Learning Activity

Curiosity   Responsibility   Communicating   Co-operating

22.3 Read through the list of facts about gas. With your partner, categorise facts (a)–(g) from the list above in the area you think it best fits on a copy of the following table. Some points can go into more than one category.

Facts for and against exploiting natural gas

	Environmental	Social	Economic
Advantage			
Disadvantage			

Discuss your categorisation of each fact with the rest of the class. Cross out and move your categorisation if you and your partner agree that someone else in the class has made a good point for it being in a different box.

Natural gas in Ireland

- Natural gas makes up about 25% of the total energy demand in Ireland.
- Over half of this natural gas comes from **native production**.
- Natural gas was first brought ashore from the **Kinsale Head** gas field in 1978. It is expected that this supply of gas will be exhausted by 2021.
- The **Corrib** gas field, off the coast of Mayo, started production in December 2015. It has a projected lifespan of twenty years.
- The balance of our natural gas requirement is **imported** from Britain by two interconnector pipelines. This gas is sourced in Britain, Norway and Russia.
- It is also planned to import **liquefied natural gas** by ship from Texas and to store it in the empty gas caverns in the Kinsale Head field. From there, it would link with the national gas **pipeline network**.
- Almost half of Ireland's **electricity** is generated in gas-powered stations. Other main users of gas are **domestic** (heating and cooking) and **industry** (raw material and heating).

Figure 22.5 The Corrib gas terminal at Bellanaboy Bridge. Some of the onshore pipeline section runs in a tunnel under Sruwaddacon Bay (right background). Can you identify the route of the tunnel from the bay to the terminal?

Learning Activity

 Communicating Co-operating Responsibility

22.4 Extraction of natural resources can have a negative effect on the environment and landscape. However, we all want to have electricity and fuel for our convenience and comfort. Most fuels contribute towards global warming and most of the ones we extract from the ground are running out.

(a) Divide the class into two groups. Each group examine one of these statements:

    (i) Switching to renewable energy is not as simple as it is being made out to be.

    (ii) Leaving fossil fuels in the ground is good for everyone.

(b) Nominate one person to summarise the group's thoughts to the other group.

Reflecting on my learning

 Reflecting Communicating Literacy

Write sentences using each of the following terms from this chapter. You may use more than one of the terms in your sentence if appropriate.

- mining
- natural resources
- natural gas
- quarrying

 PowerPoint summary

 Revision
Go to **www.edco.ie/geographynow** and try the interactive activities and quizzes.

Exploiting energy resources

23

Go to **www.edco.ie/geographynow** and try the interactive activities and quizzes.

Learning intentions

When you have completed this chapter you will be able to:

- Examine the uses of fossil fuels
- Describe the causes and consequences of acid rain
- Explain why air pollution is a health hazard in urban areas
- Examine the economic and social changes that oil production has brought about in Saudi Arabia
- Identify the renewable energy sources that will grow in importance in future decades
- Assess the arguments for and against the use of wind power and solar power.

Key terms

fossil fuels

acid rain

air pollution

sulfur dioxide

carbon monoxide

particulate matter

Saudi Arabia

petrodollars

gender segregation

renewable energy

wind energy

solar energy

The environmental consequences of the exploitation of energy resources

The **global exploitation** of energy resources has grown enormously since the Industrial Revolution began in the 1780s. Fossil fuels – coal, oil and natural gas – have powered economic growth since that time.

The environmental consequences of burning fossil fuels are very serious. These consequences include the following:

- Climate change   Link 🔗 **Chapter 20**: pages 198–203

- Acid rain

- Air pollution.

Acid rain

Acid rain is a mixture of water and gases such as sulfur dioxide and nitrogen oxides. Acid rain has a pH below 4.3 on the pH scale.

GEO FACT

pH is a measure of how much acid or base is in a liquid.

Link 🔗 **Science**: Chemical World

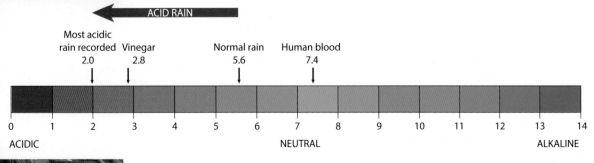

ACID RAIN →

Most acidic rain recorded 2.0 — Vinegar 2.8 — Normal rain 5.6 — Human blood 7.4

0 1 2 3 4 5 6 7 8 9 10 11 12 13 14

ACIDIC   NEUTRAL   ALKALINE

Figure 23.1 Acid rain on the pH scale

You will have studied the pH scale, acids and bases in your science course.

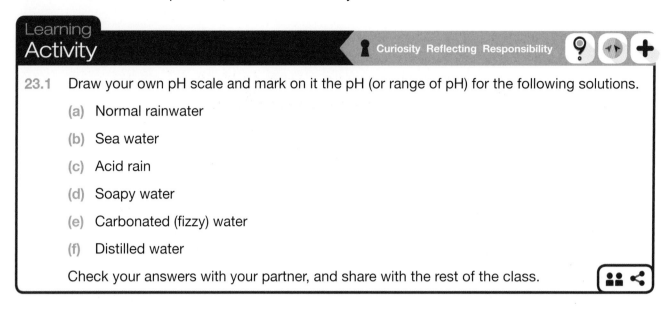

The causes and consequences of acid rain

Harmful gases are released by the **burning of fossil fuels** in power stations and from engine exhausts. When these gases mix with water vapour, they fall to earth as acid rain or acid snow. Wind blows gases from one country to another. Therefore, acid rain is an **international problem**.

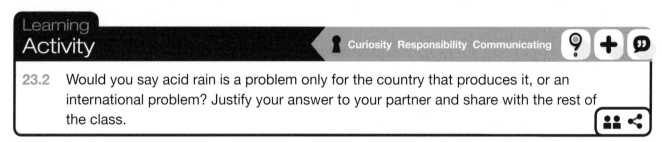

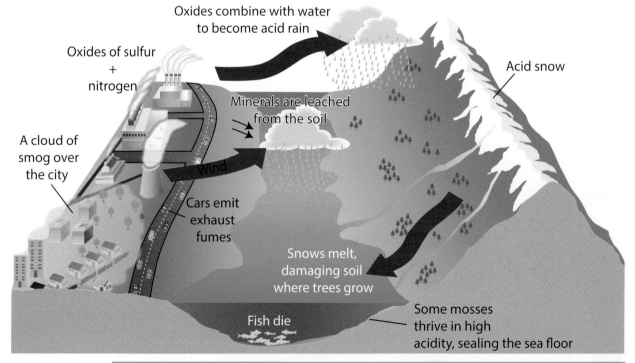

Figure 23.2 Acid rain falls on forests, lakes and farms and damages the natural world

Forests

- Acid rain leaches (washes away) **nutrients** from the soil.

- **Trees weaken** because of a lack of nutrients.

- Acid rain **damages the foliage** of trees.

- Damaged and weakened trees die from **diseases** and attacks by **parasites**.

Historic buildings

- Acid rain is very damaging to **old stone buildings**.

- The **Parthenon** in Athens, **Cologne Cathedral**, the **Colosseum** in Rome and many other famous buildings are being damaged by the effects of acid rain.

- Major **tourist attractions** are becoming less attractive.

The damage caused by acid rain

Fish life in lakes

- Rivers carry **acidic rainwater** and **meltwaters from acid snow** into lakes.

- **Fish eggs are damaged** when the pH falls below 4.3.

- The eggs don't hatch and **fish life disappears**.

- Many lakes, especially in Sweden, are **biologically dead**.

Agriculture

- **Minerals** and **trace elements** in soil, such as copper and calcium, are **washed out** of the soil by acid rain.

- Soil loses its fertility. Farmers have to replace the lost minerals with expensive **fertiliser**.

Social effects

- Acid rain affects the **quality of water supplies** from lakes.

- The concentration of **metals** in lakes rises because they are washed out of the soil by acid rain.

- The polluted water can affect **human health**, especially the health of infants.

Figure 23.3 The damage caused by acid rain

Learning Activity

Curiosity Responsibility Creativity

23.3 Research photographs that show the damage caused by acid rain. Find one picture for each of the five headings in figure 23.3. Create a similar illustration to figure 23.3, replacing the text with your labelled picture.

The solutions to acid rain

The only long-term solutions to the acid rain problem are the same as those for climate change.

Link  **Chapter 20**: page 202

Learning Activity Curiosity Communicating

23.4 Why are the solutions to climate change and the solutions to acid rain the same? Discuss this with your partner and share with the rest of the class.

Air pollution in cities

The burning of fossil fuels leads to severe air pollution in cities. The main **air polluting substances** include the following:

- **Sulfur dioxide**, mainly caused by the burning of coal and by central heating boilers.

- **Carbon monoxide**, a highly dangerous gas that comes from traffic and other processes that burn fossil fuels.

- **Particulate matter** (PM) from diesel fumes. These are minute particles that penetrate deeply into the lungs and cause respiratory conditions.

These pollutants have **social consequences**, such as health issues for many people. They contribute to chest infections and asthma. They lead to days lost at work and absence from school. They can prevent elderly people from leaving the house in cold, damp conditions in winter.

Air quality has improved but mainly in the cities of wealthy countries.

Learning Activity Curiosity Responsibility

23.5 Research the following.

(a) Which organisations set air quality standards for Ireland?

(b) Which body is responsible for monitoring pollution against those standards?

Check your answers with your partner and share with the rest of the class.

How has air pollution been reduced?

Smokeless coal is now in use in many countries.

In many cities, coal burning has been replaced by **natural gas** – the cleanest of the fossil fuels.

Link Chapter 22: page 223–25

Vehicle engines use new technologies that have **reduced emissions**.

Better use of **public transport**, which pollutes much less per passenger than cars and is environmentally more sustainable.

Rising use of **electric vehicles**, such as cars and light rail systems (e.g. Luas) release no emissions onto city streets.

Clean energy sources, such as solar and wind power, are being developed in many countries. Denmark is a leader in wind power. Spain and Germany are leaders in solar energy production.

Figure 23.4 Electric cars recharging. This sight will become very common

Learning Activity

Communicating Reflecting Responsibility

23.6 In your opinion, should the government make sure that a wider public transport network is provided in rural areas of Ireland? Justify your opinion to your partner and discuss with the rest of the class.

The oil industry: economic and social consequences in oil producing regions

Oil is more widely used than any other fossil fuel. For that reason, the economy of regions of the world that have oil reserves has been transformed in recent decades.

These regions have earned enormous sums of money from the **export of oil**. This has been most obvious in Persian Gulf countries. Billions of petrodollars have been transferred from oil importing countries to countries in the Persian Gulf over many decades.

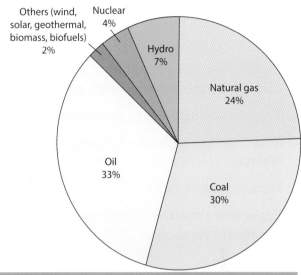

Figure 23.5 Sources of world energy consumption

Learning Activity

Communicating Literacy Co-operating

23.7 (a) With your partner, write a definition of **petrodollar**. Share this with the rest of the class.

(b) Make up another word, similar to petrodollar, but for another industry or activity. Share this with your partner, and then the rest of the class.

GEO FACT

Oil was first discovered in commercial quantities in Saudi Arabia in 1938. At that time, Saudi Arabia's people were mainly nomads who lived in the Arabian desert.

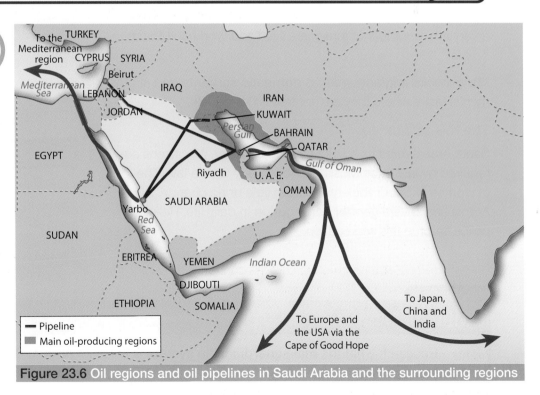

Figure 23.6 Oil regions and oil pipelines in Saudi Arabia and the surrounding regions

Oil has transformed the Persian Gulf region in some ways. The standard of living for millions of people has increased very rapidly. Education and health services have been developed. This is very clear in the case of Saudi Arabia.

Saudi Arabia

This mostly desert country has seen rapid economic change in recent decades:

- Oil exploration, production and transport have created many **jobs**.

- People from **nomadic tribes** of the Arabian desert **abandoned the desert** to work in the oil industry.

- Camels were replaced by **jeeps and SUVs**.

- Desert tents were replaced by **urban homes** and an **urban lifestyle**.

- **Incomes rose** rapidly.

- **Expensive consumer goods** from across the world became available in the shops.

Social changes

Saudi Arabia has seen **many social changes** in recent decades. The quality of life for millions of people in Saudi Arabia is now comparable to many advanced countries. Saudis have access to very good hospitals and schools.

Saudi Arabia has **ten million migrants**, a third of the total population. These are needed to fill the labour needs of the growing economy. Workers from Egypt, Pakistan, Bangladesh and other countries work in Saudi Arabia. This is a very significant social change because two generations ago, only a very small number of foreigners lived and worked in Saudi Arabia.

Many inward migrants work as **domestic servants** and at other menial tasks where they are not treated as equals.

The role of women

Saudi Arabia remains a strict **Islamic country**. All citizens are required by law to be Muslims and to obey Sharia law. The role of women in Saudi society has seen little or no change. Saudi Arabia has severe **gender segregation** in daily life. Religious police enforce this segregation.

Learning Activity — Curiosity

23.8 Write in your copy three oil-producing countries in the Persian Gulf.

Figure 23.7 The skyline of Riyadh, capital of Saudi Arabia

Table 23.1 Saudi Arabia in figures

	2017	1950
Population	30 million	3.2 million
Life expectancy	76 years	39 years
Births per mother	2.1	7.2
Urban population	82%	15%
Access to clean water	89%	Unknown
Adult literacy	87%	10%

GEO FACT

Life expectancy has almost doubled in Saudi Arabia in a little more than 60 years.

GEO FACT

Saudi Arabia is not a democracy but a **monarchy** where the king has absolute power.

Women in Saudi Arabia were not given the right to drive until 2017.

Learning Activity — Curiosity Responsibility Communicating Co-operating

23.9 Research what the **male guardianship system** is in Saudi Arabia. Discuss this with your partner.

23.10 If the male guardianship system was proposed for the women of Ireland, what do you think the reaction of Irish citizens would be? Discuss this as a class.

Future energy sources

Renewable energy

Renewable energy comes from a source that is **not depleted when it is used**. Examples include hydroelectricity, solar and wind energy. Many countries such as Germany, Sweden, Denmark and Norway are rapidly increasing their investment in renewable energy.

GEO FACT

Nuclear energy does not produce greenhouse gases.

GEO FACT

All of Germany's nuclear reactors will be closed down by 2022. This decision was prompted by the Fukushima nuclear disaster in Japan in 2011. (See chapter 4, page 30.)

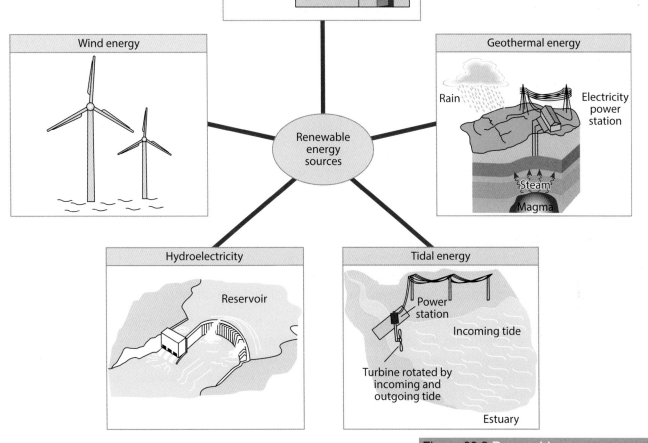

Figure 23.8 Renewable energy sources

We have looked elsewhere at some sources of renewable energy.

 Link **Chapter 3:** Geothermal energy, pages 16–17

 Link **Chapter 10:** Hydroelectricity, pages 100–103

In this section, we will look at wind energy.

GEO FACT

On the particularly gusty morning of 10 January 2017, wind energy in Ireland produced 60% of Ireland's electricity requirements.

GEO FACT

The largest wind farm in Ireland was opened in 2017 in Meenadreen, Co. Donegal. It can potentially supply the needs of 50,000 homes.

Wind energy

Wind farms have aroused some **controversy**. Arguments for and against wind farms are presented below.

In favour of wind farms

- The **wind is free**. Wind is a natural resource because it is blowing in many parts of Ireland most of the time. It is a **renewable resource**.

- Wind farms will **reduce our dependence on imported energy** such as oil from the Persian Gulf and Russia's gas fields.

- Wind energy is completely **clean**, unlike fossil fuels, which produce gases that damage our health and contribute to global warming.

- Most countries in the EU are **developing wind energy**.

- Wind turbines provide employment during the construction stage and for maintenance workers.

Link **Chapter 16:** pages 164–69

Against wind farms

- Wind turbines are very big. They cause **visual pollution**. They change the landscape.

- The **whirring noise** of the blades and the shadows that they cast upset some people. An area loses its peace and quiet.

- Wind is **unreliable**. There are calm days and nights. Electricity stations running on oil and gas are needed as a back-up at those times.

- Wind turbines may **affect wildlife** by killing birds if they are poorly sited.

Because of people's concerns, in countries such as Denmark offshore wind farms are being built.

In Ireland, a small wind farm has been built in the Irish Sea on the Arklow Bank.

Learning Activity

Curiosity Responsibility Literacy

23.11 Research the advantages and disadvantages of onshore and offshore wind turbines.

In your copy or in a word processing program, create a table using the following headings. Complete the table using the information from your research.

	Onshore wind turbines	Offshore wind turbines
Advantages		
Disadvantages		

Figure 23.9 Onshore and offshore wind turbines in the Netherlands. Can you make a case for the development of off-shore wind farms off the coast of Ireland?

Learning Activity

Curiosity Communicating Literacy

23.12 (a) Do you agree or disagree with the statement: 'Wind turbines should be built offshore if they are to be built at all.' Justify your answer to your partner.

(b) Join another pair of students and debate your stance of being for or against wind farms. Justify your thoughts.

Solar energy

Solar energy is energy from the sun. Photovoltaic (PV) **solar panels** capture the sun's energy and convert it into electricity, which can be **stored** in a battery or used by the **national grid**.

Solar energy has a bright future in Mediterranean countries, which receive as much as 2,800 hours of sunshine a year. Many developing countries in tropical regions are also suitable, but the technology is expensive.

Figure 23.10 PV solar panels in Germany are used for producing electricity

Learning Activity

Curiosity Responsibility

23.13 Consider why solar energy is a good source of energy for:

(a) Developed countries

(b) Developing countries.

Discuss your thoughts with your partner and share with the rest of the class.

23.14 (a) With your partner, research the arguments for and against solar energy.

(b) Present these in two columns, on a slide presentation or on paper.

(c) Display the results of your research around the room for the rest of the class to read.

Reflecting on my learning

Reflecting Communicating Literacy

Write sentences using each of the following terms from this chapter. You may use more than one of the terms in your sentence if appropriate.

acid rain | gender segregation | Saudi Arabia
air pollution | particulate matter | solar energy
carbon monoxide | petrodollars | sulfur dioxide
fossil fuels | renewable energy | wind energy

 PowerPoint summary

 Revision
Go to **www.edco.ie/geographynow** and try the interactive activities and quizzes.

24

Go to **www.edco.ie/geographynow** and
try the interactive activities and quizzes.

Learning intentions

When you have completed this chapter you will be able to:

- Describe the main forest regions of the world and their role in biodiversity
- Consider why humans have reduced the forests of the world and the
  consequences of deforestation
- Identify countries where reafforestation is taking place
- Describe how forests are sustainably managed in countries such as
  Sweden and Costa Rica.

Learning Outcomes

2.3 Identify how the physical landscape influences the development of primary activities

2.4 Assess the exploitation of water, fish stocks, **forestry** and soil as natural resources

2.9 Assess the interrelationships between the physical world, tourism and transport

Key terms

tropical, deciduous, coniferous forests

ecosystem

deforestation

reafforestation

renewable/infinite resources

non-renewable/finite resources

exploitation

ecotourism

sustainable management

Exploiting natural resources

Humans exploit natural resources. We have seen how water (chapter 10) and soil (chapter 13) are used by humans.

Learning Activity

🔑 Reflecting Literacy Communicating

24.1 Work in pairs. One of you take the subject of water and the other the subject of soil.

   (a) Make notes for water/soil on:

      (i) Why it is important for life on Earth

      (ii) How we use it

      (iii) Why we need to use it in a sustainable way.

   (b) Summarise (a) (i)–(iii) for your partner.

   (c) Share your answers with the rest of the class.

In this chapter we will be looking at the exploitation of forestry and in the next chapter we will look at the exploitation of fishing.

Forestry

The type of forestry found in the world depends on the climate in which it is growing:

- The **equatorial climate** supports tropical rainforest such as ebony, teak and mahogany species.

Link 🔗 Chapter 21: page 210

- The temperate climates of western Europe have native forests of broadleaf oak, beech, ash and many more.

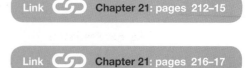
Link 🔗 Chapter 21: pages 212–15

- Cold climates support slow-growing coniferous forests of spruce, pine and larch, for example in Canada, Northern Scandinavia and Siberia.

Link 🔗 Chapter 21: pages 216–17

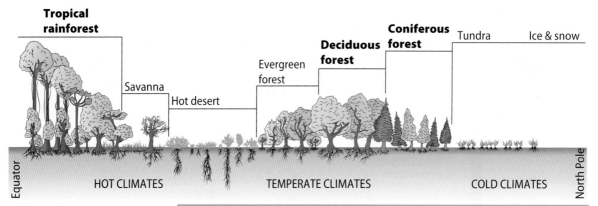

Figure 24.1 Vegetation from the equatorial region to the polar region

Forests are essential to the **life support system** of our planet. They absorb carbon dioxide and release oxygen.

Learning Activity

🔒 Curiosity Reflecting 🧭 ✈

24.2 Forests are considered to be the **planet's lungs**. Discuss with your partner why you think this term is used. Share your thoughts with the rest of the class.

24.3 On a scale of 1 (not at all) to 10 (essential), where would you rate the importance of forests in the life of all creatures on Earth? Justify your answer. Discuss your thoughts with your partner and share with the rest of the class.

Tropical rainforests and temperate forests support particularly rich ecosystems. Forests are essential to maintain the diversity of plants, animals and insects.

Link 🔗 Science: Biological world

Forests are a renewable or infinite resource. If they are managed carefully, forests can be replanted as they are harvested.

DEFINITION

Ecosystem

All the plants, animals and other living things, together with non-living materials such as water, soil and rocks, that inhabit an area and interact.

Learning Activity

🔒 Curiosity Reflecting Communicating Literacy 🧭 ✈ 💬 ✒

24.4 Write in your copy a definition of renewable and non-renewable resources, with examples of each.

24.5 (a) In pairs, discuss whether the fact that trees and forests are a renewable resource means that we can cut them down without concern. Justify your position on this question.

(b) Join with another pair to discuss this question further. Circulate a placemat template to note all your thoughts, and between you agree a summary of your discussion, to be written down by a nominated person in your group.

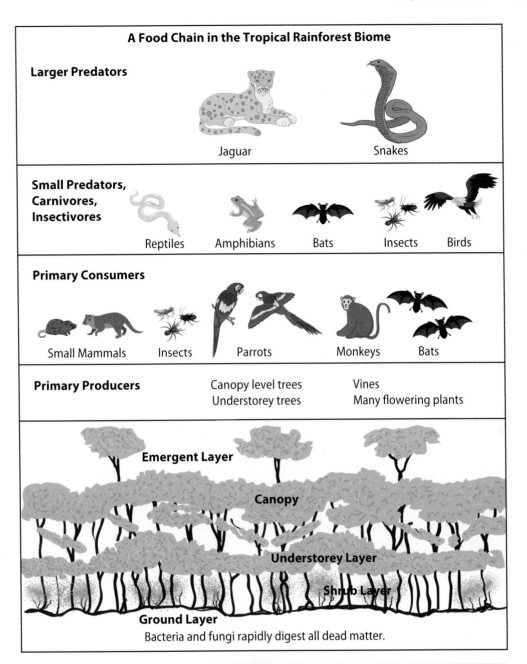

A Food Chain in the Tropical Rainforest Biome

Larger Predators

Jaguar   Snakes

Small Predators, Carnivores, Insectivores

Reptiles   Amphibians   Bats   Insects   Birds

Primary Consumers

Small Mammals   Insects   Parrots   Monkeys   Bats

Primary Producers   Canopy level trees   Vines
Understorey trees   Many flowering plants

Emergent Layer

Canopy

Understorey Layer

Shrub Layer

Ground Layer
Bacteria and fungi rapidly digest all dead matter.

Figure 24.2 A food chain in the tropical rainforest

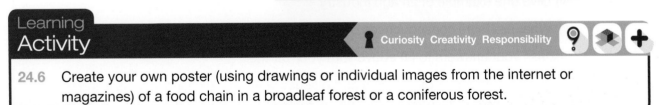

Learning **Activity**   Curiosity Creativity Responsibility

24.6   Create your own poster (using drawings or individual images from the internet or magazines) of a food chain in a broadleaf forest or a coniferous forest.

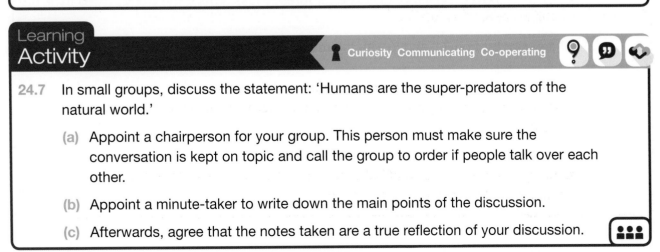

Learning **Activity**   Curiosity Communicating Co-operating

24.7   In small groups, discuss the statement: 'Humans are the super-predators of the natural world.'

(a)   Appoint a chairperson for your group. This person must make sure the conversation is kept on topic and call the group to order if people talk over each other.

(b)   Appoint a minute-taker to write down the main points of the discussion.

(c)   Afterwards, agree that the notes taken are a true reflection of your discussion.

The exploitation of forestry

GEO FACT

An area about the size of the island of New Zealand is deforested each year across the globe, mainly in tropical countries.

The world lost an area of tree cover the size of New Zealand last year

By Morgan Erickson-Davis

In 2016 the world lost an area of tree cover the size of New Zealand, according to satellite data. That's around 297,000 square kilometres, a 51 percent jump over 2015.

Fire is the primary culprit. Many fires in the Brazilian Amazon rainforest were set intentionally by people seeking to clear land for agriculture and other developments.

Indonesia also saw an increase in tree cover loss last year. This is from peatland draining and slash-and-burn agriculture as well as logging and agroindustrial expansion. In particular, West Papua showed an increase in clearing for oil palm plantations in 2016.

With the loss of forests comes the loss of valuable habitat for wildlife and ecosystem services for human communities. Trees are also big storehouses of carbon; if they're destroyed, that carbon is released into the atmosphere, advancing global warming.

Better forest management is needed to stop such high levels of tree cover loss.

www.mongabay.com, 24 October 2017

Learning Activity

Curiosity Communicating Co-operating Literacy Numeracy

24.8 Read the newspaper article above, then do the following.

(a) On your own, answer these questions:

(i) How much forestry (in square kilometres) was lost in the world in 2016?

(ii) How much forestry was lost in 2015?

(iii) What was the main cause of forestry loss?

(iv) Give one example of an agri industry.

(v) What are three consequences of removing forestry around the world?

(b) Discuss your answers to (a) above with your partner.

(c) Join with another pair of students and discuss ways in which individuals living in Ireland can help prevent/compensate for forestry loss around the world. Try to think of one way each.

(d) Share your list from (c) above with the rest of the class.

The chainsaw speeds up forestry removal

For many years, the forests of the world have been cut **more quickly than they have been replanted**. The chainsaw has greatly increased the removal of forest cover since it replaced the axe.

Learning Activity

Curiosity Communicating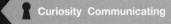

24.9 How have satellite images helped us to monitor the extent of deforestation? Discuss your thoughts with your partner and then share with the rest of the class.

Why is so much forest cleared?

Deforestation is taking place mainly in tropical and sub-tropical regions where the annual **population increase** is very rapid. Most of the cleared land is devoted to **crop production** such as rice, maize, vegetable and fruits for local people. As the population increases, people require more food, firewood for cooking and for furniture.

Land is cleared for cattle grazing, especially in Brazil. As countries such as China and Brazil become wealthier, the demand for meat grows.

Figure 24.3 Deforestation in Guyana, South America due to gold mining

Learning Activity

Communicating Literacy Co-operating Responsibility

24.10 Walking debate: Do you think living in urban environments makes people removed from nature and so they care less about sustaining forests around the world?

(a)   Consider how nature and habitats are being destroyed around the world and yet many people seem unconcerned about how devastating this can be. When your teacher says to, move to the sign that reflects how you feel about the question above: Agree, Not sure, Disagree.

(b)   Each person should give to the class a justification for why they have chosen their position. If their reason makes you change your mind about your first thoughts, move to join the other group.

(c)   When everyone has decided on their position on this subject, discuss as a class whether natural habitats in the Amazon rainforest are important to people in Ireland even though they do not live in the Amazon rainforest.

The results of deforestation

Cutting down forests affects everyone in the world.

- Tropical rainforest supports millions of **tribal people** in 70 countries from Brazil to Borneo. Tribes have used forests **sustainably** for generations by shifting agriculture and by hunting and gathering. When their forest is removed, tribes lose their traditional way of life and from necessity drift to urban centres where many succumb to petty crime, drugs or simply give up.

- As **trees are lost, diversity is lost**. Plants, birds, insects and other animals that evolved over millions of years become extinct.

- The world's capacity to **absorb carbon dioxide** is greatly reduced.

- Forests contain a wealth of **diversity**. Many plants are used in **modern medicines**. Plants that would be beneficial to us may not have been discovered and could become extinct before they are.

GEO FACT

An extract from the rosy periwinkle plant, found in Madagascar, is used in the treatment of childhood leukaemia and has resulted in a spectacular improvement in recovery.

GEO FACT

One hectare of tropical rainforest can have 650 tree species. This is more than in the USA and Canada combined.

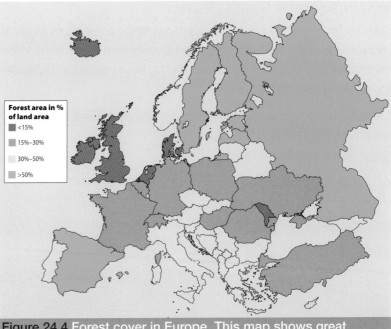

Figure 24.4 Forest cover in Europe. This map shows great variations between countries

Is the future for forests bleak?

Learning Activity

Reflecting Communicating Responsibility

24.11 Do you feel optimistic or pessimistic about the future of forests? Justify your answer to your partner. Share your thoughts with the rest of the class.

We think the answer is both yes and no. In **developing countries** where political corruption is the norm, friends and family members of the ruling classes are a law unto themselves. Officials are bribed to look the other way while forests are cleared for mining and timber exports.

However, many countries have large areas under forest cover. Several countries are making **great attempts** to increase the area of forests within their borders. These include China, Vietnam, Thailand, Turkey, Ireland and Algeria.

Examples of sustainable forestry

We will look at two examples of sustainable forestry: Costa Rica and Sweden.

Figure 24.5 The location of Costa Rica. Costa Rica is a small country with an area of 51,000 km². How does this area compare with that of the Republic of Ireland?

GEO FACT

Costa Rica is a developing country but is very socially advanced. It is known as the Switzerland of Central America because of its advanced health system.

Learning
Activity

Curiosity Responsibility

24.12 Identify Costa Rica and Sweden on a world map. (See pages 402–03.) Write in your copy which continent each is on.

24.13 Research the population of Costa Rica and Sweden and note these in your copy.

Ecotourism in Costa Rica

Costa Rica's forests are home to:

- 13,000 plant species
- 2,000 butterfly species
- 163 types of amphibians

- 250 types of reptile
- At least 870 types of birds.

 Link **Chapter 38**: sustainable tourism, pages 362–73.

The Costa Rican people see that ecotourism targeting forest diversity can be a source of employment and wealth.

For that reason, **25%** of the area of Costa Rica is given over to wildlife refuges, forest reserves and protected zones.

More than 600,000 people derive their living directly or indirectly from tourism in Costa Rica. Over 2.7 million tourists visit the country annually. These are mostly from the USA, with about half a million from Europe; the number of Chinese is increasing too.

The Costa Rican people have shown that the best thing to do with forests is to preserve them by sustainable management because the forest biomes are an economic asset.

DEFINITION
Biome
An area of the planet classified for its climate patterns, soil types, and the animals and plants that inhabit it.

Figure 24.6 Tourists enjoy the ecosystem of Costa Rica. The country's forests are a treasure chest of biodiversity

Learning
Activity

Curiosity Communicating

24.14 What do we mean when we say the forest biome is an **economic asset**? Discuss this with your partner and share with the rest of the class.

Sustainable management of forests in Sweden

Sweden is the model for all countries that wish to sustainably manage their forests. Forest resources in Sweden look after **the needs of Sweden today** with large numbers of people directly and indirectly employed in the forestry and timber industries.

- Sweden began to manage its forest sustainably in 1903 and now has more than 100 years of experience in this area.

- In Sweden, the long winter means that trees grow very slowly. Conifers take up to 70 years to mature. Therefore, sustainable timber harvesting has to be strictly controlled.

- The Swedish Forestry Agency is responsible for forest management.

- Only 1% of their timber is harvested annually.

- Cleared areas are replanted in the year after tree felling so that no time is lost.

- Forestry employs over 100,000 people and timber products are major Swedish exports.

- Forests are an important amenity for Swedish people with forest walks, camp sites and fishing lakes in many forested areas. This keeps urban people in touch with the natural world and gives Swedes a sense of ownership of the forest.

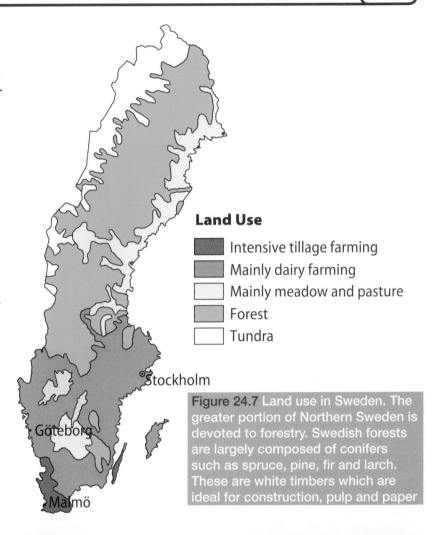

Land Use

- Intensive tillage farming
- Mainly dairy farming
- Mainly meadow and pasture
- Forest
- Tundra

Stockholm

Göteborg

Malmö

Figure 24.7 Land use in Sweden. The greater portion of Northern Sweden is devoted to forestry. Swedish forests are largely composed of conifers such as spruce, pine, fir and larch. These are white timbers which are ideal for construction, pulp and paper

Figure 24.8 Children picking mushrooms in a forest in Sweden. Swedes have a very strong attachment to their forests and landscape

Learning Activity

Curiosity Responsibility Communicating Co-operating Creativity Literacy

24.15 Research 'one million trees in one day' for Ireland. In pairs, create a poster or write a script for a question-and-answer interview as a way of advertising this initiative. Put the posters around the classroom, or perform in front of the class or record a podcast of your interview.

A few words on forestry in Ireland

Ireland lost its deciduous forest cover over hundreds of years. Forests were cut and shipped to Britain to make ships and other products. By 1924, when most of Ireland regained its independence, only 1% of Ireland was forested. Today, after a major reafforestation drive, that figure has risen to more than 10%. This is still low by European standards.

Much of Ireland's forestry is made up of fast-growing conifers such as spruce, which are not native to this country. However, timber from coniferous forests is very versatile and has many uses. There is a large demand for coniferous timber for wood pulp, paper and other timber products for the construction industry.

GEO FACT

Ireland has only one native conifer: the Scots pine.

DEFINITION

Reafforestation

The restocking of existing forests and woodlands that have been depleted, usually through deforestation.

Learning Activity

Curiosity Responsibility Creativity Literacy

24.16 Research the trees that are native to Ireland. Create a poster or booklet with the tree name and a picture to identify it. You may work on your own or in pairs.

Reflecting on my learning

Reflecting Communicating Literacy

Write sentences using each of the following terms from this chapter. You may use more than one of the terms in your sentence if appropriate.

- deforestation
- ecosystem
- ecotourism
- exploitation
- non-renewable/finite resources
- reafforestation
- renewable/infinite resources
- sustainable management
- tropical, deciduous, coniferous forests

 PowerPoint summary

 Revision
Go to **www.edco.ie/geographynow** and try the interactive activities and quizzes.

25

Go to **www.edco.ie/geographynow** and try the interactive activities and quizzes.

Learning intentions

When you have completed this chapter you will be able to:

- Explain how Ireland's continental shelf enables waters off the Irish coast to be rich in fish
- Explain how fish, if caught sensibly, are a renewable resource
- Consider Ireland's fishing industry
- Assess the reasons for and consequences of fish resources being overexploited
- Consider methods used by the EU to conserve fish stocks.

Key terms

sustainable fishing · continental shelf · spawning ground

overexploitation · trawling · fish quota

depletion · Irish Conservation Box

Fish

Fish is a very important food for many people. It is **low in fat** and contains **healthy oils**.

Sustainable fishing

Fish are a **renewable resource**. Although some are caught, others can breed and replace their numbers. If fishing is carried out **sensibly** there will be enough fish to catch. This is known as sustainable fishing.

Overexploitation

However, in many places trawlers take more fish than are replaced by breeding. This is called overexploitation (overuse) of a resource – in this case, **overfishing**.

As a result of overfishing, **fish stocks get smaller and smaller** until there are too few fish to be worth catching. We call this depletion of a resource.

Ireland's continental shelf

Irish waters have traditionally been rich in fish. The seas off the Irish coast form a continental shelf. This is an area of sea close to land in which large shoals of fish can thrive.

DEFINITION

Plankton

Tiny organisms that are too small to swim against the current and so drift in the water. They are the bottom of the fish food chain.

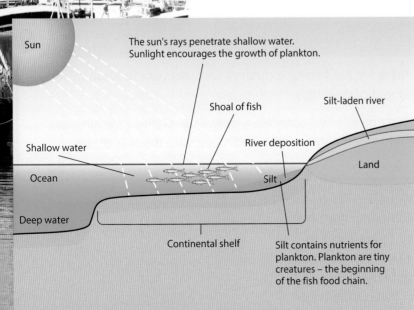

Figure 25.1 **The continental shelf: the conditions necessary for the presence of large shoals of fish**

The Irish fishing industry

The Irish fishing industry was small in scale until recent decades. Many fishermen fished in-shore for generations in **currachs**. Most trawlers were small and had small nets. Therefore, **catches were small**. This all changed when Ireland joined the EEC – now the EU – in 1973.

Fishing as a primary activity

A **primary activity** is an industry that makes use of a natural resource. Commercial **fishing** is a **primary activity** because it exploits the sea and creatures that naturally live in it.

Where this activity takes place is influenced by the physical landscape. By its nature, commercial fishing takes place off the coast of Ireland and out into the sea. In some areas, generations of men, and now women too, have made their living by fishing.

Figure 25.2 Men putting to sea in a currach. Currachs were incapable of depleting the fish of the seas. Can you explain why?

Learning Activity

Curiosity Responsibility

25.1 With the aid of an atlas or the internet, mark and label the following fishing ports on the outline map of Ireland in your Activity Book (page 68).

An Daingean/ Dingle	Clogherhead	Galway	Kilmore Quay
	Cobh	Greencastle	Rossaveal
Burtonport	Duncannon	Howth	Skerries
Castletownbere	Dunmore East	Killybegs	

A **secondary activity** is one that **processes** products from the primary activity.

Link **Chapter 37**: pages 352–61

Learning Activity

Curiosity

25.2 What secondary activities are there for the fishing industry? Discuss your thoughts with your partner, and share with the rest of the class.

25.3 If your home or school is near the coast, what secondary activities related to fishing are local to you? Discuss your thoughts with your partner and share with the rest of the class.

EU membership

When Ireland joined the EU in 1973 (known as the EEC at that time) it gave up control of its fisheries. **Ireland had to share its fisheries** with other members of the EU. Therefore, the amount of fish taken from waters around Ireland greatly increased, especially after Spain joined in 1985. More than half the fish taken from waters around Ireland today are caught by foreign trawlers.

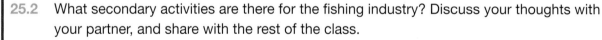

GEO FACT

The current 28 EU member states have 87,000 trawlers in total – a number that is far too high for the available fish stocks to be sustained.

Modern fishing technology

The modern trawler is well equipped
to catch fish.

GEO FACT

Very large trawlers are known as **supertrawlers.**

Figure 25.3 Unloading a catch from the deck of a trawler in Howth, Co. Dublin

Trawler skippers use detection methods such as **radar** and **sonar** to locate shoals.
Nets are invisible to fish and are unbreakable.
Hydraulic winches can lift several tonnes of fish onto the deck.
Trawlers have **cold rooms** that allow them to stay at sea for days.

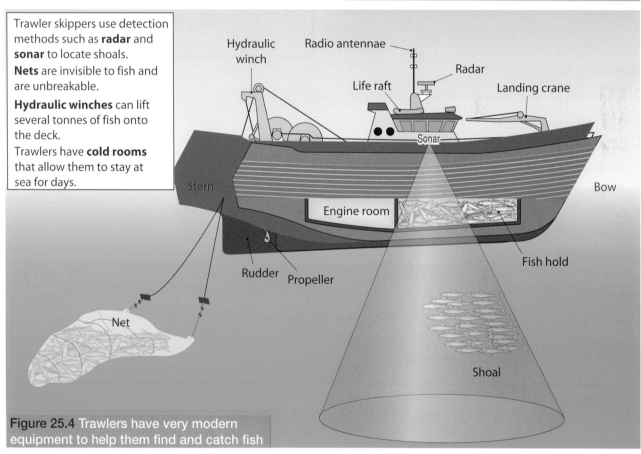

Figure 25.4 Trawlers have very modern equipment to help them find and catch fish

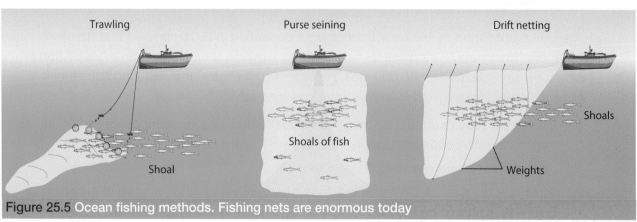

Figure 25.5 Ocean fishing methods. Fishing nets are enormous today

Endangered species of fish

Due to overfishing many species of fish caught in Irish waters are **in decline**.

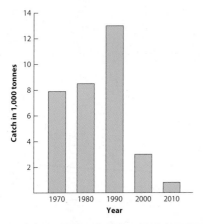

Figure 25.6 The cod catch in the Irish Sea over time. There has been a severe decline since the peak of 1990

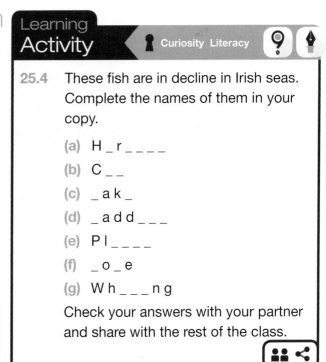

Learning **Activity**   Curiosity Literacy

25.4   These fish are in decline in Irish seas. Complete the names of them in your copy.

(a) H _ r _ _ _ _
(b) C _ _
(c) _ a k _
(d) _ a d d _ _ _
(e) P l _ _ _ _
(f) _ o _ e
(g) W h _ _ _ n g

Check your answers with your partner and share with the rest of the class.

Reasons for overfishing

The reasons for overfishing include the following:

- Too many **well-equipped** trawlers are chasing too few fish.
- The seas around Ireland cover a wide area. It is impossible to stop **illegal fishing**.
- Many juvenile fish are being caught because some fishing trawlers use **nets with a small mesh**. This reduces the next year's catch as there are fewer fish reaching maturity.
- Many trawlers catch and kill a variety of fish **and discard unwanted species** back to the sea. This is clearly unsustainable.

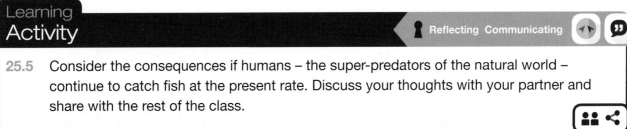

Learning **Activity**   Reflecting Communicating

25.5   Consider the consequences if humans – the super-predators of the natural world – continue to catch fish at the present rate. Discuss your thoughts with your partner and share with the rest of the class.

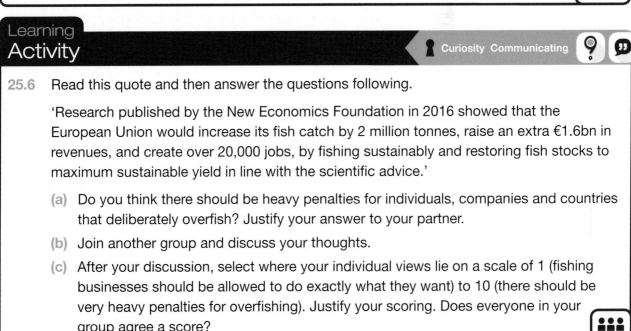

Learning **Activity**   Curiosity Communicating

25.6   Read this quote and then answer the questions following.

'Research published by the New Economics Foundation in 2016 showed that the European Union would increase its fish catch by 2 million tonnes, raise an extra €1.6bn in revenues, and create over 20,000 jobs, by fishing sustainably and restoring fish stocks to maximum sustainable yield in line with the scientific advice.'

(a) Do you think there should be heavy penalties for individuals, companies and countries that deliberately overfish? Justify your answer to your partner.

(b) Join another group and discuss your thoughts.

(c) After your discussion, select where your individual views lie on a scale of 1 (fishing businesses should be allowed to do exactly what they want) to 10 (there should be very heavy penalties for overfishing). Justify your scoring. Does everyone in your group agree a score?

Conserving fish stocks

The EU is taking steps to reduce overfishing. The **Irish Conservation Box** – an area of 100,000 km^2 – has been established. The Box is an important **spawning ground**, where herring, mackerel, hake and haddock breed. Fishing is **severely restricted** in this area.

Other steps that are used to **conserve fish stocks** include the following:

- Scientists check the numbers of particular species of fish in the seas. **Quotas** are then placed on the amount of each species that can be caught.

- The **number of trawlers** is being reduced. Owners and workers can retire with an EU pension.

- The **mesh size of nets** is fixed so that juvenile fish can escape.

- The **fishing season** for some species is shortened.

- Trawlers from **countries outside the EU**, such as Russia, are not allowed to fish in EU waters.

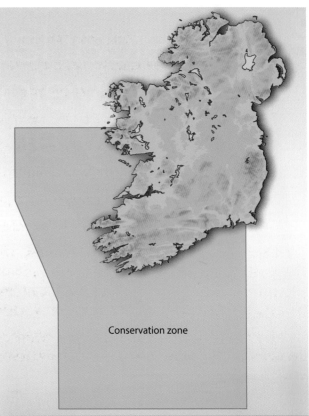

Conservation zone

Figure 25.7 A conservation zone has been created in the seas around Ireland in order to protect fish for future generations

DEFINITION

Fish quota

A limit on the amount of fish that can be caught annually.

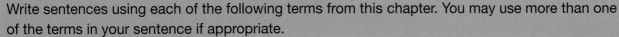

Reflecting on my learning

Reflecting Communicating Literacy

Write sentences using each of the following terms from this chapter. You may use more than one of the terms in your sentence if appropriate.

- continental shelf
- depletion
- fish quota
- Irish Conservation Box
- overexploitation
- spawning ground
- sustainable fishing
- trawling

 PowerPoint summary

 Revision
Go to **www.edco.ie/geographynow** and try the interactive activities and quizzes.

Section 2

The influence of the physical landscape on the development of primary activities

26

 Go to **www.edco.ie/geographynow** and try the interactive activities and quizzes.

Learning intentions

When you have completed this chapter you will be able to:

- Construct a definition of the term primary economic activity relating to farming
- Examine how the physical landscape has an important impact on farming
- Describe how the physical landscape of plains and river valleys supports productive farming
- Explain why the Paris Basin and the Nile Valley of Egypt are major producers of food crops
- Understand why grassland farming in Ireland is particularly important in the Central Plain and in the Golden Vale
- Describe the physical characteristics of uplands and why they are less attractive for farming than lowlands
- Present evidence for how the landscape near you affects farming practices.

Key terms

primary economic activities

physical landscape

plain

rolling landscape

granary

upland farming

irrigation

What is a primary economic activity?

Farming, fishing, mining and forestry are primary economic activities. In primary activities, raw materials including foods are extracted from Earth.

Learning Activity

 Curiosity Reflecting Literacy Communicating Co-operating

26.1 (a) In your pair, one of you think of a definition for the word **primary** and the other think of a definition for the phrase **economic activity**.

(b) Tell your partner your definition, and together combine your two definitions to explain the term **primary economic activity** specifically in relation to farming.

(c) Write your definition from (b) on a sheet of paper and place or pass these around the room. Tick the definition you like best.

Link For mining see chapter 23; for forestry see chapter 24; for fishing see chapter 25.

Farming

Along with climate and soil, the physical landscape determines the type of farming that a farmer will choose.

The physical landscape has a very **strong influence** on farming. While farming is not confined to lowlands, it is most productive on this landscape, particularly river valleys and plains.

The great river valleys of China and India supply food for hundreds of millions of people. The valley of the Nile in Egypt is another example.

We will study agriculture in the Paris Basin, which is a very large plain.

DEFINITION

Plain

A large expanse of level or rolling landscape.

The Paris Basin

The Paris Basin is one of the most productive agricultural regions in Europe. It is known as the **granary of France**. It is a very large region about the size of Ireland and is mostly a plain. Unlike Ireland, which is mainly given over to grassland farms, the Paris Basin is largely devoted to crops such as wheat, barley and maize.

Figure 26.1 The Paris Basin

Learning Activity

26.2 Construct a definition of 'the granary of France'? Look up 'granary' to check your understanding.

Curiosity

The region has well-distributed rainfall throughout the year with about 800 mm each year.

Early April temperatures are warm enough for germination of cereal seeds.

Summer temperatures average 18°C with excellent sunshine in July and August – the ripening and harvesting season.

South-facing slopes allow the vines to capture as much sunshine as possible.

The climate is West European

Ideal for tractors and combine harvesters, so machinery can be used safely and to best effect.

Parts of the southern and eastern edges of the Paris Basin have well-drained hills on whose south-facing slopes grapes are grown

The physical factors that influence farming in the Paris Basin

The landscape is flat or rolling countryside

The best-known wine region of the Paris Basin is **Champagne**, which produces the most famous sparkling wine in the world.

The soils of the Paris Basin are weathered from the bedrock of sedimentary rock and fine soils deposited by wind

The drainage is generally excellent.

The soil is easily tilled by machinery.

Learning
Activity

Curiosity Reflecting
Communicating

26.3 Examine figure 26.2. With your partner, list all the clues that indicate that this landscape is good for growing crops. Share your thoughts with the rest of the class.

GEO FACT

Intensive farming is confined to about 20% of the world's land area. The rest is either too cold, too high, too wet or too dry to support intensive farming.

Figure 26.2 **Harvesting wheat in the Paris Basin**

Upland farming

Farming is very difficult in hilly and mountainous terrain. There are several reasons for this:

- Uplands are **colder** and **more exposed** to high winds than lowlands. This is especially true of middle and high latitudes. In Ireland and many other West European countries, uplands are also **wetter** than lowlands because of relief rain.

- Uplands often have very **thin soils** because the soil has been eroded by glaciation or by rainfall runoff.

- Land on hillsides does not allow for intensive crop cultivation. Hillsides are **unsuitable for farm machinery** because of the danger and the steep gradient.

In many uplands, land with some soil is planted with **forestry** rather than farmed.

For these reasons, hill farming is far **less productive** than lowland farming. In Ireland, some uplands are used for rough grazing of hardy mountain sheep as they can tolerate the colder and wetter weather.

Figure 26.3 **Farming in the Irish landscape. The lowlands are covered in lush pasture while the upland in the left foreground has rough pasture devoted to sheep grazing**

Grassland farming in Ireland

More than 80% of Irish agricultural land is devoted to grassland farming. This is because, apart from the sunny south east, the climate of Ireland is too damp and cool for cereals.

Link 🔗 **Chapter 14: pages 155–56**

GEO FACT 🌐

Ireland's farmers grow the cheapest grass in the world because of the mild damp climate.

Just as important, much of Ireland's landscape is composed of plains. Examples are the Central Plain of Ireland and the Golden Vale of Munster. Many farms in these areas have fertile brown earth soils. The landscape of plains and gently rolling fields is suitable for tractors and silage harvesting machinery.

The Republic of Ireland has almost 7 million cattle and about 5.2 million sheep, which graze out of doors for many months on Irish pastures. Irish grassland farms produce enough beef for about 36 million people. About one million cattle are dairy cows with a high concentration of those in the Golden Vale.

Hilly farms in Ireland with very gentle slopes are also devoted to grassland farming. However, in the west of Ireland, where the rainfall is higher than in the east, the grazing season is hindered by waterlogging due to the higher rainfall and heavy soils.

Figure 26.4 Farming on the island of Ireland

GEO FACT

More than 80% of Irish beef is exported.

GEO FACT

There are more sheep than people in the Republic of Ireland.

Farming in irrigated valley landscapes

Many parts of the world do not have enough rainfall to support productive farming. However, irrigation can be used effectively in river valleys to provide bumper crops. An example is the Nile Valley of Egypt.

Figure 26.5 Farming and settlement on the banks of the River Nile in Egypt

The Nile Valley

The distance from the **Aswan Dam** to the sea is about 1,800 km. North of the dam, the landscape of the lower Nile Valley has the features of an old age stage river. The valley opens out and the valley floor becomes a flat floodplain.

Link ⌘ Chapter 10: pages 97–100

Most of Egypt's population lives here. The Nile has a huge delta which has a flat landscape and is ideal for crops.

Each year, floods covered the floodplain. The soil was fertilised by sediments. Since Egypt has very little rainfall, these annual floods have allowed people to live in the Nile floodplain and harvest crops successfully for several thousand years.

GEO FACT 🌐

Egypt is at the eastern edge of the Sahara desert.

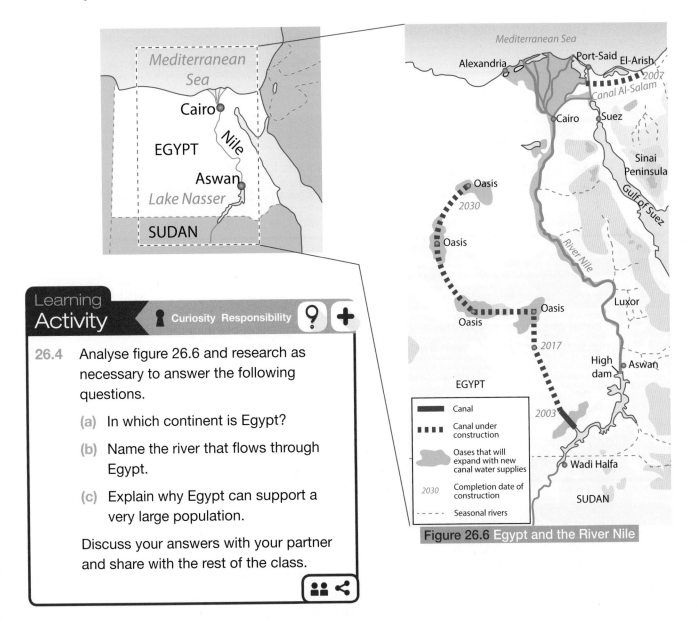

Learning Activity

🔒 Curiosity Responsibility ♀ ➕

26.4 Analyse figure 26.6 and research as necessary to answer the following questions.

(a) In which continent is Egypt?

(b) Name the river that flows through Egypt.

(c) Explain why Egypt can support a very large population.

Discuss your answers with your partner and share with the rest of the class.

Figure 26.6 Egypt and the River Nile

In the 1960s, a dam was built in Aswan to store the Nile waters for hydro-electricity and for year-round irrigation. The dam was completed in 1975. The dam releases water through canals and plastic pipes and allows farmers in the floodplain to harvest several crops a year. This provides additional food for Egypt's growing population.

In the years to come, additional oases in the western desert will be expanded through canal water from Lake Nasser.

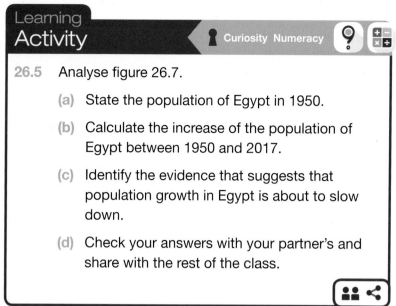

Learning Activity

Curiosity Numeracy

26.5 Analyse figure 26.7.

(a) State the population of Egypt in 1950.

(b) Calculate the increase of the population of Egypt between 1950 and 2017.

(c) Identify the evidence that suggests that population growth in Egypt is about to slow down.

(d) Check your answers with your partner's and share with the rest of the class.

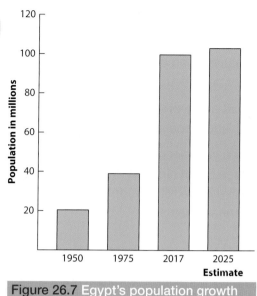

Figure 26.7 Egypt's population growth

Learning Activity

Curiosity Responsibility

26.6 The Aswan Dam has come with some disadvantages for agriculture.

(a) Research and list two disadvantages of the Aswan Dam for agriculture.

(b) Discuss these with your partner and share with the rest of the class.

Learning Activity

Curiosity Responsibility Communicating Literacy Creativity

26.7 In small groups, consider the landscape and farming taking place in the countryside near your school. In Ireland, even if you live in the city, farming is taking place not too far away.

(a) Using your own photographs or pictures from the internet or elsewhere, create a poster, slide presentation or other visual means of explaining how your local landscape impacts on farming as a primary economic activity.

(b) As a group, present your visual to the rest of the class, making sure you all take part in the presentation.

Reflecting on my learning

Reflecting Communicating Literacy

Write sentences using each of the following terms from this chapter. You may use more than one of the terms in your sentence if appropriate.

granary

plain

upland farming

irrigation

primary economic activities

physical landscape

rolling landscape

PowerPoint summary

Revision
Go to **www.edco.ie/geographynow** and try the interactive activities and quizzes.

Section 3

Exploring People, Place and Change

259

Population change over time

27

Go to **www.edco.ie/geographynow** and try the interactive activities and quizzes.

Learning intentions

When you have completed this chapter you will be able to:

- Explain why birth and death rates change over time, according to the population cycle
- Identify where population growth is rapid and where it has slowed
- Explain the demographic transition model
- Define the terms birth rate and death rate
- Consider the population growth since the middle ages
- Identify when the population explosion started
- Recognise at which stage different countries are in the demographic transition model
- Calculate the percentage increase or decrease of a population.

3.1 Use the demographic transition model to explain populations' characteristics and how populations change

Key terms

population

rate of growth

fluctuate

population explosion

developing world

developed world

demography

demographic transition

population cycle

sustainable

birth rate

death rate

natural increase

natural decrease

GEO FACT

The **Black Death** in the fourteenth century was so severe that it may have **halved** the population of Europe.

DEFINITION

Fluctuate

To rise and to fall in an uneven way.

Population growth

The **population** of the world has **increased over time**, but the **rate of growth** has been **uneven**. At some periods the population has even decreased.

In the past people died at almost the same rate as others were born. Population growth was **slow and uneven** because famine, wars and plagues killed many people. The population **fluctuated**.

Learning Activity

Curiosity

27.1 In the Middle Ages (the fifth to the fifteenth centuries) population growth was very low. Suggest one reason for this to your partner, and then share with the rest of the class.

Learning Activity

 Numeracy Curiosity

27.2 Research the population of the world today. In your copy:

(a) Write down the URL of the website or other source you used to find this information.

(b) Express the number for world population in full.

(c) Express the number for world population in billions, rounded to one decimal place.

(d) The population is increasing by about 78 million every year. How many people is this each week, as a decimal rounded to one decimal place?

Learning Activity
Numeracy Curiosity

27.3 The table shows world population from 1500 to today. Draw a line graph of these figures.

Year	Population
1500	426,000,000
1600	537,000,000
1700	585,000,000
1800	913,000,000
1900	1,578,000,000
1920	1,891,000,000
1940	2,297,000,000
1960	3,026,000,000
1980	4,449,000,000
2000	6,127,000,000
2010	6,916,000,000
Today	Use your figure from question 27.2 (b)

Source: worldpopulationhistory.org

You will see from your graph that in relatively recent years the world's population has increased dramatically. This population growth is called the **population explosion**.

Learning Activity
Communicating Literacy Co-operating Numeracy

27.4 Mark on the graph you drew for question 27.3 the point when, in your opinion, the population explosion began.

27.5 Discuss the reasons for the population explosion.

27.6 Discuss whether this level of growth is sustainable for our planet.

DEFINITION

Sustainable
Can continue for a long time.

Where is population growth greatest today?

- **Rapid growth:** Today, the greatest population growth is in **poorer countries**, also known as the **developing world**. These are many countries in south and south-west Asia and in Africa.

- **Slow growth:** The populations of **wealthier countries** (also known as the developed world), such as those in Europe and North America, where people are having few or no children.

- **Decline:** In some countries, such as Japan, the population is falling.

Learning Activity
Curiosity Co-operating

27.7 Work in pairs to name one region of the world where population growth is very high. Suggest why the population is still rising here. Share your thoughts with the rest of the class.

Figure 27.1 A crowded street in Hong Kong

The demographic transition model (population cycle)

The study of population is called **demography**. People who study population have created a **model** to help us to understand how a population increases over time. This is called the demographic transition model or population cycle.

The demographic transition model (see figure 27.2) shows the changes for a country over time in:

- The **birth rates** – measured as the number of births per thousand people in one year

- The **death rates** – measured as the number of deaths per thousand people in one year

- The **total population**.

DEFINITION

Model

A way of representing an event or trend to explain how it has occurred, and to use for predicting how it is likely to occur or continue in the future.

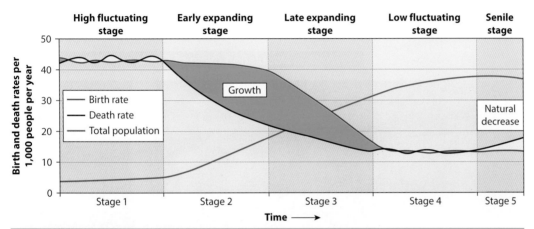

Figure 27.2 The demographic transition model (population cycle)

The five stages shown in figure 27.2 are explained in table 27.1.

Table 27.1 The five stages of the demographic transition model

Stage	1 High fluctuating	2 Early expanding	3 Late expanding	4 Low fluctuating	5 Senile
Birth rate (BR) and death rate (DR)	• BR and DR are high • High DR cancels out the high BR	• BR remains high • DR decreases rapidly	• BR declines rapidly • DR continues to decline	• BR is very low • DR is very low	• DR is greater than BR
Population change	• Very little change	• Rapid population growth	• Population growth continues but at a slower rate	• Population growth is very low	• The population begins to decline
Reasons	• Famine • Disease • Natural disasters	• Government begins to provide clean water and childhood vaccinations	• Rapid economic development • Parents are more educated and begin to plan their families	• Country is wealthy • Parents are educated • Parents have small families	• Women have very few children • There is a high proportion of elderly
Examples	• Europe in medieval times • Tribal groups today	• Mali • Kenya • Nigeria • Sudan	• Brazil • India	• UK • USA	• Germany • Japan

Learning
Activity

🔒 **Curiosity**

27.8 Identify at which stage of the population cycle Ireland is.

Learning
Activity 🔒 **Curiosity Numeracy**

27.9 Look at figure 27.3. Identify at what stage China was in 2017 in the population cycle.

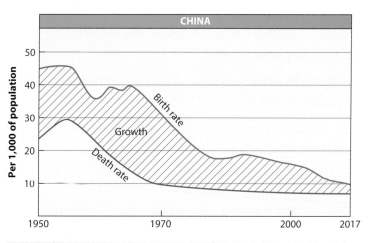

Figure 27.3 **Population cycle of China over time**

Figure 27.4 **The average household size in Pakistan is seven people**

GEO FACT

Birth rates and death rates are measured for every 1,000 people in the population, for a year. A birth rate of 40 per 1,000 means that for every 1,000 people in the particular population, there will be 40 births. So if this particular population is five million, the increase in births will be:

$$\frac{40 \times 5,000,000}{1,000} = 40 \times 5,000 = 200,000 \text{ births a year.}$$

Natural increase

Natural increase occurs when the **birth rate is higher than the death rate**.

Natural increase is given as a **percentage**, and can be calculated by subtracting the death rate from the birth rate.

When the death rate is higher than the birth rate, there is a natural decrease in population.

Calculating percentage increase of a population

In a country at stage 2, the birth rate may be 40 per 1,000 and the death rate may be 15 per 1,000.

Growth = 40 – 15 = 25 per 1,000

Convert to percentage:

$$\frac{25}{1,000} \times \frac{100}{1} = 2.5\%$$

The natural increase is **2.5% per year.**

Learning Activity

 Numeracy

27.10 What is the percentage increase in a country with the following rates? Check your answer with your partner and share with the rest of the class.

- Birth rate per 1,000 = 30
- Death rate per 1,000 = 20

Learning Activity

 Communicating Literacy Curiosity Co-operating

27.11 With the world's population growing so rapidly, how can we ensure that our planet is able to support the expanding number of people that have to be housed, fed and kept healthy? Discuss your views.

Reflecting on my learning

 Reflecting Communicating Literacy

Write sentences using each of the following terms from this chapter. You may use more than one of the terms in your sentence if appropriate.

birth rate	developing world	population cycle
death rate	fluctuate	population explosion
demographic transition	natural decrease	rate of growth
demography	natural increase	sustainable
developed world	population	

 PowerPoint summary

 Revision
Go to **www.edco.ie/geographynow** and try the interactive activities and quizzes.

Population: factors that affect the rate of population change

28

Go to **www.edco.ie/geographynow** and try the interactive activities and quizzes.

Learning intentions

When you have completed this chapter you will be able to:

- Explain the reasons why the population of a country or region changes
- Explain why the reliance of one crop, the potato, caused the population of Ireland to significantly decline
- Discuss the ethics of farming methods used to feed a growing population
- Consider the ways in which technology improves people's lives
- Compare the health of people in countries with clean water supplies to those in countries without a clean water supply
- Consider the effects of war on populations
- Compare the role of women in different societies
- Consider the impact of family planning on populations
- Compare the effects of education on population change between a developed country and a developing country.

Learning Outcomes

3.3 Examine population change in Ireland and in a developing country

You are also working towards

3.1 Use the demographic transition model to explain populations' characteristics and how populations change

3.7 Compare life chances for a young person in relation to gender equality, health care, employment and education opportunities in a developed and a developing country

Key terms

crop rotation

colonisation

food supply

irrigation

clean water

sanitation

vaccination

inequality

replacement level

family planning

literacy

Factors influencing the rate of population change

A number of factors influence the rate of population change:

1 Food supply

2 Improved technology

3 Health

4 War

5 The role of women in society

6 Education.

1 Food supply

Plentiful, nutritious food helps a population to grow. Over time, farmers have increased their crop yields by:

- Using healthier and stronger **seeds**

- Using **genetically modified (GM)** crops

- Using the method of **crop rotation**

- Using **fertilisers** to greatly increase food output per **hectare**

- **Storing** grain in **silos** so that it is not spoiled by rain or eaten by pests

- Using healthier and stronger breeds of **animals**.

With additional food supplies, the population of Europe and North America increased rapidly in the nineteenth and early twentieth centuries. Colonisation by Europeans brought agricultural advances to Africa, South America and Asia.

DEFINITION

Genetically modified crops
GM plants have had their cell structure changed artificially so that they are resistant to disease or produce more fruit.

Crop rotation
Growing a different crop in the same field each year to reduce the risk of pests and to prevent all the nutrients in the soil being used up, as different crops require different nutrients.

One hectare
= 10,000 square metres, or half the size of Croke Park stadium.

Silo
A tall tower that is used to store grain.

Colonisation
When one country takes control of another country and its people go there to live and govern.

How food supply affects populations

Reduced food supply in nineteenth-century Ireland
The population of Ireland grew from 4.5 million in 1800 to more than 8.5 million in 1845 because large families were usual. Although the majority of people were poor, they could support themselves on a hectare of land, which could produce enough **potatoes** and vegetables to feed a family.

However, the reliance on the potato crop meant that when it became **blighted by disease**, poor people's food supply declined. This was most noticeable between 1845 and 1848, a time that became known as the Great Famine. Almost a million people died and many others emigrated.

Increased food supply in Brazil
The population of Brazil grew from 17 million in 1900 to about 210 million in 2017. This was due to **high inward migration** from Europe and because of a **high birth rate**.

Brazilian farmers cleared land for agriculture. This meant that they could increase supplies of rice, maize, soybean, wheat, vegetables and fruit to feed the rapidly growing population.

Learning Activity

  Communicating Literacy Co-operating

28.1 To grow enough food to meet demand, most farmers carry out **intensive farming**. This means having a high number of animals, and using artificial fertilisers and weed killers to produce more food on a given area of land. It also means removing hedges, trees and other areas that wildlife rely on to survive. Discuss the following:

(a) What are the negative impacts of intensive farming?

(b) Is the intensive way of farming sustainable? Justify your answer.

(c) How will the loss of wildlife habitat (in Ireland and abroad, such as the clearing of the rainforests) affect people as well as wildlife in the future?

28.2 Suggest how climate change will affect food supplies and therefore populations.

2 Improved technology

Better technology can boost population growth in the following ways.

- Tractors, modern ploughs, combine harvesters and other equipment have made **farming** more efficient. This increases the **food supply**.

- In advanced countries such as the USA and those of the EU, cereals such as wheat are grown using modern technology and **chemical fertilisers**. Output of wheat per hectare is very high.

- **Irrigation** has meant that vast areas of dry land can now be farmed.

- **Drones** are used by farmers to check crops and equipment on large farms, so problems can be identified and attended to early.

- New technology has produced **medical equipment and medicines** such as antibiotics and vaccinations that save lives and decrease the death rate.

DEFINITION

Irrigation

Supplying dry land with water through canals or pipes, so that crops can grow.

Figure 28.1 A modern irrigation system in Tunisia, North Africa

Figure 28.2 Workers use modern technology to plant lettuces in a field

Learning Activity

Communicating Literacy Co-operating

28.3   Consider whether improved technology has had a negative effect on populations as well as a positive effect. What technology, and how has it affected populations? (Hint: think about large farming equipment.) Discuss your thoughts with your partner and then share with the rest of the class.

3 Health

Better health within a population generally means a lower death rate. People's health can be improved in several ways, including:

- Clean **drinking water**

- Proper **sanitation**, i.e. the proper treatment and disposal of sewage

- Childhood **vaccinations**

- A good **health service**

- **Health education**.

GEO FACT

Tuberculosis (TB) caused the deaths of more than 3,000 adults in Ireland every year until the middle of the twentieth century. It was stamped out after 1948 by a major campaign and using new drugs.

Drinking water and sanitation

Rich countries

In wealthy countries, safe drinking water has been available since the end of the nineteenth century.

In Ireland and other developed countries, **treated domestic water** supplies and **modern sanitation** are available to nearly everyone.

Poor countries

In rapidly developing countries such as Brazil, Mexico and Thailand, clean water is widely available in cities, but not in many rural areas. People who live in the countryside depend on a **well**. This water may be unsafe if it is contaminated by animals or human waste.

Millions of Brazilians live in **shanty towns** outside the large cities. There is often no safe drinking water. This can lead to outbreaks of diseases such as **cholera**.

DEFINITION

Shanty town

A poor area at the edge of a city where people live in houses made of old timber, plastic and scavenged materials.

Cholera

A disease that is passed on from the use of untreated water and results in severe diarrhoea, which can kill people within hours if not treated.

GEO FACT

There are between 1.3 million and 4.0 million cases of cholera every year worldwide. These result in between 21,000 and 143,000 deaths.

50,000 people died in Ireland from cholera in 1832.

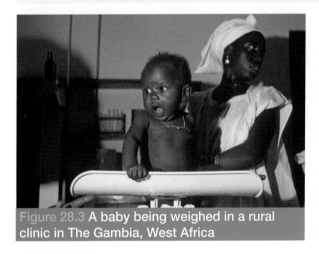

Figure 28.3 A baby being weighed in a rural clinic in The Gambia, West Africa

Figure 28.4 A girl drinking filtered water in rural Cambodia. Filtered water helps people to stay healthy

Learning Activity

Creativity Co-operating Curiosity Responsibility

28.4 (a) In small groups, research the following:

  (i) How not having clean water and good sanitation affects the lives of those people living in such conditions.

  (ii) How these people can be helped to obtain clean water and have sanitation.

(b) Create a series of posters or a slide presentation on your findings. Present these to the rest of the class, with each member of the group presenting a part of the talk.

You will need to assign tasks to each member of your group. For example: chairperson, note taker, researchers for part (a)(i), researchers for part (a)(ii), who will create which part of the presentation.

4 War

War has a major impact on people's lives. These are some of the ways:

- War **disrupts** farming and food supply, health services, water supplies and sanitation systems.
- The knock-on effect of disruptions is that people's **health** is affected.
- Modern **weapons** and **bombing** campaigns can lead to death on a terrible scale for soldiers and civilians.

War is a common occurrence in the developing world, especially in Africa, with huge numbers being killed:

- More than five million people died as a result of the civil war in the Democratic Republic of the Congo (1998–2003).
- By December 2017, after six years of war in Syria, an estimated 470,000 people had been killed, according to Human Rights Watch.

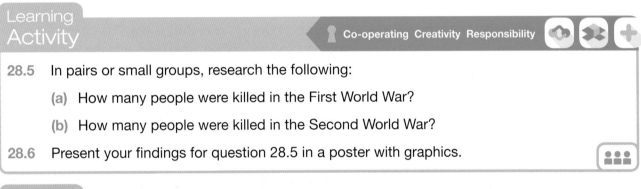

Learning Activity

Co-operating Creativity Responsibility

28.5 In pairs or small groups, research the following:

(a) How many people were killed in the First World War?

(b) How many people were killed in the Second World War?

28.6 Present your findings for question 28.5 in a poster with graphics.

Learning Activity

Communicating Literacy Co-operating

28.7 Have a class discussion on other effects of war on populations.

5 The role of women in society

There is **inequality** around the world as to the role of women and girls in their society.

In developed countries

Women in developed countries have a far higher status (position) in society than their grandmothers had. Two generations ago in Ireland and Western Europe, most women were confined to the roles of mothers and full-time homemakers. However, today many mothers also have a career.

Change was brought about by:

- The **feminist movement** – a social and political campaign started in the 1960s by women to achieve equality with men
- Availability of **education** for girls and young women
- Couples **planning their families**: the number of children and when they will have them. The number of children per mother is declining. For example:
  - In 1970, Irish mothers had an average of 4.0 children each
  - In 2016, Irish mothers had an average of 1.9 children each, a slight decrease on the previous year
  - In Germany and Italy, for instance, the average number of children per mother is 1.4. This figure is well below the **replacement level** of 2.1 children per mother.

DEFINITION

Replacement level

The average number of children born per woman in a society so that a population does not decline in the next generation.

In developing countries

In developing countries, women have much more traditional roles. In many of these countries women have **low status**. Additionally, many women do not have access to **family planning** or they have a fear of it, or they are prevented from using it for cultural or religious reasons. There is little access to education, especially for women.

In many African countries mothers have more than five children each.

DEFINITION

Family planning

When couples use contraception to plan the number of children they will have and when they will have them.

Learning
Activity

 Communicating Curiosity Literacy Co-operating

28.8   On your own, read the following article. Then in pairs discuss the points below. Share your views with the rest of the class.

The aftermath of China's one-child policy

It may be too little, too late to turn around the effects of China's one-child policy. The policy, which began in the 1970s, was to reduce the expanding population amid fears that the People's Republic would not be able to feed everyone.

China's family-planning regulations limited most urban families to a single child. This resulted in horrendous rights abuses, which included forced abortions and sterilisation. In China, boys were traditionally valued more than girls and so parents chose to abort female foetuses in the hope that the next pregnancy would produce a male.

There are many 'invisible children', as the births of second children illegally born under the policy were not recorded. They could not go to school, access healthcare, get a passport or a job; they are unable even to use the country's trains. Their parents were heavily fined and some lost their jobs.

Today, the consequences of this social-engineering experiment are clear to see. There is a growing elderly population, with the problems that brings, a huge gender imbalance and a labour shortage. The relaxation of the policy is to try to recover the population, but the number of women of child-bearing age is reducing and about three-quarters of families are unwilling to have a second child for economic reasons.

The authorities claim that the one-child policy prevented 400 million births, but researchers say that China's birthrate would have declined naturally, without the intervention of government.

(a)   On your own, consider the questions on the next page and make notes.

(b)   Discuss your thoughts with your partner and note the conclusions you draw.

(c)   Share your conclusions with the rest of the class.

Learning Activity

Questions

(i)   Outline what the one-child policy set out to do.

(ii)   Explain why the policy was despised by many people, both within China and in other countries.

(iii) Explain what is meant by the term 'invisible children'.

(iv)   State what problems the unregistered people face.

(v)   Suggest why the writer of this piece calls the policy a 'social-engineering experiment'.

(vi)   Identify any benefits of the one-child policy.

(vii) Identify the undesirable consequences of the policy.

(viii) Explain what is meant by the term 'gender imbalance'. Suggest why this has arisen.

(ix)   Suggest what problems there might be as a result of there being more men than women in China. (Some estimates are that men outnumber women by 60 million.)

(x)   Consider whether a policy such as the one-child policy could ever be right for a community. Justify your answer.

6 Education

In general, the **more educated** the population, the **smaller the average family size** and the **lower the natural population growth**. When parents are educated, they are more likely to be aware of family planning and to raise healthy children. In addition, in countries where both males and females are educated, women are more likely to have a career outside the home. It is easier to do that with a small family.

Education in developed and developing countries

Ireland and other developed world countries

In European countries, everyone goes to school and most complete second-level education. Many women combine careers with raising a family. Parents also tend to have fewer children because raising children is expensive.

Brazil

Great improvements have been made in girls' education in Brazil in recent decades. Now, 98% of girls aged 15–24 are literate, while 47% of girls complete secondary school. This helps to explain why the average number of children per mother in Brazil today has fallen from 5 children in 1970 to 1.8.

Learning Activity

 Communicating Literacy Co-operating

28.9   Consider why educated women are more likely to plan their families. Share your thoughts with a partner and then have a group discussion on this topic.

Figure 28.5 Girls on their way to school in rural Brazil. Education helps them to make choices in their lives

GEO FACT

The German population would decline without inward migration.

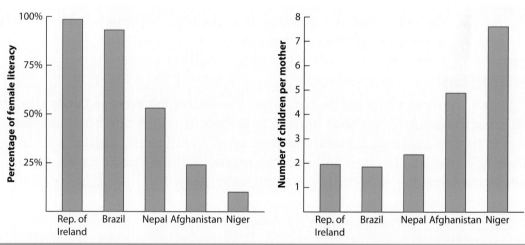

Figure 28.6 Female literacy and the number of children per mother in selected countries

Learning
Activity

Numeracy Curiosity

28.10 Study the bar charts in figure 28.6. In your copy, explain the connection between female literacy and the number of children per mother.

Learning
Activity

Co-operating Literacy

28.11 (a) Consider what life would be like if you couldn't read or write.

   (i) Consider all the things you couldn't do that you take for granted.

   (ii) In what ways would this affect you for the rest of your life?

(b) Discuss your thoughts with your partner. Add to your lists anything else they have thought of that would also affect you.

(c) Share your thoughts with another pair of students.

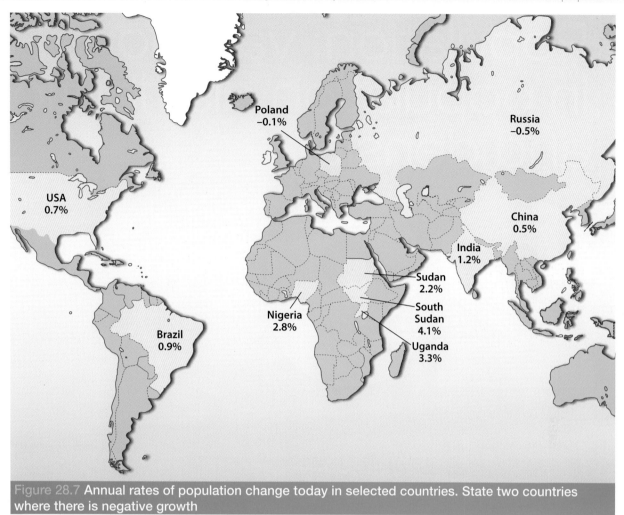

Figure 28.7 Annual rates of population change today in selected countries. State two countries where there is negative growth

How long will it take for a population to double?

- At a 1% annual growth rate, the population will double in 66 years.

- At a 2% annual growth rate, the population will double in 33 years.

- At a 3% annual growth rate, the population will double in 22 years.

Learning Activity

Curiosity Reflectiing

28.12 Consider the figures for doubling population given above. State two reasons why high growth rates in some countries at the present time may decline in the future.

Reflecting on my learning

Reflecting Communicating Literacy

Write sentences using each of the following terms from this chapter. You may use more than one of the terms in your sentence if appropriate.

clean water	food supply	replacement level
colonisation	inequality	sanitation
crop rotation	irrigation	vaccination
family planning	literacy	

 PowerPoint summary

 Revision
Go to **www.edco.ie/geographynow** and try the interactive activities and quizzes.

Population: variations in population distribution and density

29

 Go to **www.edco.ie/geographynow** and try the interactive activities and quizzes.

Learning intentions

When you have completed this chapter you will be able to:

- Explain how resources and terrain affects population density
- Consider how migrants are important to a country, and how there might also be challenges
- Consider how the Famine affected the area in which you live
- Compare the social and historical reasons for population distribution in a developed country (Ireland) and a developing country (Brazil)
- Read and interpret a population pyramid.

Learning Outcomes

3.2 Investigate the causes and consequences of migration

3.3 Examine population change in Ireland and in a developing country

Key terms

population distribution   Great Famine   population pyramid

population density   emigrate   life expectancy

resources   rural depopulation   dependent population

terrain   migrant   ageing population

The world's population

Population distribution around the world is uneven. In other words, the **population density** is not the same everywhere. Even in the same area, population density can vary over time.

Some of the factors that cause population variation are to do with:

- Resources and terrain

- Society and history.

Resources and terrain

People avoid regions that are very high, very wet and humid, or very dry. For example:

- **Greenland** has very few people because most of it is covered by an ice cap.

- **The Sahara** and other deserts are too dry for farming.

Other areas of the world have a high population density. For example:

- Many of the great **floodplains**, such as the Ganges Basin in India and the Nile valley in Egypt.

- **Western Europe**, because of its moderate climate, many excellent soils and large industrial cities.

DEFINITION

Population distribution

How people are spread over a region.

Population density

The average number of people living in a square kilometre.

DEFINITION

Resources

Any material or product that people find useful.

Terrain

The physical features of an area of land.

Learning Activity

  Curiosity

29.1 In your copy, explain why these factors of Western Europe mean it has a high population density:

(a) Moderate climate

(b) Excellent soils

(c) Large industrial cities.

GEO FACT

India and China have 37% of the world's population between them.

Learning Activity

Curiosity Numeracy

29.2   Examine figure 29.1. In your copy, write down the percentage of the world's population found in North and South America combined.

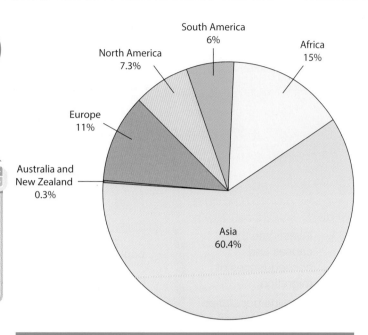

Figure 29.1 **Percentage share of the world's population by continent**

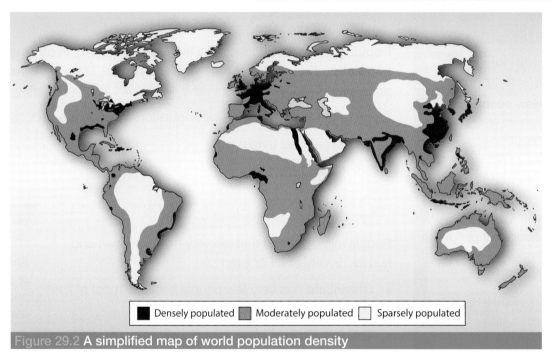

☐ Densely populated ☐ Moderately populated ☐ Sparsely populated

Figure 29.2 **A simplified map of world population density**

Society and history

We will look at social and historical factors that cause variations in population distribution and density using two examples: Ireland and Brazil.

Population change in the Republic of Ireland over time

The population of the 26 counties of the Republic of Ireland has changed a great deal over time. Before the Great Famine of 1845–48, the population grew very rapidly for these reasons:

- People married early and had **large families**

- The **subdivision** of farms into **small plots of land** meant that every **son** got land to live off and nobody had to **emigrate** for work

- The small plots of land could grow enough **potatoes**, the main food crop, to feed the large families.

Learning
Activity

Curiosity

29.3   Consider why sons were given land but not daughters. Suggest how this might have affected population in a small area. Discuss your thoughts with your partner, and then share with the rest of the class.

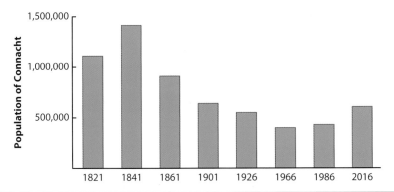

Figure 29.3 **The population change of Connacht over time. People emigrated in the past because of the lack of resources**

The impact of the Famine

- The **Great Famine** of the 1840s halted population growth.

- Many thousands of people **died of hunger** and famine fever in the West of Ireland and many more **emigrated**.

- After the Famine, farmers no longer subdivided their land. The **eldest son** inherited the family farm.

- The eldest son married only after the younger family members had left home. In general, people **married later** and had fewer children, so **families got smaller**.

- People continued to **emigrate** for the next hundred years, and others left the rural areas to live in **towns and cities**.

Learning
Activity

Co-operating Creativity Responsibility

29.4   In small groups, research how the Great Famine affected population in your area/town/city. Maybe it had an effect on your own families.

Write an essay, or create a series of drawings, poster or another visual on how your locality was affected by the Great Famine.

Figure 29.4 **Abandoned houses in Great Blasket Island off the coast of Kerry. The last remaining inhabitants left the island in 1953**

As a result, the population of Ireland declined steadily from the time of the Great Famine until the 1960s. This was unique in the whole of Europe at that time. Population distribution in Ireland became more uneven, and population density sharply decreased.

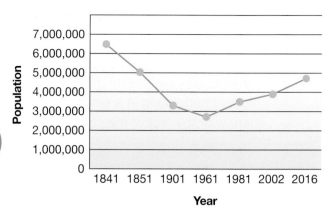

Figure 29.5 **Changes in the total population of the 26 counties (the area of the Republic of Ireland) since 1841**

More than 400,000 people emigrated from the Republic of Ireland in the 1950s, because of the lack of jobs and the gradual mechanisation of agriculture.

Population growth in recent decades

Population decline was halted and reversed from the 1960s onwards. The government under Taoiseach Seán Lemass encouraged **multinational companies** to invest in Ireland. Ireland joined the **EEC** (which later became the EU) in 1973. These two factors helped **job creation** in Ireland.

The 2001 census had to be postponed until 2002 because of Foot and Mouth disease.

Learning Activity

Curiosity Responsibility

29.5 Research why Foot and Mouth disease caused the census of 2001 to be postponed. Share your answer with your partner and then the rest of the class.

The **Celtic Tiger** years that began in 1995 and ended abruptly in 2008 also helped to create jobs in Ireland. Irish and international companies invested in Ireland. Many internet and social media companies chose Ireland as their European headquarters.

This led to a sharp increase in the numbers of migrants entering the country for work. Some of these inward migrants were returning Irish people and others were skilled workers from many countries. The population of **urban centres** grew very rapidly.

However, some rural areas in the West of Ireland continued to lose people to nearby towns and to the Dublin region, where many jobs were available. When rural areas lose people to towns and cities, rural depopulation takes place.

The growth of Dublin

Dublin, as the **economic engine** of the Republic of Ireland, has grown more rapidly in recent decades than other regions of the Republic. The populations of the counties surrounding Dublin have grown too, because many people in those counties work in the Dublin region. People have also moved out of Dublin to live in the towns of the nearby counties such as Meath, Louth and Kildare because homes are cheaper there.

Celtic Tiger

The name given to the time when the Irish economy grew rapidly with the help of large foreign investment.

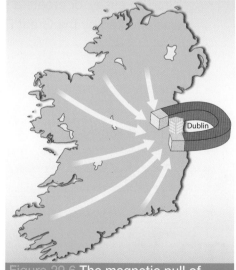

Figure 29.6 **The magnetic pull of Dublin is due to the many jobs in the region**

The population of Dublin city and county had reached 1,345,402 in 2016. This accounts for about 28% of the population of the Republic of Ireland.

The population of the provinces of the Republic of Ireland

The population of Ireland is unevenly distributed because of the large population in Dublin city and county and the increasing populations in the counties surrounding Dublin. Leinster has more than 55% of the population of the Republic. Therefore, population densities in many counties of Leinster are higher than in the west.

The population of Connacht is low because of the mountainous nature of much of the landscape, the small towns (apart from Galway city) and a long history of outward migration since the Great Famine.

Munster has more than twice the population of Connacht because it has three cities and large expanses of excellent agricultural land resources such as the Golden Vale.

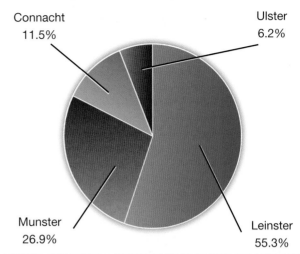

Figure 29.7 The population of the Republic of Ireland by province, 2016 census (*Source*: CSO)

Brazil

Population density varies across Brazil and has also varied over time.

Table 29.1 **Brazil's population in figures**	
Population 2017	210 million
Population density	24 per km² (Rep. of Ireland: 68 in 2016)

Original inhabitants

The first people to live in Brazil crossed the Bering Strait from Asia to Alaska and spread down through the American continent. It is estimated that **five million** inhabitants lived in Brazil before the European discovery of the Americas. They were mainly **hunter-gatherers**. Brazil had a very low population density, spread throughout the country.

DEFINITION

Migrate
To move from one country to another.

Migrant
A person who moves from one place to another.

European settlers

After the European discovery of the Americas, waves of **Portuguese** colonists arrived and settled along the **east coast** of Brazil.

The **coastal climate** was suitable for growing coffee, cotton and sugar cane.

Ports such as **Rio de Janeiro** were built so that sugar, coffee and other produce could be exported to Europe.

Population density rose sharply on the east coast because of the **high birth rate** and also because people continued to **migrate** from Europe into the twentieth century. Many migrants from Germany, Italy and Switzerland settled on the cooler coast of southern Brazil.

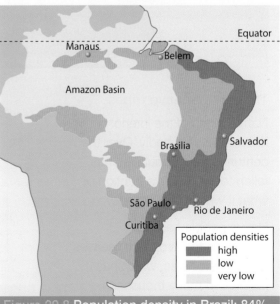

Figure 29.8 Population density in Brazil; 84% of the population live in urban centres

GEO FACT

Brazil covers almost half of South America.

Migration into the interior

In the 1960s, the Brazilian government began to encourage settlement in the interior of the country.

- A new capital, **Brasilia**, was built 1,000 km inland.
- New **roads** were opened up and settlers were offered **free land**.
- Vast **mineral resources**, such as iron ore and precious metals, were discovered.

Settlement in the interior is not easy for the following reasons:

- Much of the **land is infertile** as heavy rains leach away the minerals from the soil.
- The natural vegetation of the Amazon Basin is dense **tropical rainforest**.
- The **climate is extreme**, with high temperatures and humidity.

For those reasons, the Amazon Basin has been called a **green hell**. The result is that many new settlers have sold their farms in the interior to large companies and ranchers. Vast estates now raise cattle or grow **soya beans** and **crops for biofuels**. A small number of workers use machines to work these estates.

Therefore, fifty years after the modern attempt to settle the interior began, **population density in the interior remains low**. East coast cities continue to expand.

DEFINITION

Biofuels

Energy sources that can be extracted from corn, sugar cane, grasses and organic waste.

Figure 29.9 A road cuts through a recently deforested area. Roads have been built through the Amazon rainforest to encourage migration into the interior

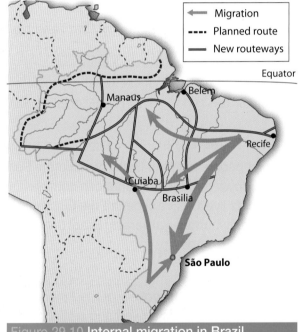

Figure 29.10 Internal migration in Brazil

The fate of native tribes

Native tribes of the interior have fared very badly. Over the centuries their population has fallen to 200,000 – a fraction of what it was 500 years ago.

Native people have low resistance to European diseases such as **measles**, which has resulted in many thousands dying.

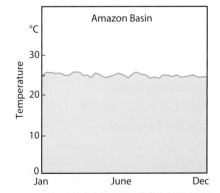

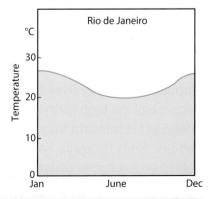

Figure 29.11 Temperatures in the Amazon Basin are hot all year round. Temperatures along the coast of Brazil vary, e.g. in Rio de Janeiro

Figure 29.12 Members of a Brazilian tribe in a reserve in Brazil

Learning Activity

Communicating Literacy Co-operating

29.6 The Brazilian rainforests are being cut down at a great rate. This has a global impact as the rainforests are **vital** to the planet's wellbeing.

(a) Discuss whether other countries should be able to prevent a particular country (in this case, Brazil) from using its resources as it wants.

(b) If you think other countries can have a say in what another country does, should they compensate that country somehow?

Learning Activity

Curiosity Co-operating

29.7 Consider how climate change will affect population density and how it will impact on:

(a) The areas of the world directly affected by weather changes.

(b) The areas of the world where people will flee to, to escape the effects of climate change.

Discuss your thoughts with a partner and then share them with the rest of the class.

Link Chapter 20: pages 198–203

Population pyramids

A **population pyramid** is a visual representation of a community's **population structure**, i.e. the make-up of a population in terms of age and sex.

The picture shows at a glance whether the population of a country is young or elderly. It helps us work out the percentage of people aged over 65 and the percentage of children of 14 and younger. These two age groups are the **dependent population** because they depend on money from the working age groups (the **economically active**) to look after them in economic terms.

How to read a typical population pyramid

- Age groups are arranged in bars in five-year spans.

- The length of each bar shows the numbers of people in each age group.

- Children's age groups are at the bottom of the pyramid; the oldest age groups are at the top.

- The male population is on the left and the female population is on the right.

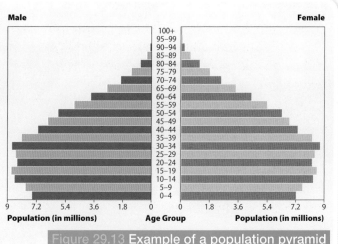

Figure 29.13 **Example of a population pyramid**

Population pyramids of three countries

We will look at the population pyramids for three countries at different stages of the population cycle: Brazil, Ireland and Germany (see table 29.2).

Table 29.2 **Fertility rates and life expectancy in three countries**

	Fertility rate	Life expectancy
Brazil	1.8	75 years
Ireland	2.0	81 years
Germany	1.4	80.9 years

DEFINITION

Fertility rate

The average number of babies born per woman in a population.

Life expectancy

How many years a person is likely to live.

GEO FACT

A fertility rate of 1.8 means that 10 mothers will have 18 children between them.

The population pyramid of Brazil

- The pyramid of Brazil has a **fairly broad base** and a **young age structure**. This is because, until recent years, Brazil had a high birth rate.

- The pyramid gets **narrower at the base**. This is because mothers in Brazil have had fewer babies in recent years as parents plan their families. This shows that the birth rate is falling.

- The bars of **young adult** age groups are wide. This is good for the **economy** of the country because Brazil has a large, young and energetic labour force.

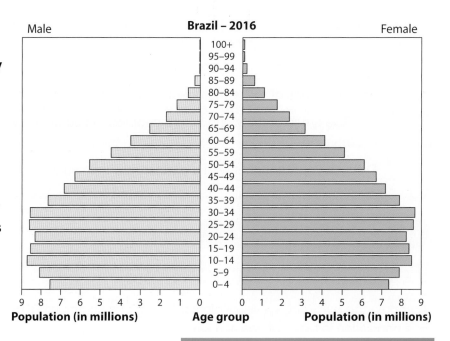

Figure 29.14 **Population pyramid of Brazil**

- The pyramid of Brazil is very **narrow at the top**. This is because Brazil has a **low life expectancy**, so the percentage of Brazilians aged over 65 is low.

The population pyramid of Ireland

- The pyramid is **narrow** in the age groups from 15 to 29. One reason is because the **fertility rate was in decline** when those age groups were born.

- However, the **birth rate has increased** in recent years. We see this because the bars for the youngest age groups have widened a little. One reason is that thousands of young adults migrated into Ireland during the **Celtic Tiger years** and became parents.

- The bars showing the 30–44 age groups are **wide**. This is because birth rates were higher when those people were born. **Inward migration** of East European adults also helps to explain the high numbers in those age groups.

- **Life expectancy is high** in Ireland. At the top of the pyramid, we can see that great numbers of people live into their eighties in Ireland, with **women living longer than men**.

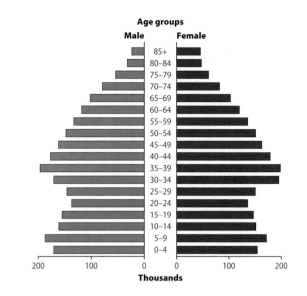

Figure 29.15 **The population structure of the Republic of Ireland, 2016 (*Source*: CSO)**

Learning Activity — Curiosity

29.8 In your copy, suggest one reason for the increase in the population of children in Ireland.

Learning Activity — Curiosity Responsibility

29.9 Research what CSO stands for and what this organisation does. In your copy, write a short paragraph on your findings.

The population pyramid of Germany

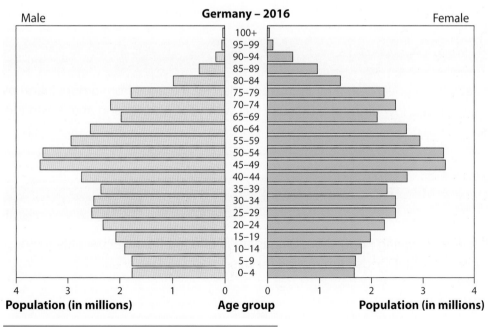

Figure 29.16 **Population pyramid of Germany**

Learning Activity

 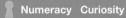

29.10 With reference to the population pyramid in figure 29.16, complete the following sentences in your Activity Book (page 162) by picking the right word from each set of choices.

(a) Germany's population pyramid has a **broad / narrow** base. This shows that Germany has a **high / low** birth rate.

(b) The base of the pyramid is getting **narrower / broader**. This shows that the birth rate is continuing to **increase / decrease**. Because of family planning, mothers had **many / few** children during recent decades.

(c) The percentage of older people is **high / low**. This is because of **high / low** life expectancy. Germany has an **ageing / young** population.

(d) On average, women have **higher / lower** life expectancy than men in Germany. This is shown by the **wider / narrower** top bars on the top **right / left**-hand side.

Learning Activity

29.11 Suggest one effect of an ageing population in a country such as Germany. Write your answer in your copy.

Who uses population pyramids?

Population pyramids are used by people who **plan for the future needs of a population**.

For example:

- Brazil has a high percentage of young people. Government planners can see that schools have to be built for them and teachers trained to teach Brazil's young people.

- In Germany, many people are elderly. The government has to plan for their health and transport needs. Caring for the elderly will also be a challenge for health services.

Learning Activity

29.12 Suggest what a government might have to plan for if it sees from a population pyramid that its country has a low birth rate. Discuss this with your partner and share with the rest of the class.

Learning Activity

29.13 Because of its ageing population, Singapore is offering financial benefits to couples who have a third child. Discuss the reason for this.

Figure 29.17 Elderly people practising tai chi in Berlin. Germany has an ageing population

GEO FACT

In Japan, where the population is at stage 5 of the demographic transition cycle, robotics are being used in coffee shops and even in residential homes for the elderly.

Reflecting on my learning

 Reflecting Communicating Literacy

Write sentences using each of the following terms from this chapter. You may use more than one of the terms in your sentence if appropriate.

ageing population	life expectancy	population pyramid
dependent population	migrant	resources
emigrate	population density	rural depopulation
Great Famine	population distribution	terrain

 PowerPoint summary

 Revision
Go to **www.edco.ie/geographynow** and try the interactive activities and quizzes.

Population: people on the move

30

Go to **www.edco.ie/geographynow** and try the interactive activities and quizzes.

Learning intentions

When you have completed this chapter you will be able to:

- Define migration
- List reasons for migration
- Differentiate between a migrant, an emigrant and an immigrant
- Consider what it would be like to be an emigrant/immigrant.

Learning Outcome

3.2 Investigate the causes and consequences of migration

Key terms

migration   pull factors   emigrant

barriers to migration   individual migration   immigrant

push factors   migrant   refugee

Migration

Migration, as we saw in chapter 29, is the **movement of people from one place to another**.

Migration may be:

- From one country to another: international migration
- Within a country: internal migration
- From the city to the suburbs for lifestyle reasons
- From rural areas to towns because of economic opportunities.

Migration of people has occurred throughout history and continues today.

Migration may be individual or organised.

Individual migration

Individuals or families migrate from one place to another because some things about where they live are **repellent** to them. Repellent reasons **push** them away. These are called push factors. Reasons may include:

- Overcrowding
- Unemployment
- Poverty
- Hunger
- Drought
- War
- A lifestyle change.

People also migrate because the places to which they move are **attractive** in some way. Attractive reasons **pull** migrants to a particular place or region. These are called pull factors. Reasons may include:

- Better job opportunities
- A better climate
- Fertile land
- A peaceful society
- A lively social scene
- The presence of friends and family members who have already migrated to that place.

There are often **barriers to migration** which may stop or slow down people who want to move. Barriers might be:

- **Poverty** – travel costs can be high.

- **Family** – there may be somebody at home who needs looking after.

- **Visas** – many countries require a foreigner to have a visa in order to enter the country. These can sometimes be difficult to get.

- **Bans on migration** – some countries have restrictions on their citizens leaving, and some countries do not allow people of certain nationalities to enter.

Many Irish people have **emigrated** to Britain and the USA, especially since the Great Famine. Many **immigrants** from Eastern Europe now live in Ireland.

By the end of 2016, 760 **refugees** had arrived in Ireland under the Irish Refugee Protection Programme (IRPP), the government's humanitarian programme for people fleeing conflict in Syria and other war-torn countries in the Middle East and north Africa.

Migration studies

Here are some real-life experiences of young people who emigrated out of or immigrated into Ireland in recent years.

DEFINITION

Migrant

A person who moves from one country or place to another.

Emigrant

An outward migrant who leaves their birth country and travels to another.

Immigrant

An inward migrant who enters a country from another country.

Refugee

A person who has been forced to leave their country to escape war or for political, religious or social reasons.

Nicola

I am an Irish doctor and I am 30 years old. I studied medicine in UCD. I worked in hospitals in Dublin for five years after becoming a doctor. Some of my doctor friends had already gone to Australia to work in hospitals and for further training. I took the plunge at the end of 2013 and I am working in Melbourne in a large hospital. The work is challenging. However, I am well paid and the outdoor lifestyle suits me. I have many friends, both Irish and Australian. I applied for residency in Australia at the end of 2014.

I keep in touch with my family using Skype and with my friends on Facebook, Instagram and Snapchat. For that reason, I am not really lonely, even though Australia is very far away. I returned to Ireland to

Figure 30.1 Nicola emigrated from Ireland to work in Australia

spend Christmas with my family last year. In five years I will be a medical consultant and I hope to return to Ireland then to continue my career.

Learning Activity

Co-operating Communicating Literacy Responsibility

30.1 In your group, discuss how when Nicola returns to Ireland her experience in Australia will help in her work.

30.2 Do you think it is a good thing to work in a different country for a short or even a long time, even if you intend returning to Ireland? Consider the benefits of working in another country. Discuss this with the rest of the group.

30.3 Imagine you are going to move with your family to a different country.

(a) What would you miss about Ireland?

(b) What wouldn't you miss about Ireland?

Alternatively, if you have moved to Ireland from another country in recent years:

(a) What do you miss about the country you left?

(b) What do you not miss about the country you left?

Write your answers in your copy.

Stanislaw

My name is Stanislaw. I am Polish and am in my late thirties. I came to Ireland in 2004 when Poland joined the EU. Why Ireland? Ireland in 2004 was booming and was known as the Celtic Tiger. In addition, I had free movement throughout the EU.

I am a mechanic and had many years of experience when I came to Ireland. I had no trouble getting a job in a large town in the Midwest region of Ireland. I have worked in the same garage since I came to Ireland. The pay is fine – a lot better than in Poland – but the cost of living is high here as well. I do a little overtime when I need extra cash.

Figure 30.2 **Stanislaw is a Polish immigrant working in Ireland**

I returned to Poland to marry my girlfriend, Zofia, in 2006. She then came to Ireland with me. Learning English is a major challenge for me. I was never very good at languages in school. Zofia, who is much better at English, is helping me to write this.

We have two children; both are Irish citizens and their English is excellent. We speak Polish at home, so the children will be bilingual. Zofia works part time in a crèche.

Ireland has been good to us and we have many Polish friends and some Irish friends here. A Polish priest is attached to this parish. He says Mass in Polish every Sunday and we meet the Polish community at Mass.

We now have enough money to return to Poland to buy a house. Both our parents are getting on in years and they miss us and their grandchildren. Ireland has been good to us and when eventually we leave, we will be sorry to go.

30.4 How has Stanislaw contributed to the Irish economy? Provide suggestions for your teacher to write on the board.

30.5 Imagine moving to a non-English-speaking country – for work, for example.

(a) What do you think the challenges would be?

(b) How would you try to overcome the challenges?

Alternatively, if you have moved to Ireland from a non-English speaking country, what were the challenges you faced or are facing with the language difference?

Provide suggestions for your teacher to write on the board.

Migration in the Mediterranean in recent years

Many migrants have made the dangerous journey from North Africa to European countries. For instance, in 2016, 181,000 migrants crossed from Libya to Italy. Migrants pay traffickers to provide boats to cross the Mediterranean Sea.

The countries from which these migrants came in the first half of 2017 are shown in table 30.1.

Table 30.1 The countries of origin of migrants who crossed the Mediterranean to Italy in the first six months of 2017

Country of origin	Percentage	Number of migrants
Nigeria	14.8%	14,120
Guinea	9.6%	9,193
Ivory Coast	9.0%	8,635
Bangladesh	8.6%	8,241
Syria	6.5%	6,182
The Gambia	6.0%	5,689
Senegal	5.1%	4,834
Mali	5.0%	4,825
Morocco	4.9%	4,712
Eritrea	4.7%	4,536
Other countries	25.8%	24,403

Source: UNHCR, the United Nations Refugee Agency

Learning Activity

Curiosity Numeracy Co-operating Communicating

30.6 These questions relate to table 30.1.

(a) In your pairs, one of you create a pie chart from the middle column of the table; the other create a bar chart from the third column of the table, rounding each figure to the nearest 500.

(b) With your partner, imagine you are going to present a television news show: would you use the table, the pie chart or the bar chart to support your report? Justify your answer.

Learning Activity

Curiosity

30.7 Write the answers to the following in your copy.

(a) Name the two non-African countries listed in table 30.1.

(b) Name the East African country in table 30.1.

Why did these people leave their countries in 2017?

There were several push factors:

- **Civil unrest** in Nigeria
- **Civil war** in Syria
- **Poverty** in most of the countries – all those in table 30.1 are in the developing world
- Some migrants have **relatives already in Europe** and hope to join them
- Some migrants are **economic migrants** – they want to better their life chances in Europe.

Learning Activity

Curiosity

30.8 Could any of the factors listed to the left be considered pull factors in some circumstances? Write your answer in your copy. Explain your answer.

The challenges of the journey for refugees

There are many challenges for these migrants, such as:

- Migrants from West Africa cross the Sahara by truck. The **terrible heat** can lead to dehydration and death.

- Migrants often **pay their life savings** to traffickers in North Africa to cross the Mediterranean to Italy or Italian islands.

- Many migrants die on the crossing every year. This is because they are put into **flimsy and overcrowded boats** by traffickers.

- When they arrive in Italy, they face **months of detention** in refugee centres while their applications are processed.

DEFINITION

Trafficker

A person who buys or sells something illegally. People traffickers help migrants move to other countries when they don't have the right to go there. The traffickers charge a lot of money, or they force the migrants to work in terrible conditions.

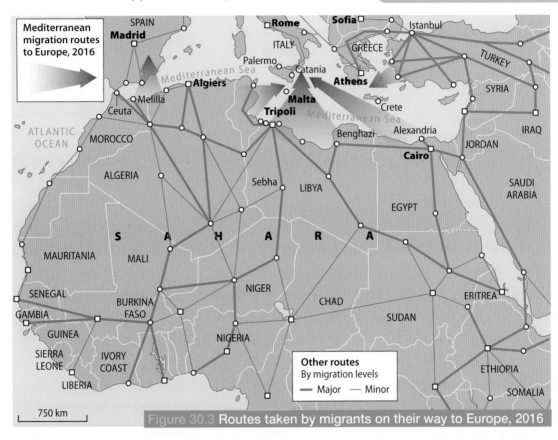

Figure 30.3 Routes taken by migrants on their way to Europe, 2016

Learning Activity

Literacy Responsibility

30.9 Try to imagine you are one of the migrants who has to leave your home because it is no longer safe for you to live there. Tonight is your last night in your home. In your copy, write your diary for today to describe in a paragraph or two how you are feeling about the coming journey with your family and what your future might hold.

Figure 30.4 LÉ Eithne is one of two Irish rescue boats that along with many others have helped to save thousands of migrants in the Mediterranean

What has been the EU response to the increase in migration numbers?

For many years southern European countries such as Greece, Italy and Spain have been the points of entry for migrants. However, many migrants prefer to travel northwards into the wealthier countries, such as Germany, France and the United Kingdom.

The EU has **failed to act with one voice** in relation to migrants who reach the EU's Mediterranean shores. The Syrian refugee crisis of 2015 showed this. For instance, Poland, Hungary and the Czech Republic refused to take migrants from Syria in recent years. Many border fences were built at crossing points to prevent migrants from southern Europe entering their countries.

The **cost of providing shelter, food and other necessities** to migrants is high. For instance, Italy expects that the cost in 2017 will be €4.6 billion – a billion euros higher than in 2016.

In 2017, Austria placed armoured cars and troops at the Brenner Pass to prevent migrants from crossing into Austria from Italy. Part of the reason for this may be that Austria took in more than 1% of its population – 90,000 people – mostly Syrians, in 2015. Many Austrian people supported political parties that were against the further intake of migrants.

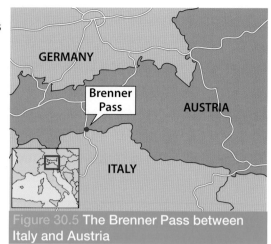

Figure 30.5 The Brenner Pass between Italy and Austria

Learning Activity

Communicating Literacy Co-operating Responsibility

30.10 Walking debate: Do you think Ireland should accept more refugees?

(a) Consider how refugees could help Ireland. Consider how they could be a challenge for Ireland. When your teacher says to, move to the sign that reflects how you feel: Agree, Not sure, Disagree.

(b) Each person should give to the class a reason for why they have chosen their position. If their reason makes you change your mind about your first thoughts, move to join the other group.

(c) When everyone has decided on their position on this subject, discuss as a class whether Ireland should be thinking only in terms of how helpful or challenging refugees could be for the country. Should Ireland be more sympathetic to the fact that people are migrating possibly to save their lives?

Learning Activity

Co-operating Communicating Responsibility

30.11 (a) On your own, consider the following questions.

(b) Discuss your thoughts with your partner.

(c) Debate these questions with the rest of the class.

   (i) Should the EU help 'young and ambitious' migrants to come to their countries to fill the gap in the jobs market?

   (ii) If the 'young and ambitious' are welcomed into Europe, should they be able to bring their families with them?

   (iii) Is it morally right for 'young and ambitious' migrants to be welcomed to a country, but not the 'old and unskilled'?

The EU's ageing population

EU countries are at stage 4 or 5 of the demographic transition cycle (see table 27.1 on page 263) . Therefore, birth rates are low. The population of several countries such as Germany and Italy will decline without inward migration. A strong argument can be made that the EU needs young and ambitious migrants to fill the jobs market and maintain its population.

Communicating Literacy Co-operating

30.12 On your own, read the following article and make notes on the questions below. Then discuss your answers with your partner and share your views with the rest of the class.

Not even a million migrants will reverse Germany's looming demographic decline

By Aamna Mohdin

Germany has registered its biggest population jump in more than 20 years. The overall population rose by 978,000 in 2015, a 1.2% increase. The total now stands at 82.2 million. It's been growing for the last few years after a worrying decline in the first decade of the 2000s.

This increase is largely due to Germany's record influx of migrants, according to the Federal Statistics Office. The European economic powerhouse took in just over one million asylum-seekers last year – more than the US has in the past 10 years.

The incoming migrants were spread evenly across the country; each German state received a quota [share] based on its population and tax revenue. The European Union tried to enforce a similar resettlement quota among other member countries last year, but with far less success.

While the record number of migrants entering the country will slightly increase the population, not even a million migrants will reverse Germany's long-term population decline. A spokesperson for the Federal Statistics Office, said that a look at the past shows that phases of high net immigration to Germany are usually followed by sharp drops. *Source:* qz.com, 30 August 2016

Questions

(i) Define the term migrant.

(ii) Explain why there has been a big increase in migrants into Europe in the last few years.

(iii) In your opinion, is such a big migration of people over a short time manageable for the countries they enter? Justify your answer.

(iv) You can see from the article that Germany's population has been in decline. In your opinion, is it good for Germany to accept the migrants entering the country? Justify your answer.

Asylum-seeker

A person who leaves their own country because they fear for their life (e.g. because of the country's political situation or because of war), and travels to another country in the hope that they will be allowed to live there.

Net immigration

When the number of people coming into a country to live (immigration) is greater than the number of people leaving a country (emigration).

 Reflecting Communicating Literacy

Reflecting on my learning

Write sentences using each of the following terms from this chapter. You may use more than one of the terms in your sentence if appropriate.

| barriers to | emigrant | individual migration | migration | push factors |
| migration | immigrant | migrant | pull factors | refugee |

 PowerPoint summary

 Revision
Go to **www.edco.ie/geographynow** and try the interactive activities and quizzes.

Population: future population change

31

Go to **www.edco.ie/geographynow** and try the interactive activities and quizzes.

Learning intentions

When you have completed this chapter you will be able to:

- Examine the future of population growth
- Consider the optimistic (hopeful) view of population growth
- Consider the pessimistic (gloomy) view of population growth
- Explain how fertility rates impact on population growth
- Decide whether you are pessimistic or optimistic about population growth.

Learning Outcome

3.3	Examine population change [in Ireland and in a developing country]

Key terms

optimistic view of population growth

pessimistic view of population growth

fertility rate

The future

People who study populations have different views about population growth in the future.

The population of the world has grown from 1.6 billion in 1900 to 7.5 billion in 2017. Will that rate of increase continue into the future? If it does, the population will reach nearly 10 billion by the middle of the twenty-first century. There are pessimistic and optimistic views about this.

The optimistic view

The more hopeful (optimistic) view is that the present growth rate in the world's population (see table 31.1) will continue to slow down and that the population will reach a steady level within a few decades. Optimists make the following points:

- The population in several **developed countries**, for example Japan and Russia, is decreasing as the population ages. Many more wealthy countries, especially in Europe, will show the same trend over the next decade.

- Many **developing countries**, such as Brazil, have seen dramatic declines in births per mother in only a few decades. This will happen in many other countries as they move across the population cycle.

- **China** has the world's largest population – almost 1.4 billion. However, Chinese population growth has slowed and the population is likely to begin to fall after 2030.

- As **Sub-Saharan Africa** (Africa south of the Sahara desert) develops and mothers become better educated, this region will also see a decline in births per mother. It is already happening in South Africa, where female literacy is 94% among young women.

Table 31.1 Population increase per annum

Year	Additional population on previous year
1990	87 million
2002	79 million
2017	78 million

What do these figures tell us about the global rate of increase?

297

The pessimistic view

The less hopeful (pessimistic) view is that the population of the world will continue to expand quickly. Pessimists make the following points:

- The population of the **world** is still **growing at more than 1%** a year.

- **India** will add more than 300 million to its present population by 2050 and overtake China's population.

- The population of **Africa** is likely to increase by 900 million by 2050 because the birth rate is still high. African countries are generally at stages 2 and 3 of the demographic transition model. Mothers in most countries in Sub-Saharan Africa have an average of five children each. These children will grow up to have children of their own.

GEO FACT

Nigeria's population is expected to overtake that of the USA by 2050.

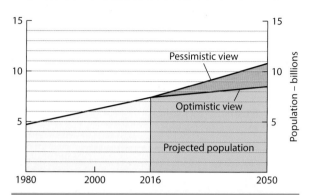

Figure 31.1 Forecasts for future population growth

Learning Activity

Numeracy Curiosity Communicating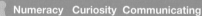

Examine figure 31.1 and answer the following questions. Check the answers with your partner and share with the rest of the class.

31.1 What was the world's population in 1980?

31.2 Calculate the increase in the population between 1980 and 2016?

31.3 According to the optimistic view of the world's projected population, what figure will the population of the world reach by 2050?

Learning Activity

Co-operating Literacy Communicating Reflecting

31.4 **Debate:** Do you have an optimistic or a pessimistic view of population growth?

(a) Split the class into four groups. Within your group, discuss whether you are optimistic or pessimistic about the rate of population increase in the future.

(b) Move to one side of the room if you are optimistic, and the other side if you are pessimistic, to join like-minded classmates from the other groups.

(c) Choose one person from your new group as the spokesperson for your group's view: optimistic or pessimistic.

(d) The spokespeople from each side debate for five minutes on whether there is more reason to be optimistic or pessimistic about the future of population growth. At the end of the debate, change sides if the other side has convinced you to follow their view.

What proportion of your class is hopeful for the future, and what proportion is not?

Fertility rates

What happens to the number of humans will depend on how fast **fertility rates** fall.

Learning Activity

Literacy Communicating Numeracy Co-operating

31.5 In your copy, construct a definition of 'fertility rate'.

31.6 In your copy, write out the following sentence, filling in the gaps.

Over _____ generations, three-child families will have _____ as many children as two-child families.

31.7 Explain why the diagrams in figure 31.2 are:

(a) A useful illustration of fertility rates.

(b) Simplistic, and not showing the full picture.

Discuss your answers with your partner and share with the rest of the class.

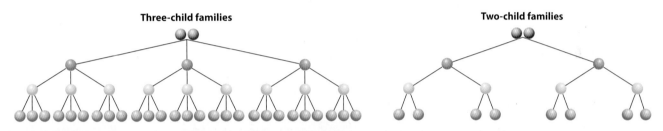

Three-child families   **Two-child families**

Figure 31.2 **In three generations, three-child families produce more than three times the number of people that two-child families produce**

Learning Activity

Communicating Literacy Co-operating

31.8 In chapter 28, we looked at China's one-child policy. Discuss whether other countries could take this approach in the future, and whether you think they should.

Reflecting on my learning

Reflecting Communicating Literacy

Write sentences using each of the following terms from this chapter. You may use more than one of the terms in your sentence if appropriate.

fertility rate

pessimistic view of population growth

optimistic view of population growth

PowerPoint summary

Revision
Go to **www.edco.ie/geographynow** and try the interactive activities and quizzes.

Population: global patterns – the North/South divide

32

Go to **www.edco.ie/geographynow** and try the interactive activities and quizzes.

Learning intentions

When you have completed this chapter you will be able to:

- Analyse how we live in an unequal world
- Look at the social inequalities between the developed world (the North) and the developing world (the South)
- Compare child mortality rates in the developed world and the developing world
- Consider the reasons for low/high child mortality rates
- Compare life expectancy rates in the developed world and the developing world.

3.7 Compare life chances for a young person in relation to gender equality, health care, employment and education opportunities in a developed and a developing country

Key terms

the North   child mortality   malnutrition

the South   life expectancy

An unequal world

In the world as a whole, there are sharp social inequalities among regions, related in part to population characteristics.

There are two major economic regions in the world:

- The **developed** world (**the North**). Almost all babies survive infancy and most people have long lives. People have safe drinking water, plenty of food and a good quality of life.

- The **developing** world (**t he South**). Most children are born to poor parents. Many babies die in infancy and many children, especially girls, do not attend school.

We live in an unequal world. We will examine how unequal it is in relation to:

- Child mortality

- Life expectancy.

Child mortality in the developed world

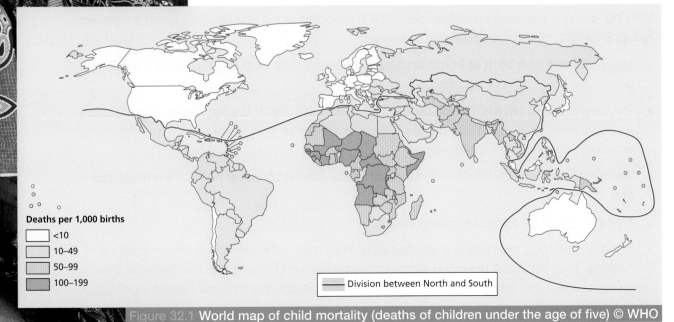

Deaths per 1,000 births

- <10
- 10–49
- 50–99
- 100–199

Division between North and South

Figure 32.1 **World map of child mortality (deaths of children under the age of five)** © WHO

The child mortality rate is **very low in the developed world** (the North), where children's health is a priority.

There are several reasons for low child mortality:

- **Healthy mothers** have healthy babies.

- Women receive **excellent care** during pregnancy.

- Most women have their babies in **maternity hospitals** where the health of mothers and babies can be monitored.

- Young children receive many **vaccinations** to protect them against diseases that used to kill.

- **Clean water** – free of harmful bacteria – is available on tap.

- **Sanitation systems** keep cities free of health hazards.

- Parents are well educated and know the importance of providing a **balanced diet** for their infants.

- There is good access to a **wide range of foods** to make sure that children have a healthy diet.

> **DEFINITION**
>
> **Child mortality rate**
>
> The average number of children who die under the age of five for every 1,000 born per year.

> **DEFINITION**
>
> **Sanitation**
>
> Conditions relating to public health and hygiene, in particular adequate sewage disposal and the provision of clean drinking water.

Figure 32.2 **Young babies in Ireland**

Learning Activity

Communicating Co-operating Responsibility

32.1　(a)　Discuss the most important features of a balanced diet.

　　　(b)　Discuss the barriers to people in a developed country still not eating a balanced diet. Discuss how these barriers might be overcome.

Child mortality in the developing world

Why do so many babies and children die in the developing world (the South)? There are several reasons for this, many of them related to **poverty**:

- Many mothers **give birth at home** in villages where medical care is unavailable. Therefore, babies die from birth complications.

- The poorer the family, the more likely it is that a mother's health is poor. **Unhealthy mothers** are more likely to have babies who are underweight. These babies are at risk from measles, whooping cough and other infections.

- There may not be access to a wide range of foods, so children **may not have a balanced diet**.

- There is often **little access to clean water**.

- In many countries, **mothers are uneducated**. They may not know about the importance of hygiene. They often use **unboiled water** to feed babies and young children because they are unaware of the dangers. This can cause stomach infections; this can lead to diarrhoea, dehydration and the death of a young child in a short time.

- **Poor sanitation** systems can also lead to outbreaks of disease.

- Major efforts are being made to vaccinate babies and young children against **killer infections**, even in the poorest countries. However, **malaria** and **measles** still cause many young children to die in the developing world, especially in Africa.

- The best way to prevent malaria is to sleep under a treated **mosquito net**, which prevents mosquitos from being able to get to the person while they sleep. However, in Sub-Saharan Africa, most children do not have mosquito nets. This leads to many deaths.

Figure 32.3 Sleeping under a mosquito net helps to prevent malaria

Learning Activity

Co-operating Curiosity Communicating

32.2 In small groups, examine figure 32.4. Between you, decide on and list the visual clues for why illness is common here.

GEO FACT

One child dies every ten seconds as a result of hunger.

Figure 32.4 A very poor part of Nairobi, Kenya

Learning Activity

Co-operating Curiosity Communicating Literacy Creativity Responsibility

32.3 **(a)** In pairs or small groups, research:

(i) How malaria affects people.

(ii) How mosquito nets help to prevent malaria.

(iii) How much a mosquito net costs.

(iv) A charity that helps to provide mosquito nets. (It can be an Irish charity or an overseas one.)

(b) Create a poster, or magazine, radio (recording) or simple TV advert (video) explaining the above and urging people to donate to the purchase of mosquito nets. Be sure to give the web address of the charity.

Life expectancy in the developed world

The age at which people die depends on where in the world they live. People live much longer in rich countries than in poor countries. Life expectancy in developed countries (the North) is high for many reasons.

Learning Activity

Co-operating Communicating Literacy Responsibility

32.4 In small groups, consider the reasons that life expectancy is high in developed countries. One person from each group give one of their group's reasons to be written on the board. Once all groups have contributed one reason, another person from each group can give a second reason if it hasn't already been noted.

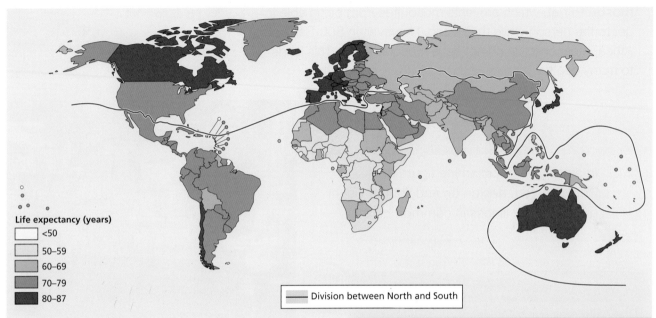

Life expectancy (years)

	<50
	50–59
	60–69
	70–79
	80–87

—— Division between North and South

Figure 32.5 **World map of life expectancy © WHO**

Life expectancy in the developing world

Life expectancy **varies greatly** between countries in the developing world (the South). This is because countries in the developing world are at different stages of development. However, countries where life expectancy is low have some common characteristics:

- Child mortality is **high.**

- **Malnutrition** affects the poor in developing countries. Malnourished people are more likely to die of malaria, TB and other diseases.

- Tens of millions of people drink **water that is unsafe** and contains bacteria. This leads to continuous infections that can shorten people's lives.

- Over 500,000 **women die in childbirth** each year, most of them in poor countries.

- In 2015, 36.7 million people were living with **HIV/AIDS**. The majority are in Sub-Saharan Africa, the world's poorest region. This condition has reduced life expectancy in several countries. This is because there are poor health services and most victims cannot afford **expensive drug treatments**.

Many countries in the developing world experience terrible **wars**. The civil war in the Democratic Republic of Congo between 1998 and 2003 caused the deaths of about five million people. Many other countries, including Sudan, South Sudan, Liberia, Iraq, Syria and Yemen, have experienced conflicts in recent years.

DEFINITION

Malnutrition

Poor health caused by a lack of food or a lack of the right type of food.

GEO FACT

795 million people in the developing world suffer from malnutrition.

GEO FACT

In Ireland in 2017, life expectancy was 78.7 years for men, 83.3 years for women.

Learning Activity

 Curiosity Literacy Responsibility

32.5 Research current wars. Write your answers in your copy and then share them with the class.

(a) Name three wars that are taking place around the world.

(b) Who is at war in each?

(c) How many deaths have there been in each of these wars since they started?

Figure 32.6 A grandmother in Tanzania caring for the two children of her deceased daughter

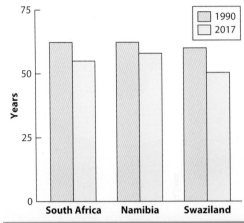

Figure 32.7 The reduced life expectancy 1990–2017 for three countries due to deaths caused by HIV/AIDS

Improvements in life expectancy

Almost all developing countries outside Sub-Saharan Africa have seen increased life expectancy in recent decades. This is because of the efforts made by governments, the World Health Organization (WHO), and other organisations to improve life expectancy. China and India are examples of countries that have increased life expectancy.

Table 32.1 Improvements in life expectancy in China and India over time

Country	1990	2017
China	68	76
India	59	68

Learning Activity

 Communicating Literacy Curiosity

32.6 Consider the reasons for life expectancy increasing in countries such as China and India. Discuss these with your partner, and then share your thoughts with the rest of the class.

Reflecting on my learning

 Reflecting Communicating Literacy

Write sentences using each of the following terms from this chapter. You may use more than one of the terms in your sentence if appropriate.

child mortality   malnutrition   the South

life expectancy   the North

 PowerPoint summary

 Revision
Go to **www.edco.ie/geographynow** and try the interactive activities and quizzes.

Life chances for young people in different parts of the world

33

Go to **www.edco.ie/geographynow** and try the interactive activities and quizzes.

Learning intentions

When you have completed this chapter you will be able to:

- Describe how young people's life chances differ between countries such as Ireland and India
- Explain how gender inequality can be a problem for girls and for women in countries such as Ireland and India
- Identify health care issues in Ireland and India
- Compare the educational opportunities in Ireland and India
- Assess employment opportunities in Ireland and India.

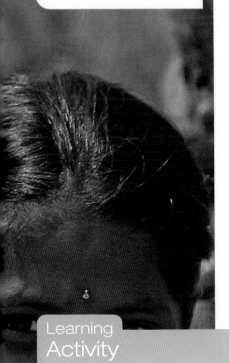

Learning Outcome

3.7 Compare life chances for a young person in relation to gender equality, health care, employment and education opportunities in a developed and a developing country

Key terms

life chances   education   employment

gender equality   health care

Life chances

Link  Chapters 28 and 32

Life chances are the opportunities that young people have in order to improve their quality of life and to develop their full potential.

In previous chapters, we have seen that death rates and life expectancy vary a great deal across the world. Similarly, the life chances of young people differ between those living in developed countries and those living in the least developed countries.

A person's life chances are influenced by:

- The level of **gender equality** that exists in their culture

- Their **educational options**

- The **health care** that is available to them

- **Employment opportunities** in the economy.

In this chapter, we will compare the life chances that exist for young people in **Ireland**, an economically developed country, and the life chances that exist for young people in **India**, an economically developing country.

Learning Activity

Curiosity Reflecting Communicating Literacy

33.1 Consider the opportunities available to young people in Ireland, and what you know or can imagine about the opportunities available to young people in India.

(a) On your own, create a table in your copy with the following headings. Make each row deep enough to fill in about four lines. Then fill in one thing you know or think might be true about opportunities that are or are not available for young people in the two countries.

	Ireland	India
Gender equality		
Educational opportunities		
Health care		
Employment opportunities		

Learning Activity

(b) Share your completed table with your partner. Add to your table anything they thought of that you didn't.

(c) Join with another pair and share your tables. Add to your table anything they thought of that you didn't.

Gender equality

Gender equality means treating women and men equally.

Ireland

One hundred years ago, women's roles in Ireland were very different from those of today. At that time, Ireland, apart from north-east Ulster, was an **agricultural society**. Within this society:

- Many women's marriages were arranged
- Very few women owned property
- Women were tied to the traditional roles of wife and mother
- Women in general did not plan their families
- Very few women worked outside the home.

Women today have lifestyles that are very different from the lives of their grandmothers.

Figure 33.1 **Women in a traditional role in Ireland in the past**

GEO FACT

In 1918, women aged 30 years and above were given the vote in Ireland for the first time.

Changes in the role of women

Now, many women work outside the home. There is a combination of reasons for this:

- **Free secondary education** was introduced in 1967. This increased education levels for girls and boys. Today, young women enter third level education in greater numbers than young men.

- **The Women's Liberation movement** of the 1970s – an international movement – led to many changes in the status of women.

- **Gender equality laws** gave women equal pay and equal status for equal work in the job market.

- **Crèches** enable mothers to go to work.

- Many women choose to work outside the home for **personal** and **economic reasons**.

- Mothers today have, on average, two children each, giving them **more freedom** to work outside of the home.

- The great increase in the **cost of homes** means that in many homes two people have to work to pay the mortgage or rent.

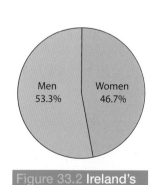
Men 53.3%   Women 46.7%

Figure 33.2 **Ireland's workforce in 2015**

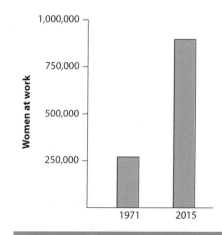
Women at work

Figure 33.3 **The number of women at work in Ireland has increased enormously in recent decades**

GEO FACT

As a group, women in Ireland were paid almost 14% less than men in 2014, even though women do better at school and university than men.

Learning Activity

Curiosity

33.2 Read the geo fact on the left. Suggest one reason why women in Ireland are still paid less than men as a group. Discuss this with your partner and share with the rest of the class.

Learning Activity

Curiosity Responsibility

33.3 It is not only women that have equality rights in the workplace. Research the following and make notes in your copy.

(a) State the name of the act of Oireachtas that legislates for equality at work.

(b) Explain how the act defines 'discrimination'.

(c) How many areas does the act specify for which people are legally covered to be treated equally? State three of them.

(d) State your source(s) for the information you found for questions (a)–(c).

India

Gender equality for girls and women in India is far behind that of Ireland. Girls are not valued as much as boys. Some expectant parents who can afford the operation, will even abort female foetuses.

As they grow up, girls are often prevented from attending school, especially in rural areas, and therefore girls are less literate than boys.

The age of marriage for girls is very young, as you can see from figure 33.4.

GEO FACT

Indira Gandhi was prime minister of India between 1966 and 1977, and again between 1980 and 1984, when she was assassinated. She was the first, and to date the only, woman prime minister of India.

GEO FACT

Literacy rates in India for people over the age of 15: women 63%; men 81%.

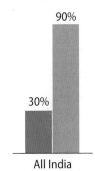

Age of marriage of women in India

- ■ Percentage of women under 18 who are married
- ■ Percentage of women under 25 who are married

Figure 33.4 Percentage of young women who are married at under 18 and under 25 years in India

Learning Activity

Curiosity Numeracy

33.4 Examine figures 33.4 and 33.5. What can you determine about the relationship between the two sets of data? Discuss your findings with your partner and then share with the rest of the class.

Illiterate women

38.1%

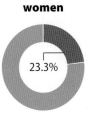

Literate women

23.3%

Women in third level education

5.2%

■ Percentage of women married below the age of 18

Figure 33.5 Education levels of young Indian women of 18 years of age and under, who are married

Millions of Indian girls are forced to marry at an early age because they are considered **an economic burden** to their families. In addition, the younger a girl is when she marries, the lower the cost of a dowry to her family.

GEO FACT

Dowries were common in Ireland even into the 1960s.

DEFINITION

Dowry

Money given by a bride's family to her husband's family when she marries.

Figure 33.6 Indian women do heavy physical work, such as working in the fields and carrying water

In India, a bride becomes the **property of her husband**. Generally speaking, girls are guided by their fathers, wives are guided by their husbands and old women by their sons.

Women regularly experience **violence and abuse** at the hands of male members of the family. Brides may be murdered if the husband's family considers the dowry she has brought with her to be too small. These crimes are of course illegal but the culprits are often not caught and punished.

Hindu **widows**, no matter how young, may not remarry and must wear white rather than their former brightly coloured clothes. Many are shunned by their community.

However, in educated families, girls go to school and often become college graduates. These women enter the professions and many become very successful. A small number of women have done very well in the banking world and are on an equal footing with their male counterparts. These are the exception rather than the norm.

GEO FACT

A blessing frequently given to a young married couple in India: 'May you be blessed with a hundred sons.'

GEO FACT

In order to provide personal security for women in India, certain sections of trains and buses are female only.

Learning
Activity

Curiosity Communicating Co-operating Literacy

33.5 Read the following extract of an article from *Hindustan Times*. Then, in small groups, discuss the questions below.

> **From then to now: How India's battle for gender equality has changed over time**
>
> *By* HT Brand Studio, 24 July 2017
>
> With male domination being so deeply entrenched both in our mindset and our laws, Indians have long since accepted the current social situation as the default one. Even in the most progressive families, daughters are still entitled to far less than sons, from playtime and education to choosing a life partner and inheriting property. No sooner than they are of age, girls are expected to help out in household duties – largely unpaid and unrecognized tasks that they're meant to fulfil throughout their lives. This unequal distribution of resources and opportunities continues into adulthood with significant wage gaps and indiscriminate sexism in everyday affairs. Similarly, boys who grow up seeing their mothers unquestioningly handle all the housework will automatically grow up expecting their wives and daughters to follow suit.

Learning Activity

> The conversation today, therefore, is no longer just about law and order; it also highlights a woman's right to dignity, respect, and equality across all spheres of public and personal life.
>
> www.hindustantimes.com, 24 July 2017

(a) Could the extract apply equally to Ireland as to India? Discuss how the two countries are similar and different in this respect.

(b) One of your group should draw a line with ten marks labelled 1 (not much) to 10 (a great deal). Pass the paper around your group, and from your reading of this section on gender equality, each of you assign a score on how great you consider the difference between the way women are treated in the two countries.

Educational opportunities

Link 🔗 Chapter 40: pages 384–95

Ireland

In Ireland, **educational opportunities** for children and young people are among the **best in the world**.

Here are some **facts about education in Ireland**:

- Education is **compulsory**.

- Teachers are extremely **well trained** for four years in teacher training colleges.

- Most students remain in school until the **Leaving Certificate**.

- **Girls achieve higher grades** than boys on average.

- A high percentage of students attend **third level** courses in universities and colleges. Students are awarded places based on their Leaving Certificate points. The points system is pressurising but very fair.

Table 33.1 Irish education figures for 2017	
Number of students in education (primary to tertiary)	1.09 million
Number of students in third level education	174,000
Government expenditure on education	€8.8 billion
Compulsory school years	6–16
Percentage of second level students who complete the Leaving Certificate	90.5%
Percentage of 30–34 year olds with third level qualifications	51%

- More girls **graduate** from third level colleges and universities than boys.

- Ireland's young people are among the **most educated in the world**. The percentage of 30–34 year olds in Ireland with third level qualifications is among the highest in the EU, but is not as high as in Japan and South Korea.

Attendance in third level education

Young people's participation in third level education depends partly on parents' income and where they come from. For instance:

- In Dublin's wealthiest districts, up to 99% of students go on to college.

- In the most disadvantaged districts of Dublin, fewer than 20% of students go on to college.

GEO FACT 🌐

In 1950, only 4,500 students sat the Leaving Certificate. Today, the figure is almost 60,000.

Students can choose from a great variety of third level courses. **STEM** (**S**cience, **T**echnology, **E**ngineering, **M**athematics) courses are in high demand. Graduates in these fields of study have a great variety of jobs available to them. Ireland comes 15th of all countries ranked for their educational attainments in science and maths.

However, at the other end of the scale is the small percentage of second level students, usually from disadvantaged areas, who drop out at various stages of post-primary school. The life chances of those students are seriously reduced. They possess few skills and their job opportunities are more limited. They are more likely to be **unemployed**.

There are also opportunities for young people who don't go on to third level studies to work in trades and services.

Learning Activity

Curiosity Communicating Co-operating

33.6 In small groups, use the brain droplets handout that your teacher will give you to help you think of barriers to fully avail of Ireland's education system. Pass the sheet round so each of you writes one idea in a droplet before passing on to the next person. Keep passing the sheet round the group until nobody has anything to add. You may discuss any point before adding it.

Share your thoughts with the rest of the class.

India

Educational opportunities in India depend largely on the **wealth** of a young person's family. Every city in India has private fee-paying schools. These schools are run by private individuals and by organisations such as religious orders and congregations. For instance:

- The Irish Christian Brothers have 21 schools. Their schools may be very large and can have more than 2,000 students on the rolls.

- The Loreto Sisters have 22 schools for girls.

Many fee-paying schools teach through the medium of English.

Here are some **facts about education in India**:

- Classes range from kindergarten to Class 12, after which young people can go on to university or other third level colleges.

- Many Indian students concentrate on **STEM** fields of study because career opportunities await them both at home and abroad.

GEO FACT

English is increasingly the language of business in Indian cities today.

Figure 33.7 A village school in rural India

- Most children go to **state-run schools**.

- In state-run schools, especially in rural areas where the most of the population lives, school **facilities are very poor** with dirt floors, no desks, windows without glass and classrooms without cooling fans.

- Teachers in many parts of India are very **poorly trained**.

- Pupil **absenteeism** is high, especially among girls, in rural areas.

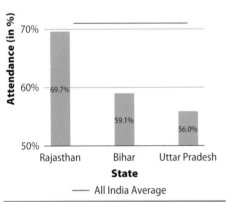

Attendance in primary school by state (on the day of the survey)

Attendance (in %)

80%

70%

69.7%

60%

59.1%

56.0%

50%

Rajasthan   Bihar   Uttar Pradesh

State

—— All India Average

Figure 33.8 **Attendance in primary school by state**

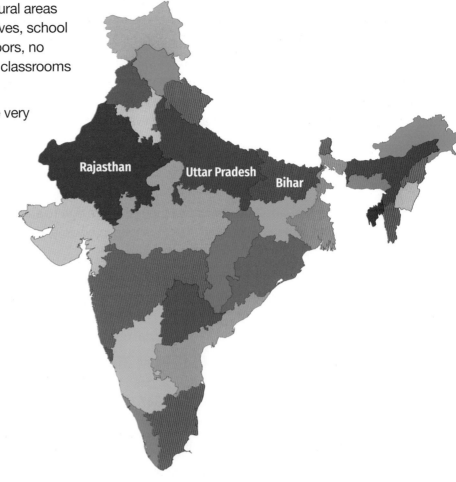

Rajasthan   Uttar Pradesh   Bihar

Figure 33.9 **The states of India**

Learning **Activity**

Reflecting Responsibility Communicating Literacy

33.7 Examine the photo at figure 33.10. Create a table or write about 250 words comparing this schoolroom with your experiences of school. What is the same and what is different?

Figure 33.10 **A schoolroom in Varanasi, a poorer part of India**

313

Health care

Ireland

By global standards, the life chances for Irish children in terms of health and health care are excellent. Life expectancy in Ireland is one of the highest in the world. Irish people have excellent nutrition due to a generally high standard of living.

Table 33.2 Ireland – health-related facts

Life expectancy	82 years
Child mortality	4 per 1,000 under five years of age
Major causes of adult death	Cancer, stroke, heart disease

Infant and child mortality are as low as they are in neighbouring countries in Western Europe. Infectious diseases, such as TB, among adults have been controlled for decades with modern medicines.

The major causes of **adult deaths** in Ireland today are age related. Many **health conditions** are related to **life style**, particularly when it results in obesity. This may lead to high blood pressure, high cholesterol and joint deterioration.

Hospital standards are generally high. Ireland has a **two-tier health system**. For the people who have **health insurance** (who account for just under 50% of the population), quick access to hospitals and consultants is very good and they receive speedy treatment for medical conditions.

However, for the rest of the population – those who do not have insurance or who have **medical cards** – access to hospitals is much slower. In August, 2017, there were 687,000 people on waiting lists, and they may be on a waiting list for up to two years.

GEO FACT

€14 billion was spent on the health budget by the Irish government in 2017.

The only solution to an improved health service is **higher taxes** so that the health budget can be expanded. A bigger budget will allow new wards to be opened and the hiring of additional medical staff.

Table 33.3 Life expectancy in years in Ireland and India – change over time

Life expectancy	1960	2017
Ireland	70	82
India	41	68

Learning Activity

Reflecting Responsibility Communicating

33.8   'Higher taxes will pay for better health care.' Have a class discussion on whether you would be willing, when you are earning, to pay higher taxes if it means the health care in the country could be improved. Justify any comments you make.

India

Health care is one of the more **challenging** areas of Indian society. The major cities have fine hospitals with modern practices and standards. However, only the wealthy can afford to pay for hospital care. Health insurance is not popular among wealthy Indians. More than one billion Indians could not afford health insurance even if they wanted to buy it.

Children are **vaccinated** against infections the same as they are in wealthy countries. All children in cities have vaccination services available to them. However, in the countryside, where 67% of the population lives, the uptake of vaccination services is not as high as it is in cities.

A real challenge arises in the case of a **medical emergency**. In the countryside, a health worker or doctor in the village health centre will decide if the patient can be treated there.

For example:

- The **village health centre** will treat ailments such as malaria or a broken bone. Children suffering from gastric and chest infections are given antibiotics. A GP charges about 40 rupees (60 cents) for a visit and medicine. All but the very poor can afford this.

- In a more serious case such as appendicitis, pneumonia or TB, the patient is referred to the **district hospital** in the nearest town, which could be many kilometres away.

- In an emergency case such as a heart attack, organ failure or hepatitis, the patient will be referred to a **city hospital**. The patient may not survive in the time it takes to reach the city hospital.

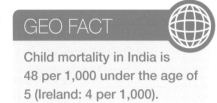

GEO FACT

Child mortality in India is 48 per 1,000 under the age of 5 (Ireland: 4 per 1,000).

Learning
Activity

 Curiosity Responsibility

33.9 Using a street plan, map or website, research how many kilometres it is to the nearest emergency department hospital from your school.

Employment opportunities

Ireland

The **employment opportunities** in Ireland were very good in 2017, with almost 2.1 million people at work, mostly in services.

The numbers of people at work in Ireland varies. When the recession of 2008 occurred with the **collapse of the Celtic Tiger**, unemployment rose to more than 15%. Thousands of young people went abroad for work, many of whom have yet to return and may never do so. By October 2017, with the recovery of the economy, unemployment had declined to 6.1%.

There are a number of job opportunities for highly qualified university leavers, such as:

- **High-tech** companies, e.g. Google, Microsoft, Intel, HP and Boston Scientific, which employ graduates in computer sciences and other fields.

- **Financial services**; this is largely because of the International Financial Services Centre – the IFSC – in Dublin. By 2017, more than 500 financial companies and banks located in the IFSC provide almost 40,000 jobs.

- **Biomedical and biotech** multinationals in the medical devices sector are clustered in Galway, employing more than 6,000 people.

However, for some, including early school leavers, these highly skilled jobs are beyond their reach. There are many other jobs that skilled and unskilled people can do, but some people remain unemployed long term. Training programmes are available for people who wish to upgrade their skills.

There is government support for people on low incomes or who are unemployed. Other benefits exist, such as Child Benefit, maternity allowance, sickness benefit and the state pension.

Employment opportunities differ considerably for young women and young men.

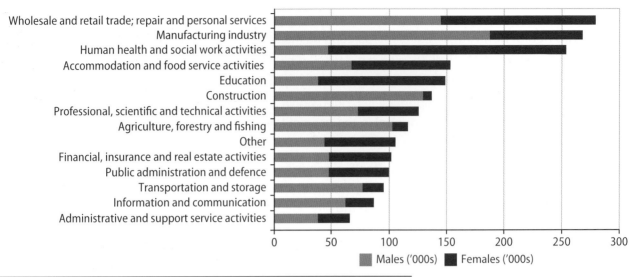

Figure 33.11 **Male and female employment by sector in Ireland, 2016**

Learning Activity

  Curiosity Numeracy

33.10 Examine figure 33.11. Answer the following questions.

  (a) Which sector employs a roughly equal number of women and men?

  (b) (i) Which sector has the highest proportion of women to men?

  (ii) Redraw this sector as a pie chart.

  (c) (i) Which sector has the highest proportion of men to women?

  (ii) Redraw this sector as a pie chart.

  (d) If you were explaining inequality to someone, would you present them with the bars from the bar chart, or with the pie charts you have drawn? Justify your answer.

  (e) Do you think it is the lack of equal opportunities that give the results shown in figure 33.11, or are the inequalities for other reasons? Explain your answer.

  (f) Discuss your answers with your partner and share with the rest of the class.

India

Employment opportunities in India are very different from those in Ireland:

 GEO FACT

Child labour still exists in some parts of India, depriving children of the chance of going to school.

- The majority of people work in the **countryside** on the land. Much farm work is done by hand or with animals. Farmers and farm labourers produce most of the food requirements of the 1.344 billion people of India. Output per person is low.

- Large numbers of people including children work as **brick makers** in brickfields.

- There are jobs in **manufacturing**. They include cotton and clothing **factories** and **heavy industries** such as steel and car assembly.

- Many **call centres** and **printers** are located in India and organisations around the world use them because labour is cheaper than in their own countries.

Figure 33.12 **Women at work on a construction site in India**

Figure 33.13 **A call centre in Bangalore, the high-tech centre in India**

If Indian people do not work, they go hungry because there is **no unemployment benefit**, children's allowances or state-provided old-age pensions. Therefore, Indian people are very enterprising, particularly in the cities. For example:

- Working as carriers of goods from shop to customer.

- Selling vegetables and other foods to the passing trade.

- Having street kitchens preparing cooked food.

- Collecting material for recycling, concentrating on one product, such as plastic water bottles, or paper or packaging cardboard.

- Providing services to the huge population, such as driving rickshaws or taxis, making pottery, leather working, shoemaking and carrying out repair work of all kinds.

For educated people, there are growing opportunities. India is enjoying a high-tech boom. The city of **Bangalore** is India's equivalent of the USA's Silicon Valley. Many children of the wealthy go to college and become engineers. These bright, well-educated young people can work in modern growth sectors such as the computer industry. Many of them move abroad to highly paid jobs.

> **GEO FACT**
>
> One-fifth of India's population of 1.3 billion people (270 million) is living below the poverty line.

Link ◯◯ Silicon Valley: **chapter 36,** pages 345-346

Learning Activity

👤 **Curiosity Responsibility** 💡 ➕

33.11 Investigate India's largest employers. Answer these questions.

(a) What is the name of India's largest employer?

(b) How many people does it employ?

Check your answers with your partner.

(c) What is India's second largest employer?

(d) How many people does it employ?

Reflecting on my learning

👤 **Reflecting Communicating Literacy**

Write sentences using each of the following terms from this chapter. You may use more than one of the terms in your sentence if appropriate.

education · gender equality · life chances · employment · health care

 **PowerPoint summary**

 Revision
Go to **www.edco.ie/geographynow** and try the interactive activities and quizzes.

Rural and urban settlement in Ireland

34

Go to **www.edco.ie/geographynow** and try the interactive activities and quizzes.

Learning intentions

When you have completed this chapter you will be able to:

- Describe where early settlers lived in Ireland
- Explain how altitude, gradient, aspect and drainage influence rural settlement in Ireland today
- Describe three patterns of rural settlement in Ireland today
- Consider the importance of Vikings, Normans and others in the origin of urban settlement in Ireland
- Explain why the coast, river valleys and river crossing points are important in the location of Irish urban settlement.

Learning Outcome

3.4 Consider the factors affecting the location and origin of rural and urban settlement in Ireland

Key terms

settlers	crannóg	monastic settlements
archaeologists	aspect	Viking settlements
middens	rural settlement	Norman settlements
ring forts	nucleated settlement	Plantation settlements
fulacht fia	linear settlement	coastal settlements
hill fort	dispersed settlement	bridging points
promontory fort	urban settlements	market town

The factors affecting the origin and location of rural settlement in Ireland

The landscape shows evidence of human settlement, past and present. The **location** of initial settlement in an area is related to:

- Where people were coming from
- Their need for water, food, defence and communication.

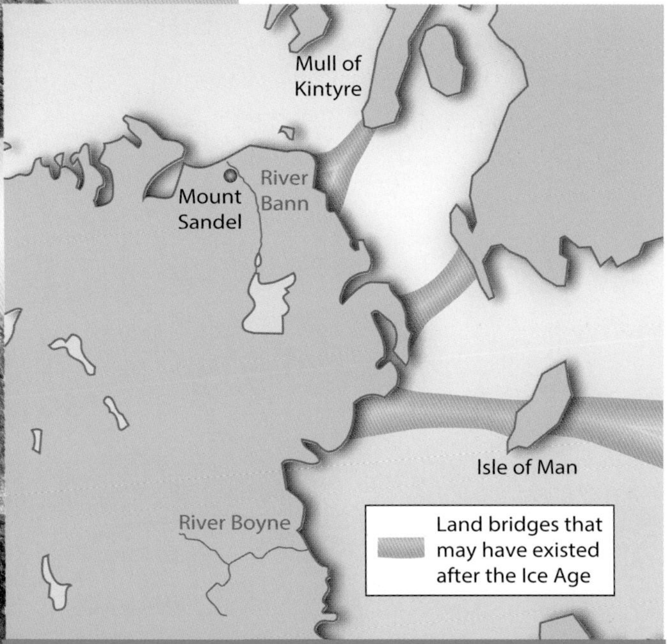

Figure 34.1 Land bridges probably connected Ireland to Britain after the Ice Age

Pre-Christian settlement – before the 5th century AD

Settlers came to Ireland about 9,000 years ago. The first settlers probably arrived in the north-east of Ireland. They may have come on foot via land bridges that connected Ireland with Britain after the Ice Age, when the sea level was much lower.

Where did early settlers live?

Archaeologists have uncovered many sites of early settlements. Sites are found along river valleys and beside lakes, e.g. the Boyne Valley and Lough Gur in Co. Limerick.

The early settlers were **hunters and food gatherers**. They hunted wild pigs, hares and deer. They caught salmon and gathered hazelnuts. We know this because archaeologists have examined their rubbish heaps, which on OS maps are called **middens**. These settlers are known as **Stone Age** people, because they used stone and bone weapons.

DEFINITION

Archaeologist

A scientist who studies the remains left by humans in the past.

Learning Activity

Curiosity Communicating

34.1 Suggest two reasons why hunter-gatherers settled near rivers and lakes. Justify your reasons to your partner and share with the rest of the class.

Early farmers

New Stone Age farmers came to Ireland around 4000 BC. These farmers brought seeds and domesticated animals. They lived in **farmsteads** called **ring forts**. They cooked meat in a cooking area known as a **fulacht fia** (which means 'the cooking pit of the deer'); you can see many of these on the Ordnance Survey map extract in figure 34.2.

The early settlers built large stone graves known today as **megalithic tombs**. Many of these tombs are found in the Burren in Co. Clare and along the Boyne river valley. These tombs tell us where early settlers lived. People were also buried in burial places which are known as **barrows**.

GEO FACT

Up to 20,000 ring forts are still found in Ireland. The Celtic ráth, or ring fort, was also known in Celtic times as lios, caiseal, cathair and dún.

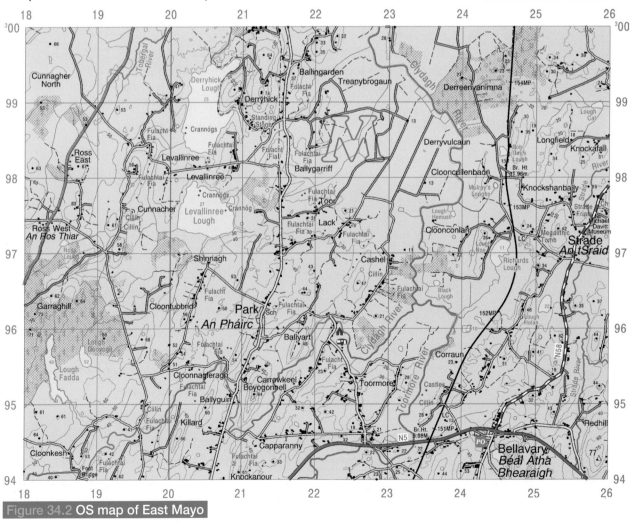

Figure 34.2 OS map of East Mayo

Learning Activity

Curiosity Communicating Reflecting

Examine figure 34.2 and answer the following questions.

34.2   Discuss with your partner how you can find archaeological sites on OS maps. Share this with the rest of the class.

34.3   Look at the ring fort at Boyogonnell, M 212 952.

(a)   Identify the symbol used that tells you this is a ring fort.

(b)   State the altitude in metres at which the ring fort is located.

(c)   Suggest a reason why the ring fort was built at that location.

(d)   State the six-figure grid reference for another ring fort built on a similar site.

Discuss your answers with your partner and share with the rest of the class.

34.4   (a)   What is the plural of **fulacht fia**? Check your answer with your partner.

(b)   State the six-figure grid reference for one fulacht fia shown on figure 34.2. In pairs, check each other's grid reference.

(c)   Suggest why many fulachtaí fia are found close to rivers and streams. Discuss this with your partner and share with the rest of the class.

34.5   State the grid reference for one megalithic tomb shown on figure 34.2. In pairs, check each other's grid reference.

The Celts and defence

At about 500 BC, the Celts came to Ireland. They were **Iron Age** people who built defensive settlements. They built **hill forts** on high ground and **promontory forts** on small headlands along the coast. They also lived in **crannógs** on small islands in lakes.

The Celts spoke Irish. Today, we have many place names that have their origin in the Celtic era, for example:

- **Dún** (fort), e.g. Dún Aenghus, Dunmore, Doonbeg
- **Inis** (island), e.g. Inishmore, Inishfree
- **Ráth** (ring fort), e.g. Rathmore, Rathnew.

> **DEFINITION**
>
> **Crannóg**
>
> An artificial island in a lake on which people built houses, kept animals and lived in safety from hostile clans.

Figure 34.3 **A crannóg in Knockalough Lake, Kilmihil, Co. Clare**

34.6 State the six-figure grid reference for one crannóg shown on figure 34.2. In pairs, check each other's grid reference.

34.7 Figure 34.2 shows several sites of one other type of archaeological feature.

(a) Identify this feature.

(b) Provide a brief definition of this feature.

Discuss this with your partner and share with the rest of the class.

The location and origin of rural settlement

Several factors influence the origin and location of rural settlement. Some factors **attract** settlement and other factors **repel** settlement.

GEO FACT

- In regions near to the Equator, people can live at very high altitudes because temperatures are far higher.

- In Peru and Bolivia, people live and farm at altitudes of 3,800 m in Andean plateaus.

Table 34.1 Factors that repel or attract settlers		
Physical factors	**What repels settlers**	**What attracts settlers**
Altitude In Ireland, most people live below 200 metres	Above 200 metres: • Low-lying cloud and exposure to severe weather (too cold, windy and wet) • Soils are generally thin and infertile, or entirely absent because of erosion	Below 200 metres: • Better weather conditions • Good soil for crops and grazing
Gradient	Steep slopes: • Have poor soil • Are difficult and dangerous for using machinery Many slopes are therefore forested	Flat or gently sloping land generally: • Has fertile soil • Is easier to build houses and roads on
Shelter	No shelter from strong winds and bad weather conditions	Shelter from strong winds and bad weather conditions. These areas are found in valley floors and in sheltered coastal harbours
Drainage	Wet, marshy or boggy lowlands where the drainage is poor	Areas that are well drained, i.e. where surface water either percolates downwards through the soil and rock or is drained by rivers and streams
Aspect This is the direction in which a settlement faces	North-facing slopes because of cold northerly winds and more shade	South-facing slopes because they are warmer and receive more sunshine

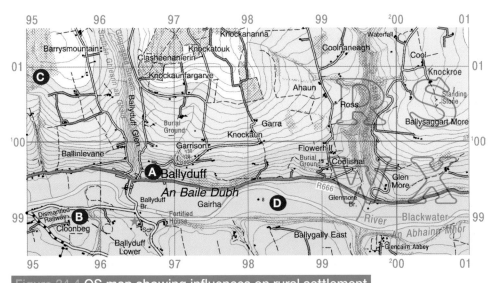

Figure 34.4 OS map showing influences on rural settlement

Learning Activity

Curiosity Communicating

34.8 Examine figure 34.4. Discuss answers to the following questions with your partner and share with the rest of the class.

(a) What factors have attracted settlement to A and B?

(b) Explain why there is an absence of settlement at C and D.

34.9 Using Scoilnet maps, examine your local OS map. Discuss the following questions with a partner. Then share your thoughts with the rest of the class.

(a) What does the map tell you about why settlers were attracted to this area?

(b) Where nearby is there an absence of settlement? What does the map tell you about why this area repelled settlement?

Patterns of rural settlement

There are three patterns of rural settlement, as shown in table 34.2.

Table 34.2 **Patterns of rural settlement**

Settlement	Pattern	Where found
Nucleated settlement	A cluster of houses	▪ In limestone land ▪ At crossroads
Linear settlement	Houses are in a line along a road	▪ On coastal roads ▪ At the foot of a mountain ▪ Along an exit road of a town or village
Dispersed settlement	Individual houses are scattered around the countryside	▪ Many are farmhouses

34.10 For each of the bullet points in the third column of table 34.2, suggest a reason why settlement can be found in this place. Create a table of 'Where found' and 'Reasons' with your partner, and share with the rest of the class.

34.11 Examine figure 34.5. Name the type of settlement circled at A, B and C.

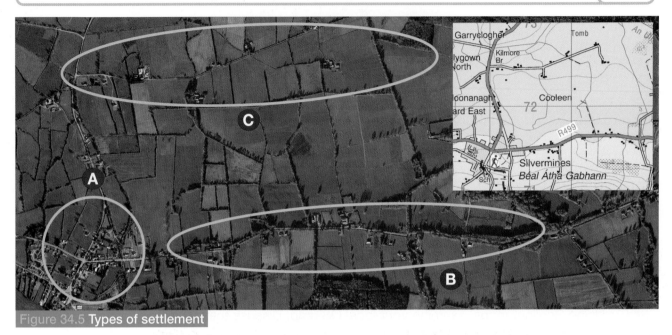

Figure 34.5 **Types of settlement**

How can we explain the settlement patterns in figure 34.5?

A has a clustered settlement and is a small village with no more than a few hundred inhabitants. It is a village in the countryside which provides services to the community of the local parish. These services are likely to include a church, a school, a few small shops and probably a filling station.

B is an example of linear settlement. People who live in this line of settlement along the road are quite close to the village. They may have bought a site from a local farmer and received planning permission to build a house. People choose to live in linear settlements because of the privacy that their own grounds give to them and because they live in a natural setting.

C is an example of dispersed settlement. These houses are most likely owned by farmers who have cattle and sheep. Each farmhouse is surrounded by a farm. Farmers live on their farms because cattle and sheep have to be watched over every day. Dairy cows are milked twice a day.

The origin and location of urban settlements

Urban settlement refers to cities and large towns. These are **built-up** areas and the buildings are **grouped** closely together. On an OS map, built-up areas are coloured **grey**.

Urban settlements owe their origin and location to:

Link 🔗 Chapter 35: pages 332–41

- Historical factors
- Physical factors.

Historical factors

Many different groups of settlers came to Ireland from across the seas. Their settlements grew into towns and cities **over time**. Each wave of settlers chose particular locations for their settlements.

Figure 34.6 **The Norman castle in Trim, Co. Meath – the largest Norman castle in Ireland**

Viking settlements

Vikings were **Scandinavian seafaring people**. They were plunderers who attacked monasteries for their gold and silver treasures. At the end of the eighth century, Viking invaders landed in Ireland. They had already established coastal settlements in Britain and Iceland. Over time, the Vikings settled along the coast, in harbours and at the mouths of rivers. Dublin is the best example.

Many coastal settlements in Ireland owe their origin to the Vikings. Many settlements ended with the word **fjord**, meaning an inlet. Fjord over time became **ford**, e.g. Carlingford, Wexford, Waterford.

Norman settlements

The Normans invaded Ireland in the twelfth century. Normans wanted land and they settled in the country's best land of the east and south.

Normans were great castle builders. Since their castles were built of stone, you can still see ruins of many of these castles. Towns that were founded or developed by the Normans include Trim, Carrickfergus, Kilkenny and Athenry.

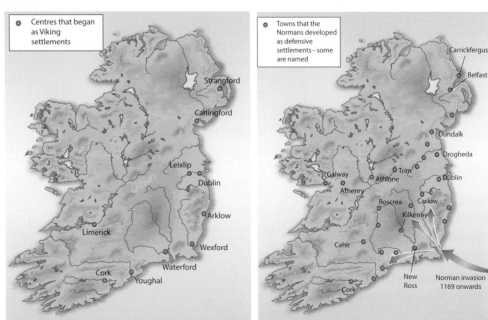

Figure 34.7 Urban centres in modern Ireland that owe their origin to Viking and Norman settlers

325

Monastic settlements

The ruins of early monasteries are found all over Ireland. Monks built monasteries in **remote** places, e.g. Scattery Island, Glendalough, Gougane Barra and Skellig Michael.

Some monasteries became centres of learning. For instance, Clonmacnoise monastery in Co. Offaly became an important seat of learning from the eighth century to the twelfth century. Scholars came to Clonmacnoise from all over Europe.

GEO FACT

The Irish word for monastery is **mainistir**. Can you think of any place names in Ireland with the word mainistir or monaster in them?

Figure 34.8 **Part of the ancient monastic site in Skellig Michael off the coast of Kerry**

Learning Activity

Curiosity Responsibility Creativity Communicating Co-operating

34.12 In small groups, you will research place names in your area. You will look at one of these places in detail, and then present your findings to the class.

(a) Research (using maps, guide books, the internet, etc.) settlements near you that owe their origin to Viking, monastic or Norman settlement.

(b) Choose one of these places to investigate further. Establish details of what group of people settled here; when and why they settled here; and how the name came about. If possible, include details on how the settlement grew.

(c) Prepare a talk or presentation on (a) and (b) above (8–10 sections or slides), including maps and illustrations. Each of you take part in presenting your findings to the rest of the class.

Plantation settlements

English and Scottish **planters** came to Ireland in the sixteenth and seventeenth centuries. Examples included the Laois-Offaly, Munster and Ulster **plantations**.

In planted counties, **fortified towns** were built to protect the settlers from the native Irish people. Many towns in Munster and Ulster owe their origin to plantations.

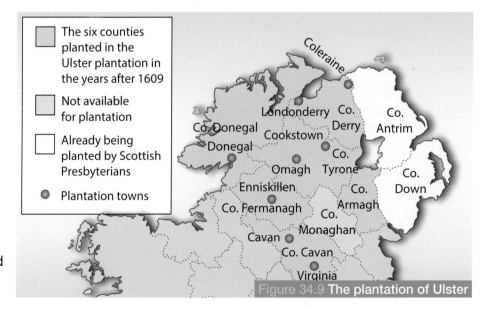

The six counties planted in the Ulster plantation in the years after 1609

Not available for plantation

Already being planted by Scottish Presbyterians

● Plantation towns

Coleraine
Londonderry Co.
Co. Donegal Cookstown Derry
Donegal
Co. Tyrone
Omagh
Enniskillen
Co. Fermanagh
Co. Monaghan
Cavan
Co. Cavan
Virginia

Co. Antrim

Co. Down

Co. Armagh

Figure 34.9 **The plantation of Ulster**

Plantation

An organised colonisation by the British government. English and Scottish settlers (**planters**) were encouraged to settle in lands in Ireland that had been confiscated from rebellious Irish chiefs.

Learning Activity

Curiosity Responsibility

34.13 Some plantations in Ireland failed because not enough settlers came. Investigate:

(a) Which six counties were successfully planted

(b) The province they were in

(c) The years in which this took place.

Physical factors that have encouraged urban settlements

Land quality

Agricultural land is one of Ireland's greatest resources. **Fertile** land attracts settlement, as we have seen. Towns that were founded in the centre of a fertile agricultural plain thrived. This was because they became market towns for the produce from the surrounding area. These towns also provided services for the local population.

The Normans settled mainly in the rich agricultural lands of Leinster and east Munster. For example:

Figure 34.10 Mitchelstown, Co. Cork is surrounded by excellent land

- Maynooth is surrounded by the fertile plains of Kildare

- Kilkenny became the market centre for farmers in the fertile lands of Co. Kilkenny. Kilkenny also has the advantage of being an important bridge point on the river Nore.

The coast

All over the world, settlements have developed on coastal locations. Every coastal county in Ireland has coastal settlements.

 Link Chapter 35: page 335

Learning Activity

Curiosity Responsibility

34.14 Create a table with two columns: 'Coastal counties of Ireland', and 'An example of a coastal settlement'. For each coastal county you have named in column one, refer to the internet or an atlas to name a coastal settlement in that county in column two.

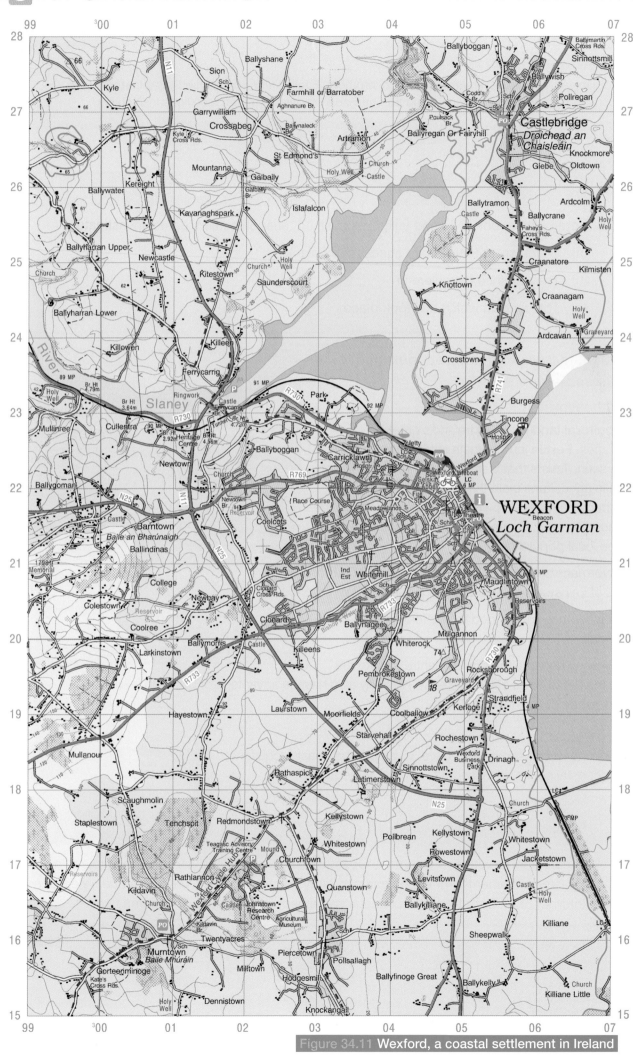

Figure 34.11 Wexford, a coastal settlement in Ireland

Learning Activity

Curiosity Reflecting

34.15 Examine the OS map of Wexford at figure 34.11. Answer the following questions in your copy.

(a) What is the approximate total area in km² of the built-up area of Wexford?

(b) The town of Wexford is at the mouth of which named river?

(c) Explain two pieces of evidence found on the OS map that suggest that the coast is popular with tourists.

(d) What activity is found at T 043 227?

(e) What service is found at T 050 223? Explain why this is located in Wexford.

Coastal locations offered and still offer many advantages for the development of settlements.

Learning Activity

Curiosity Co-operating Reflecting

34.16 Work in pairs.

- Draw a Venn diagram – two overlapping circles.

- Give your diagram a heading: 'Pros and cons of coastal settlement'.

- Label the circle on the left: 'Reasons for settlement'; label the circle on the right: 'Reasons for settlement growth'.

- Add the items given in bold in the list on the right to the left circle or the right circle; or, where the reason for settlement is a reason for the town's continued existence, in the area where the two circles overlap. If an item on the list is a disadvantage to settling on the coast, write it anywhere outside of the circles.

▶ Coastal areas are **more prone to storms** and storm damage.

▶ **Bays and harbours** offer shelter to fishing fleets.

▶ Some people can survive or make a living from **fishing**.

▶ **Ports** enable trade with distant lands.

▶ The **sea levels rising** will cause flooding.

▶ **Tourism** generates income for the area.

▶ **Coastal erosion** can cause loss of land and buildings.

▶ **Fresh water** is available from rivers running into the sea.

Rivers and river valleys

Rivers and river valleys have attracted settlement in Ireland since ancient times. Many towns are located at **bridging points** on rivers.

Learning Activity

Curiosity Communicating

34.17 Suggest why bridging points became settlements. Discuss this with your partner and share with the rest of the class.

DEFINITION

Bridging point

Where a river is narrow enough or shallow enough to cross (bridge), by travelling through the river or building a bridge over it.

The Irish word **áth** means **ford**, a crossing point on a river. Many towns in Ireland contain this word, e.g. Bail Átha Luain (Athlone), Baile Átha Cliath (Dublin) and Droichead Átha (Drogheda).

The largest urban centres on the island of Ireland are all located at river mouths or on the banks of river estuaries. These include Belfast, Sligo, Limerick, Cork and Waterford. These centres are located at the **lowest crossing point** on which they are located.

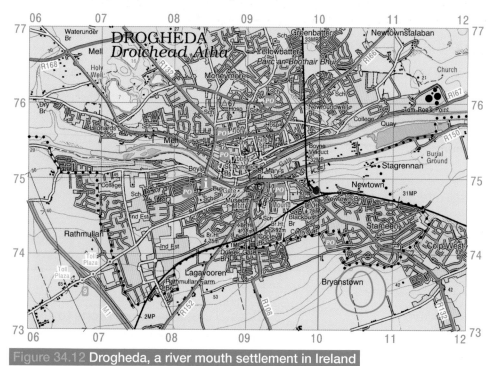

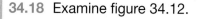

Figure 34.12 Drogheda, a river mouth settlement in Ireland

Learning Activity

Curiosity Communicating

34.18 Examine figure 34.12.

(a) State the number of bridges that cross the river in the town.

(b) Suggest why the bridges were built at these points.

(c) Explain why Drogheda's location as a bridging point helped the settlement to grow.

(d) Look at the bridges in the centre of Drogheda which cross the river Boyne. Suggest why traffic problems could occur at certain times of the day on those bridges.

(e) Explain why the building of the M1 motorway may have eased traffic within the town of Drogheda.

Compare your answers with your partner's, and share with the rest of the class.

Learning Activity

Curiosity   Responsibility   Communicating   Co-operating

34.19 Work on your own or in pairs to research an urban settlement located on a river near you.

(a) Using a map if necessary, determine your nearest town or city that has been built in a river valley (this may be the town you live in, or one nearby).

(b) For the town you named in part (a), research why it developed (for example, it might be a port town, a Norman town, a Plantations town or an ecclesiastical centre).

(c) Using an OS map or aerial photographs (search the internet or look at Scoilnet maps), count how many bridges there are within the town.

(d) Draw a sketch map of the town, clearly showing:

  (i) The river

  (ii) The bridges within the town boundaries

  (iii) The original area of settlement (if you can discover this)

  (iv) A label explaining the reason why settlers stayed here.

(e) Put your sketches around the classroom walls. Make sure you look at everyone else's and make notes on what you liked about their posters that you will try to incorporate into your future work.

Reflecting on my learning

Reflecting   Communicating   Literacy

Write sentences using each of the following terms from this chapter. You may use more than one of the terms in your sentence if appropriate.

archaeologists	hill fort	Plantation settlements
aspect	linear settlement	promontory fort
bridging points	market town	ring forts
coastal settlements	middens	rural settlement
crannóg	monastic settlements	settlers
dispersed settlement	Norman settlements	urban settlements
fulacht fia	nucleated settlement	Viking settlements

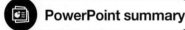 **PowerPoint summary**

 Revision
Go to **www.edco.ie/geographynow** and try the interactive activities and quizzes.

The causes and effects of urban change in an Irish city

35

Go to **www.edco.ie/geographynow** and try the interactive activities and quizzes.

Learning intentions

When you have completed this chapter you will be able to:

- Explain the causes and effects of urban change that have caused Ireland's population to become more urbanised
- Describe how Galway city changed from being a small defensive settlement to the large urban centre it is today
- Account for the fact that Galway became a tourist destination
- Relate Galway's population growth to its educational, medical and manufacturing facilities
- Apply the reasons for population growth to other areas of Ireland
- Examine the effects of population growth, including urban sprawl and traffic congestion
- Describe how urban regeneration has given Galway city centre a facelift
- Apply the principles from the Galway case study to an urban area near you.

3.5 Examine the causes
and effects of urban
change in an Irish
town or city

Key terms

urbanised

urban sprawl

urban regeneration

defensive settlement

traffic congestion

retail centre

route focus

traffic management

infrastructure

ring road

GEO FACT

In 1946, only 38% of the population lived in urban areas in Ireland.

GEO FACT

Within the EU, Ireland has one of the lowest percentages of its population living in urban areas.

Urban change

Throughout the twentieth century and continuing now, the Republic of Ireland has become more urbanised. This means that more people live in towns than live in the countryside. By 2017, **63%** of the population of the country lived in urban areas. This has led to population growth in cities and towns throughout the country. Over recent decades, cities and towns have grown in size and economic importance.

To explain the causes and effects of urban change in Ireland, we will look at the case study of **Galway city**.

Galway's origins

Galway began as a defensive settlement about 800 years ago. A Norman lord built a castle in the area. Walls were built to protect the settlement from attack. Norman families began to **trade** with France and the settlement became a **port**. However, throughout its history, Galway experienced many changes and the settlement acquired new functions.

Figure 35.1 **The location of Galway city in the west of Ireland**

DEFINITION

Defensive settlement

A place where people settled in order to defend their land and people.

GEO FACT

Galway is known as the City of the Tribes.

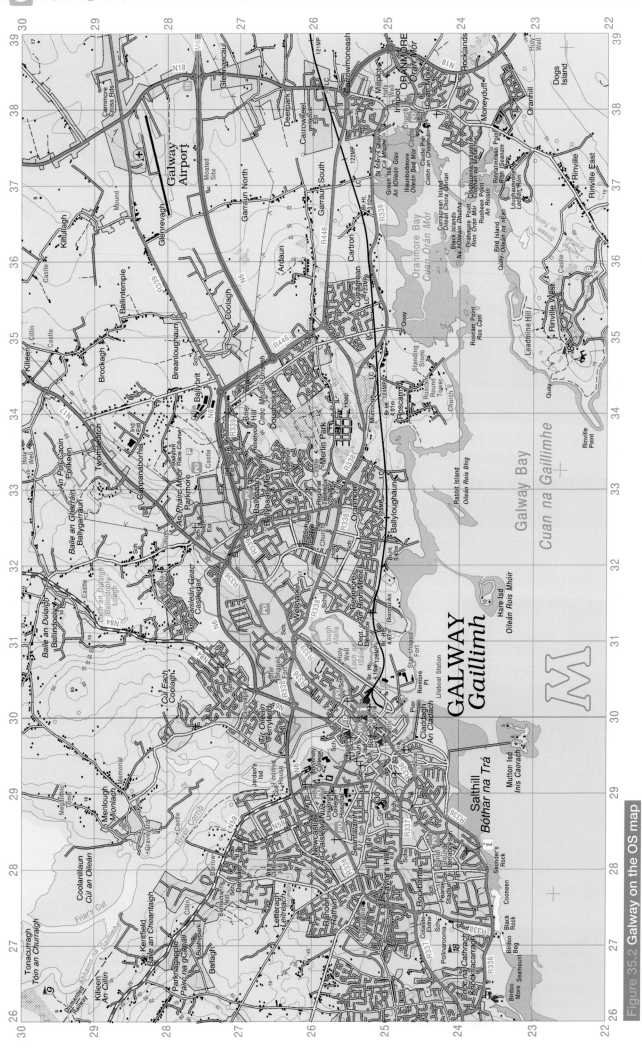

Figure 35.2 Galway on the OS map

Learning Activity

Curiosity

35.1 Examine the OS map of Galway city (figure 35.2) and answer the following questions.

(a) Where is the city centre? Explain your answer.

(b) What institution is found at M 294 259?

(c) The industrial estate at M 324 275 is well served by road transport. Verify this statement using evidence from the map.

(d) The city has many attractions for tourists. Assess the map to justify this statement.

(e) The city has a major teaching hospital. Identify this on the map and state the grid reference.

Learning Activity

Curiosity Responsibility

Find answers to the following questions. Discuss your answers with your partner, then share with the rest of the class.

35.2 Find out why Galway has the nickname City of the Tribes.

35.3 If you do not live in Galway, find out the nickname of your county and why it is called that.

35.4 Does your town or village have a nickname? What is it, and why is it called that?

Learning Activity

Curiosity Communicating Responsibility

35.5 In small groups, discuss why we give our counties, cities, towns and villages nicknames.

Port function

Galway was a major **port** in the West of Ireland for centuries. The city developed around the port because **foreign trade** created wealth.

- **Exports** included hides, wool and smoked fish.

- **Imports** included cloth, brandy and wine from France.

Learning Activity

Curiosity Reflecting

35.6 Identify the port on the OS map extract at figure 35.2. State its six-figure map reference.

35.7 Why would the port have been important to the less wealthy inhabitants of Galway? Discuss your thoughts with your partner and share with the rest of the class.

The city became a route focus

Link  Chapter 34: page 329

Galway city became a **route focus** as goods such as butter and animal hides were brought from the surrounding area to the port for export. The city became a **bridging point** on the **Corrib** river. In the nineteenth century, the railway reached Galway. This caused further change because passengers came to the city from the east and a tourist trade began.

DEFINITION

Route focus

Where many routes meet.

Learning
Activity

Curiosity

35.8 Consider the result of more tourists coming to Galway. Suggest how it affected work and population. Discuss your thoughts with your partner and share with the rest of the class.

The railway also brought **goods** to the city. Galway's **market function** grew because of this and **shops** developed to serve the people of the surrounding areas.

Galway became a commercial centre

Over time, shops, inns and eating houses grew in Galway city centre. The centre became densely built up. This area became the city's central business district (CBD). By the end of the twentieth century the CBD occupied the entire city centre. Businesses included banks, financial companies, department stores, pubs, restaurants, hotels and offices of law firms and accountants.

Educational developments

Galway became a **university city** in the nineteenth century. This was the only university in the West of Ireland at the time. The university, now known as **NUIG** (National University of Ireland in Galway), brought about many changes. College **staff** were employed and the population grew because of the additional numbers of **students**.

In recent decades, Galway has become home to **GMIT** (Galway Mayo Institute of Technology). **UHG** (University Hospital Galway) is a teaching hospital. These bring in more students, all of whom need accommodation, travel and other services.

The city is also a **major medical centre** with several big hospitals. These hospitals are large **employers** and have also brought about increases in the population of the city. The daily needs of the hospitals such as food and medical suppliers also require large numbers of workers.

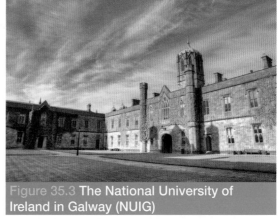

Figure 35.3 **The National University of Ireland in Galway (NUIG)**

Learning
Activity

Curiosity

35.9 With your partner, research the following:

(a) The names of the higher level educational institutions and hospitals in your county, or that are nearest to you if your own county has none.

(b) The type of urban setting they are in, i.e. a small town, a large town or a city.

(c) Draw a sketch map of the town or city, marking on it the institutions you listed in (a).

(d) Display your sketch maps around the class, and look at everyone else's to make sure you found all the institutions.

A manufacturing function

In recent times, Galway has become a **major manufacturing location**. Many multinational corporations (**MNCs**) involved in the research and manufacture of medical devices are located in the city. These include Boston Scientific, the largest employer in the West of Ireland. There are more than 6,000 people working in the medical devices sector in Galway.

Figure 35.4 Many medical devices companies are in Galway

Learning Activity

Curiosity Responsibility Communicating Co-operating Creativity

35.10 In small groups, investigate the manufacturing industries in your area (your nearest town or city). Present your findings to the rest of the class.

(a) Determine the names of:

(i) One local business manufacturing for a local market

(ii) One local business manufacturing for a national market

(iii) One MNC.

(b) Are most manufacturing businesses local, national or multinational in your area?

(c) Is there a lot of one particular type of manufacturing business? What is it?

(d) Identify a particular part of town or county where a lot of manufacturing businesses operate from.

(e) Suggest why this part of the town/city has grown as a manufacturing area.

(f) Present your findings to the rest of the class as a slide presentation, podcast in the form of an interview or poster presentation. Involve all members of your group in the presentation.

Population growth in Galway

Tourism, educational institutions and manufacturing businesses have brought **further growth** in Galway and **surrounding villages**. The result is that in the 2016 census, the population had grown to almost 80,000 people.

Table 35.1 Population change in Galway city, 1901–2016	
1901	13,426
1946	20,400
1971	29,400
1996	57,400
2016	79,504

Source: Central Statistics Office

Learning Activity

Numeracy

35.11 Calculate the percentage increase in population:

(a) From 1901 to 2016

(b) From 1996 to 2016.

Check your answers with your partner's, and share with the rest of the class.

Learning
Activity
Reflecting Responsibility Communicating Literacy Creativity

35.12 Draw a spider diagram for Galway or your own town or city to illustrate how its modern functions have helped its population to grow. Put these around the class for everyone to see.

The effects of population growth

Galway city's population has **expanded** sharply since 1901, as we saw in table 35.1. This has affected the infrastructure of the city, i.e. its buildings and roads.

Building

Population growth has led to a major increase in the size of Galway's **built-up area**. The city has expanded into the countryside. Urban sprawl has occurred because Irish people prefer to live in homes with front and back gardens.

Learning
Activity
Curiosity Communicating Co-operating

35.13 How sustainable is urban sprawl? Discuss this as a class.

Villages close to Galway have also grown because of **overspill** of the population into the surrounding countryside. Oranmore is an example. Athenry, Spiddal and Barna have also grown very rapidly in recent times. Some people who work in Galway prefer to live in those villages for **economic and social** reasons.

Learning
Activity
Curiosity Communicating Literacy

35.14 Discuss the following with your partner and then share your thoughts with the rest of the class.

(a) Suggest two reasons why some people prefer to live in a small village instead of in a large urban area.

(b) What life stages might these people be at?  Link Business Studies

Learning
Activity
Curiosity Communicating Literacy

35.15 Examine the photograph in figure 35.5 and answer the following questions.

(a) Locate the Central Business District (CBD) in Galway and state the section of the photograph it is in. Explain how you know this is the CBD.

(b) Imagine you are a tour guide. Choose three points of interest that you would show to tourists. Justify your choices.

(c) Identify and describe locations that show evidence of urban sprawl.

(d) The rail terminal is ideally located for rail travellers. Justify that statement.

(e) Galway is seen as a very attractive city in which to live. Describe the evidence in the photograph to support that statement.

(f) Identify and describe two places where traffic gridlock is likely to occur at certain times. Justify your answer.

Discuss your answers with your partner and share with the rest of the class.

Figure 35.5 Aerial photograph of Galway

Traffic congestion

As is the case in most other cities, the growth of Galway city has led to **traffic problems**. Many people living in the suburbs use their cars to get to work in the city centre. This leads to traffic **congestion** during the main commuting times (known as the **rush hour**), when traffic moves very slowly or is at a standstill for some time. The **narrow streets** of the city centre make the challenge of traffic congestion even greater.

As in other cities, **traffic management** steps have been put in place to keep traffic moving. These include one-way streets, traffic lights and no-parking zones.

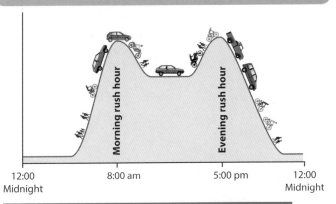

DEFINITION

Urban sprawl

The uncontrolled spread of a city into the countryside.

Figure 35.6 Rush hour traffic peaks twice a day

Figure 35.7 **Examples of traffic management in Galway. How do these aid traffic management?**

The final stretches of the N6, a national primary routeway, has become a **ring road** for traffic to bypass the city centre. The ring road has been upgraded to dual carriageway in some stretches to cope with heavy traffic. An outer ring road is planned. The ring road helps to divert traffic from the city centre.

Learning Activity

Curiosity Communicating Co-operating Creativity

35.16 Work in small groups to assess traffic management in your nearest town or city.

(a) Using a placemat template, each of you provide an example of traffic management in your town or city. Keep circulating the template until you have run out of examples.

(b) Draw a sketch map of your town or area of city and mark on it the examples you have identified in (a) above.

(c) Place your maps around the room and compare your examples with those of other groups.

(d) Discuss as a class whether you think these traffic management measures are necessary, and what would be the consequences of not having them.

Urban regeneration

Many cities experience **urban decay** as older buildings in the city centre fall out of use. Galway is no exception to this. Many buildings in areas close to Eyre Square and the docks area of the city fell into **disrepair** during the twentieth century.

As the economy of the country developed, these areas were **regenerated**. The run-down areas were given a **facelift**. Old unsafe buildings were removed. In their place, shopping centres, offices and apartment blocks were built. Streets were **pedestrianised**. Eyre Square received an elaborate **makeover**. Markets take place here at various times.

Figure 35.8 The Christmas market in Eyre Square

With the growth of the city's population, the number of **shoppers** grew. The city has become a major **retail centre** for the region and much employment has been created in the city in the retail and hospitality sectors.

Learning Activity

 Curiosity Responsibility Communicating Co-operating Creativity

35.17 In small groups, research an area in your town, or a town near you, that has undergone urban regeneration since the 1990s.

  (a) Name the area.

  (b) What was there before, and what is there now?

  (c) Try to find some before and after photographs.

  (d) Display your findings as a self-running slide show on a computer or as a series of posters on the wall.

Learning Activity

Curiosity Responsibility Communicating Co-operating Creativity Literacy

35.18 Is there an area in your nearest town or city that would benefit from urban regeneration?

  (a) Name the area.

  (b) Find pictures of the area.

  (c) Propose how the area could be regenerated.

  (d) Sketch what you think it could look like.

  (e) Present your ideas as a self-running slide show on a computer or as a series of posters on the wall.

Reflecting on my learning

 Reflecting Communicating Literacy

Write sentences using each of the following terms from this chapter. You may use more than one of the terms in your sentence if appropriate.

defensive settlement	retail centre	route focus	traffic	urban sprawl
	ring road	traffic congestion	management	urbanised
infrastructure			urban regeneration	

 PowerPoint summary

 Go to **www.edco.ie/geographynow** and try the interactive activities and quizzes.

Global patterns of economic development

36

Go to **www.edco.ie/geographynow** and
try the interactive activities and quizzes.

Learning intentions

When you have completed this chapter you will be able to:

- Identify the dominant economic regions of the world today
- Explain why the economic development of some regions is far behind the most advanced regions
- Compare an economically advanced region with a less economically advanced region
- Show that even in wealthy countries, some regions are economically challenged.

Key terms

economic development

dominant economic regions

Silicon Valley

entrepreneurial culture

economic core

free trade zone

Asian Tigers

workshop of the world

special economic zone

inward investment

transport infrastructure

economic driver

regional assemblies

Distribution of economic development

Economic development is **unevenly distributed** across the globe. Some regions are very advanced economically. Other regions, especially in parts of South Asia, Sub-Saharan Africa and parts of Latin America, are far behind in economic terms.

The dominant economic regions of the globe

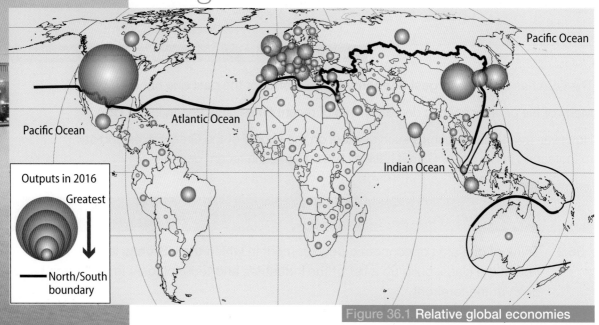

Figure 36.1 **Relative global economies**

Three regions dominate economic development in the world today.

Learning Activity

Curiosity Communicating

36.1 Examine figure 36.1 and, with the aid of an atlas, answer the following questions.

(a) What are the three regions that dominate the world's economic development?

(b) Are these mainly in the northern hemisphere or the southern hemisphere?

(c) Which country is the largest economy in the world?

(d) Which country is the second-largest economy?

(e) Suggest why we consider the countries of Europe to be an economic region.

Discuss your answers with your partner and then share with the rest of the class.

Most of the world's wealth is concentrated among the people of the three dominant regions you have identified from figure 36.1. These regions are the **drivers of the global economy**. The majority of the world's manufacturing and service industries is located in these regions.

GEO FACT

New York is a global financial capital.

The USA

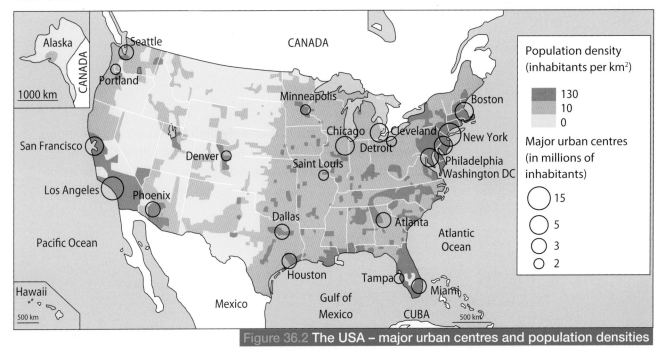

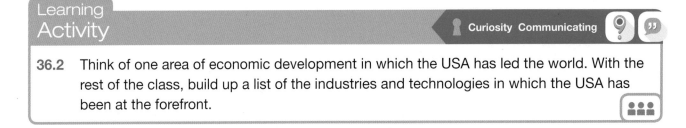

Figure 36.2 **The USA – major urban centres and population densities**

The USA has been the **largest economy in the world** for the past one hundred years.

Many of the great economic developments of recent times have begun in the USA.

However, traditional industries such as steel on the shores of the Great Lakes and car manufacture in the city of Detroit have all but collapsed in recent decades.

Learning Activity

Curiosity Communicating

36.2 Think of one area of economic development in which the USA has led the world. With the rest of the class, build up a list of the industries and technologies in which the USA has been at the forefront.

Learning Activity

Curiosity Responsibility Communicating Literacy

36.3 Locate the Great Lakes on a map showing the whole of the USA. Describe their location in one or two sentences so that someone else could find them quickly.

36.4 Which state is Detroit in? Make sure you can point to its location on the map at figure 36.2.

Much of this development has occurred in **Silicon Valley** in California.

Silicon Valley, California

Silicon Valley is in the vicinity of the City of San José, located close to San Francisco. It is the nickname of possibly the **most important high-tech centre** in the world. The headquarters of many of the best-known multinational companies are located in Silicon Valley, as you can see from figure 36.4. Many of these companies have literally changed the way we live.

GEO FACT

Seattle is the home of Microsoft, the software giant.

Figure 36.3 Silicon Valley with the new Apple HQ taking shape in the foreground

Learning Activity

Curiosity

36.5 Name two computer technology companies and one social media company that are based in Silicon Valley.

The importance of Silicon Valley

The main reason for the extraordinary importance of Silicon Valley in the global economy is the **University of Stanford**. The university has Nobel prize winners on its past and present staff. Stanford researchers are on the cutting edge in various fields of science and computing.

The MNCs as well as the university attract very **inventive and creative people** from all over the world. Some of the best and brightest engineers and scientists move to Silicon Valley to work.

The **entrepreneurial culture** of the Valley has encouraged countless start-ups, many of which have grown to become household names the world over.

There is worldwide demand for new health care products, internet technology, laser technology, drone and military technology and security systems. Silicon Valley companies develop these systems for a **global market**.

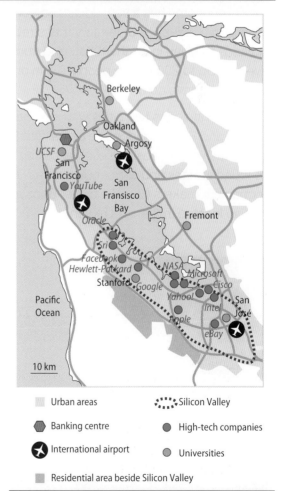

Urban areas	···· Silicon Valley
Banking centre	● High-tech companies
✈ International airport	○ Universities
Residential area beside Silicon Valley	

Figure 36.4 Silicon Valley and the San Francisco Bay area

The region manufactures some of the products that are developed there, but a large portion of its products are manufactured in China, Vietnam and Mexico.

GEO FACT

Mark Zuckerberg's personal fortune was valued at $70 billion in 2017. He started Facebook in 2004.

Learning Activity

 Curiosity Communicating

36.6 Consider the following questions, then discuss your answers with your partner. Share your thoughts with the rest of the class.

(a) What is a disadvantage of many of the world's best scientists moving to Silicon Valley to work?

(b) Why are many of the products developed in Silicon Valley manufactured in other countries?

(c) What is a consequence for Silicon Valley of manufacturing processes being undertaken in other countries?

The EU

Economic development is very **advanced** in much of the EU. Some EU members, such as Germany, Britain, France and Italy, are among the largest economies in the world.

The EU economy has a very advanced economic core. The core is found in a great belt of territory that stretches from the British midlands to Milan in northern Italy and from Paris to southern Sweden. Up to 200 million people live in or close to the EU economic core.

This region includes two cities with a global influence: London and Paris. London is a global financial centre; French fashion houses and cosmetics companies are found in Paris and surrounding areas. The great German car makers (BMW, Daimler Benz and others) are also located in the core region.

Figure 36.5 The Central Business District of Frankfurt, the home of the European Central Bank

Core economic regions

* The UK is expected to leave the EU in 2019

Figure 36.6 A simplified map of the economic regions of the EU

Learning Activity

Curiosity

36.7   With the help of an atlas, name the countries that are found in the EU economic core.

The advanced economic development in Europe

There are several reasons that explain why economic development is advanced in Europe. They are:

DEFINITION

Free trade zone

An area where goods may be imported and stored or processed for re-export or to move into the country's market without having to pay duties to the customs authorities.

- Many countries in Europe have been **industrialised** since the nineteenth century.

- The region has a **well-educated labour force**. In addition, many **highly skilled** people from overseas work in EU countries.

- The development of the EEC (now the EU) in 1957 created a free trade zone between its member states. Trade increased between member states as demand for goods increased and more countries joined the EU. The standard of living rose.

- West European **transport routes** are among the most modern in the world. This encourages the cheaper and quicker transport of goods between countries and further increases trade.

- Western Europe is surrounded by seas which have some of the busiest **shipping routes** in the world. European ports such as Rotterdam import raw materials and fuels to maintain the economy of western Europe.

- European **universities** and other **research centres** are involved in the research of new products in healthcare, biotechnology, space technology and food processing. Many of these developments are converted into new products that are manufactured for a global market.

East Asia

Japan grew to become one of the world's largest economies in the second half of the twentieth century. After 1960, the economies of South Korea, Taiwan, Hong Kong and Singapore followed. So successful were these economies in the production of televisions, cameras and other consumer goods that they became known by the nickname the Asian Tigers.

Since 1980, these **tiger economies** have been joined by the largest country in east Asia: China.

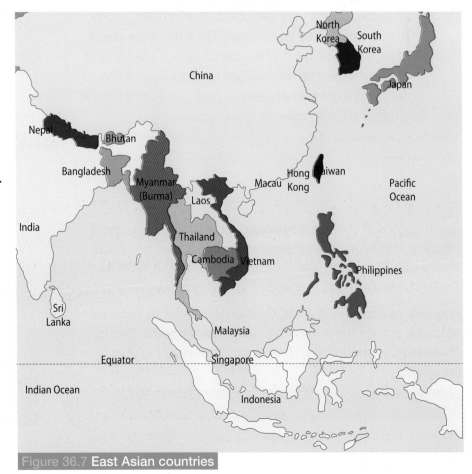

Figure 36.7 East Asian countries

GEO FACT

China is by far the largest manufacturer of motor cars in the world today with an output of 24 million cars in 2016.

The importance of China in the global economy

China is today's **workshop of the world**. After 1978, China embarked on rapid industrialisation. **The** country has the **largest labour force in the world**. China invited MNCs from Japan, South Korea, Taiwan, the USA and other countries to invest in its industrial development. Now millions of Chinese workers are engaged in assembly work in the manufacture of computers, cameras, smartphones, sports gear and other consumer goods.

The east coast of China and east China generally have seen the greatest economic development. **Special economic zones** (SEZs) and other development centres were built in coastal regions.

China is now the **largest exporter** of goods in the world. The biggest container ports in the world are on the east coast of China.

Many people predict that just as the economy in the twentieth century was dominated by the USA, so the twenty-first century global economy will come to be dominated by China. Only time will tell.

Learning **Activity**

Curiosity Numeracy

36.8 At home, check your own clothes and other goods to see where they were made. On a separate piece of paper, make a list of the items (about 10–15) and the countries they were made in. Do a tally of the items for each country and in your copy create a pie chart of the countries of manufacture.

Regions with slow economic development

Some regions of the **less developed world** are making good progress with economic development, such as eastern Brazil, the Persian Gulf region and large areas of East Asia in China, Thailand, Malaysia and Vietnam.

However, much of South Asia, Central Asia and Sub-Saharan Africa are among the poorest and **least developed** in the world. These regions contain the 47 most slowly developing countries in the world.

GEO FACT

Of the 2,000 largest companies in the world in 2016, only 21 were African.

GEO FACT

The Apple iPhone is assembled in China.

GEO FACT

Britain was the 'workshop of the world' in the nineteenth century.

Figure 36.8 The Central Business District (CBD) of Shanghai, the financial and commercial capital of China

DEFINITION

Special economic zone

An area of a country where business and trade laws are different from rest of the country to help boost economic development.

Glasses Headphones Smartphone Bag T-shirt Watch Jacket Belt Jeans Socks Training shoes

Figure 36.9 Chinese-made goods are worn by teenagers the world over

Reasons for slow economic development

There are many reasons that these countries are developing very slowly:

- Many of the countries are **landlocked**. They are far from the world's great sea trade routes.

- They have very **low levels of foreign trade**.

- Their **exports** are mainly unprocessed goods such as agricultural raw materials. These include raw cotton, coffee beans, cocoa beans, peanuts and unpackaged tea. The **price** of these products **fluctuates**. If there is a glut of the product on the world market, the price collapses.

- Many of these countries and regions experience **civil wars and political instability**. In 2017, countries with dangerous political situations included Yemen, Afghanistan, South Sudan and the Lake Chad Basin of Africa. Development during a civil war is impossible.

- Some of the world's poorest countries are ruled by **corrupt and/or incompetent leaders** whose only ambition is to remain in power and enrich themselves and who care nothing for the welfare of their people.

- Vital **inward investment** by multinationals is **very low or non-existent**.

We live in an unequal world.

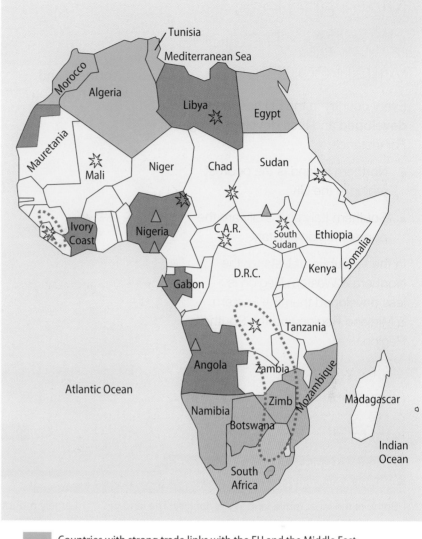

	Countries with strong trade links with the EU and the Middle East
	An emerging economic power in Africa
	Weak economies heavily dependent on South Africa
	Countries with oil and/or agricultural export
	Very weak economies – among the least developed countries
☆	Recent conflicts
△	Oil/gas reserves
⋯	Mineral resources

Figure 36.10 **Africa is the poorest continent and is held back by poor political leadership, corruption and conflict**

Learning Activity

Curiosity   Communicating   Co-operating   Reflecting

36.9   In small groups, complete a fish-bone chart to summarise what you have learnt about regions of the world with slow economic growth.

One person should write on the chart and make sure that everyone in the group contributes suggestions for it.

Place your charts around the classroom for everyone to look at.

More and less developed regions within countries

Every country in the EU has **more developed** and **less developed** regions. For instance:

- Northern Ireland is the poorest region in the UK

- Southern Italy and Sicily are the poorest regions in Italy.

In the Republic of Ireland, the Northern & Western Region is less developed than the Eastern & Midland Region and the Southern Region.

Contrasting regions in Ireland

Northern and Western Region

Eastern and Midland Region

Southern Region

Figure 36.11 **Regional assemblies in Ireland**

Table 36.1 Regions of Ireland compared

Eastern & Midland region	Northern & Western region
Some of the most **fertile land** in the country. The land of counties Meath, Louth, Kildare, Dublin and parts of other counties have brown earth soils which are very productive	Largely **mountainous land**, especially in counties Galway, Mayo and Donegal. Mountainous land gives farmers a very low income
The soil suits the more profitable **tillage farming**, i.e. barley and wheat production. North Co. Dublin has large areas devoted to horticulture for the Dublin market nearby	Because of leached soils, mountainous terrain and damp climate, most farms are small and concentrate on the less profitable **sheep and cattle farming**
More than **48% of the population** and the **highest population densities** live here It benefits from the **inward migration** of young educated people from the other regions of the state and from abroad	Only **18% of the population** and **very low population densities** live here There is a high percentage of **elderly farmers** and young people **migrate** to more prosperous regions
Apart from Dublin, the region has many large and **thriving towns** such as Portlaoise, Drogheda, Navan and Newbridge MNCs, such as Google, move here and invest in the region	The region has a **peripheral location**. It is far from Dublin, the centre of power and influence in the Republic. Because of its low population, it has fewer TDs in the Dáil than other regions to represent the region Apart from Galway city, Sligo, Castlebar and Letterkenny, the region's **urban centres are small**. This makes the region less attractive for major MNCs to invest in
Has the **best infrastructure** in the country. Dublin is the hub of the Irish transport system with motorways and railways radiating outwards from Dublin to the provinces, and a very large international airport	Has a **less advanced infrastructure** than other regions. There is only one international airport: Knock, Co. Mayo
Dublin city and suburbs are located in this region. Dublin city and county had a **large population** of 1,345,402 in 2016, and is continuing to grow Dublin is the economic driver of the state and is the leading financial, commercial, manufacturing, educational, tourist and media centre in the state	For generations, young people have migrated outwards from the region to the east of Ireland and abroad to find work and a higher standard of living. This is an example of a **brain drain** The region had a **small population** of 850,000 people in 2016

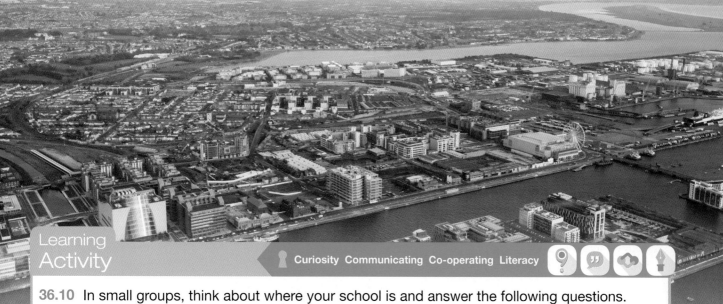

Figure 36.12 Dublin's Docklands. Which buildings do you recognise (find at least two)?

Learning Activity

Curiosity Communicating Co-operating Literacy

36.10 In small groups, think about where your school is and answer the following questions.

(a) In which region of Ireland are you?

(b) Is your school in a rural, town, city outskirts or city location?

(c) Assess the 10 km radius of your school under the following headings:

    (i) What sort of land is in the area?

    (ii) What is the main type of farming?

    (iii) What is the population density (low, medium, high)?

    (iv) What is the nearest large town or city and how far away is it? (You may be in it!)

    (v) What MNCs are in the area (name up to three of the nearest ones)?

    (vi) What is your assessment of the infrastructure of the area (road network, airports, bus routes)?

    (vii) In your experience, are young people migrating to the area or away from the area, or staying there?

Reflecting on my learning

Reflecting Communicating Literacy

Write sentences using each of the following terms from this chapter. You may use more than one of the terms in your sentence if appropriate.

Asian Tigers	free trade zone	special economic zone
dominant economic regions	inward investment	transport infrastructure
economic development	regional assemblies	workshop of the world
entrepreneurial culture	Silicon Valley	

 PowerPoint summary

 Revision
Go to **www.edco.ie/geographynow** and try the interactive activities and quizzes.

Economic activities

37

Go to **www.edco.ie/geographynow** and
try the interactive activities and quizzes.

Learning intentions

When you have completed this chapter you will be able to:

- Differentiate between primary, secondary and tertiary sectors
- Provide examples of jobs that fall into the three economic activities
- Explain the term footloose industry
- Analyse the factors that lead to the location of a secondary activity
- Identify secondary activities near your school
- Investigate a local secondary activity.

2.5 Describe a local secondary activity in relation to its function and the factors that influence its location

Key terms

sector

economic activity

primary

secondary

tertiary

services

resource material

transport facilities

labour force

high-tech manufacturer

market location

multinational company

capital

footloose industry

industrial estates

government policy

The information in this chapter will help you to research a secondary activity in your area. (See Activity Book, page 206.)

Economic activities

There are three sectors of economic activity, as shown in table 37.1.

Table 37.1 Economic activity

Type of economic activity	What it is	Examples
Primary sector	Raw materials are produced from Earth	▪ Farming ▪ Fishing ▪ Forestry ▪ Mining
Secondary sector	Workers in factories use raw materials to manufacture or assemble goods that people can buy	▪ Manufacturing steel components ▪ Assembling mobile phones ▪ Building ▪ Sewing ▪ Food processing
Tertiary or services sector	People provide services that other people require	▪ Teaching ▪ Hairdressing ▪ Accountancy ▪ Nursing ▪ Retail

The workforce in more developed and less developed economies

In **poor countries**, most people are working in the **primary sector**, as farmers, fishermen and women and miners.

As a country's **wealth grows**, more of its people work in **manufacturing** and in **services**. In **very wealthy** countries, most people work in **services**.

Learning Activity

Curiosity Communicating
Literacy Numeracy

37.1 Examine the pie charts in figure 37.1.

(a) State which of the charts shows a developing country and which shows a developed country.

(b) In pairs, one of you justify your answer for choosing the chart for the developing country, and the other justify your answer for choosing the chart for the developed country.

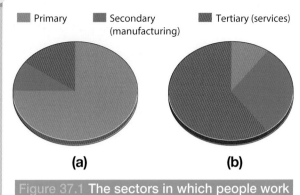

Legend: Primary | Secondary (manufacturing) | Tertiary (services)

(a)   (b)

Figure 37.1 The sectors in which people work

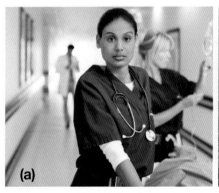

(a)

(b)

(c)

Figure 37.2 Working in the economic sectors

Learning Activity

Curiosity Reflecting

37.2 Look at the photos in figure 37.2. Identify the economic sector that the job in the photos (a)–(c) represents. Agree your answers with your partner.

In Ireland – a wealthy country compared to many others – most people work in the **tertiary** or services sector.

We have looked at primary activities in **chapters 22 to 26**. In this chapter, we will look in more detail at secondary economic activities, particularly those where you live.

Table 37.2 The percentage of the Irish workforce in each of the three economic sectors of the economy

Primary	8%
Secondary	28%
Services	64%

Secondary economic activities

A secondary economic activity is one in which **raw materials are processed into products**.

Inputs	Processes	Outputs
Resource materials (e.g. raw materials, power, workers)	Turn into products	Products

Waste |

Learning
Activity

 Curiosity

37.3 Consider the manufacture of shoes and answer the following questions.

(a) What will be:

(i) The inputs?

(ii) The processes?

(iii) The outputs?

(b) Will it matter where the shoe factory is located? Justify your answer.

(c) Discuss your answers with a partner. Join with another pair of students and share your thoughts on this secondary activity.

Footloose industry

Modern industry, unlike industry in the past, tends to be **footloose**.

Many manufacturing industries are footloose. The reasons for this are shown in figure 37.3.

 DEFINITION

Footloose industry

Manufacturing business that is not tied to one location.

Industrial estates are widely dispersed both in Ireland and abroad. In Ireland, the **IDA** has encouraged many companies to set up light industry in small towns.

Ring roads around cities such as Dublin, Cork, Limerick and Galway attract footloose manufacturing industry.

The labour force today is generally car-owning. This allows factories in small towns to draw its workforce from rural areas.

Why are modern industries footloose?

Electricity is widely available. Electricity is the main source of energy for manufacturing today.

Excellent transport on national road and rail routes allows the transport of resource materials to factories in many locations.

Light industry products – high in value and low in weight – can be distributed cheaply to markets.

Figure 37.3 Reasons for industries being footloose

Industrial estates/parks

Industrial estates/parks are areas where lots of businesses operate in close proximity to each other. They attract footloose industries and offer many advantages to **industrialists**.

Learning
Activity

Curiosity Communicating Co-operating Responsibility

37.4 In small groups, consider why industry owners are attracted to industrial estates. What do they have to offer? Nominate one person to be your group's spokesperson, and each group give a reason to the rest of the class.

37.5 Most towns have industrial estates. What is the name of the one nearest to your school? In your group, make a list of the businesses on that industrial estate.

Figure 37.4 **Shannon Industrial Estate, Shannon, Co. Clare. Describe what you see. How does the proximity of the airport act as a good factor of location for industrial plants?**

Factory location

The location of a factory is based on a number of factors, as shown in figure 37.5.

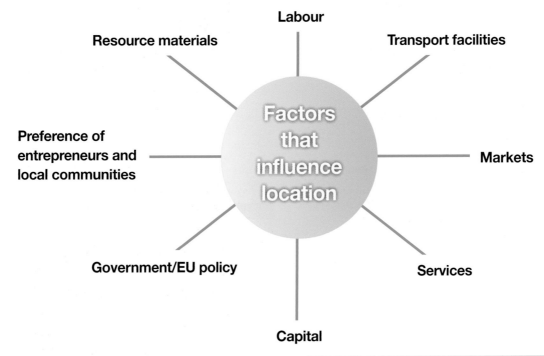

Figure 37.5 **Factors that influence factory location**

We will explain how these factors influence factory location by looking at the case study of **Intel Ireland**, a light industry in Leixlip.

Intel

Resource materials

- When resource materials are **small and light**, as in Intel, factories are **not tied to a resource location**, because transport costs are low.

Intel is a **light industry** using light resource materials that include silicon wafers. These are mainly imported by air through Dublin Airport.

Labour

- Every factory requires a workforce: the people who work there. Factories employ people with the **skills they need**.
- Large factories need a **pool of workers** who live reasonably close. Workers are more mobile today because many can afford cars.

Intel is a **high-tech manufacturer**. Therefore, it needs **highly educated workers**. Many Intel workers are graduates of universities in Dublin, Maynooth and elsewhere. The residential town of **Leixlip**, Maynooth and Dublin's western suburbs provide the pool of workers the factory needs.

Transport facilities

- **Roads, rail, ports and airports** are vital to manufacturing plants for the transport of raw materials and finished products.
- Many manufacturing plants are built near **motorways**, dual carriageways and **ring roads** for easy access.

Intel is well served by transport networks. The **M4 motorway** is only two kilometres to the south. This is evident on the OS map on page 359. The M4 connects with the M50 and **Dublin Airport** – ideal for importing and exporting light materials.

Markets

- This is **where the goods are sold**.
- Some factories, such as bakeries, are located **close to the market** because the goods are perishable and bulky.
- Where a product has a high value and low bulk, the factory can be **far from the market**.

Intel is a major **multinational company**. Its **market is global**: it supplies microchips to companies all over the world. Because microchips are high value and low bulk (very small), they can be made far from where they are sold.

Services

- Factories need services, including **water**, high-voltage **electricity** and **telecommunications**.
- Telecommunications include telephone and high-speed **broadband** services.

Water is taken from the nearby **Liffey** and purified for the Intel plant. Electricity is supplied to Intel by Electric Ireland.

Telecommunications are vital to the success of Intel. Intel managers can hold **video-conferences** with customers across the world using Ireland's telecom services. Ireland's telecom services in Leixlip meet international standards.

Capital

- **Companies need capital** – the cash to buy land, build and equip a factory and get established.
- **Banks provide loans** to companies that have good prospects for growth.

Intel is a highly profitable global company. It **invests** huge sums in researching and developing next-generation microchips. The Leixlip plant has been upgraded and expanded over the years at huge capital cost by Intel itself.

Government/EU policy

- Governments use **tax incentives** on company profits to attract companies.
- Ireland has a **low corporation tax** on company profits to attract foreign companies to the country.
- The **IDA** encourages companies to invest in Ireland.

Government policy was a key reason for the location of Intel's Leixlip plant. The Irish government, through the IDA, actively supported the establishment of Intel in Leixlip in 1989 with **grants** and **tax incentives**.

Preferences of entrepreneurs and local communities

- Local communities welcome companies that do not pollute the **environment**.
- However, they may object to plants that present **health and safety risks**, e.g. incineration plants.

The Leixlip plant is located on a pleasant greenfield site, a former stud farm. Intel was welcomed by local communities as the plant is a modern, clean facility without emissions into the atmosphere. It is also a very large employer.

DEFINITION

IDA
The Industrial Development Authority

Figure 37.6 Leixlip, Co. Kildare with the Intel plant at the left centre on a greenfield site

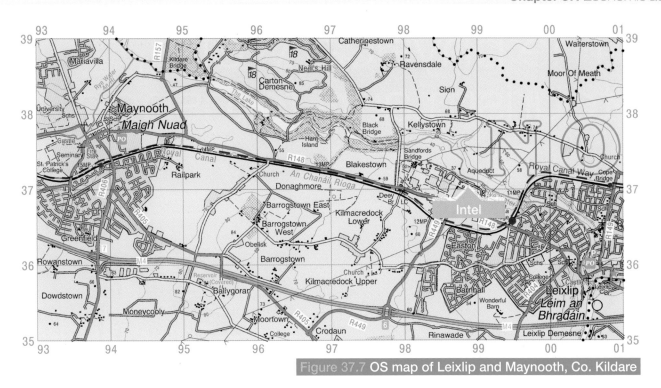

Figure 37.7 **OS map of Leixlip and Maynooth, Co. Kildare**

Learning
Activity

Curiosity Reflecting

37.6   Examine the OS map at figure 37.7 and answer the following questions.

(a)   The Intel plant is well served by road and rail. What evidence on the OS map supports this statement?

(b)   What evidence in the OS map suggests that many of Intel's workers may live in Maynooth and Leixlip?

(c)   An energy source, visible on the OS map, runs close to the Intel plant. What is it?

(d)   Draw a sketch map of the area shown in the OS map, and include the following:

(i)   The M4 and the R148

(iii)   The ESB power line

(ii)   The Intel plant

(iv)   The built-up area of the town of Leixlip.

Reflecting on my learning

Reflecting Communicating Literacy

Write sentences using each of the following terms from this chapter. You may use more than one of the terms in your sentence if appropriate.

capital	industrial estates	resource material
footloose industry	labour force	transport facilities
government policy	market location	
high-tech manufacturer	multinational company	

 PowerPoint summary

 Revision
Go to **www.edco.ie/geographynow** and try the interactive activities and quizzes.

The physical world, tourism and transport

38

Go to **www.edco.ie/geographynow** and try the interactive activities and quizzes.

Learning intentions

When you have completed this chapter you will be able to:

- Explain why tourism is so important for many countries
- Define ecotourism
- Provide examples of different types of tourist destinations
- Outline the impacts of tourism on the landscape
- Describe tourism in Spain, now and for the future
- Explain how transport is vital for tourism, particularly in Spain
- Describe the concerns of anti-tourism protesters
- Explain sustainable tourism, with particular reference to Spain and Ireland.

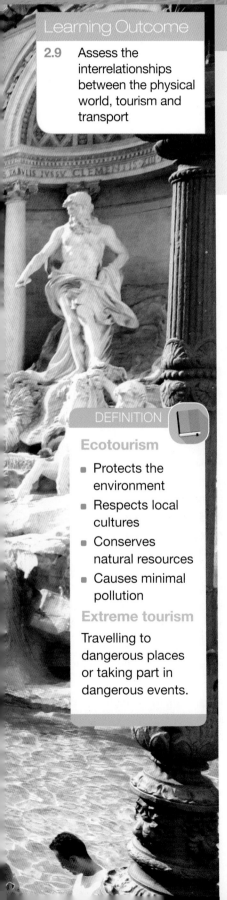

Key terms

- tourism
- attractions
- ecotourism
- economic impact
- social and cultural impact
- environmental impact
- transport
- mass tourism
- anti-tourism
- sustainable tourism

DEFINITION

Ecotourism

- Protects the environment
- Respects local cultures
- Conserves natural resources
- Causes minimal pollution

Extreme tourism

Travelling to dangerous places or taking part in dangerous events.

Tourism

Tourism is a key driver for **socio-economic progress** in both developed and developing economies. Since the 1950s, tourism has experienced continued growth to become one of the fastest-growing economic sectors in the world. Today, the business value of tourism is greater than that of oil exports, food products or the car industry.

Growth of tourism

There are several reasons why **tourism has increased** over the last sixty years:

- People have more disposable income
- The increase in the length of leisure time and paid holiday leave
- Improvements in transport infrastructure, especially air and road
- Wider range of type of holiday: package holidays, DIY holidays, cruises, ecotourism, extreme tourism, etc.
- Media: advertising, internet bookings
- Expansion of tourist services: variety of accommodation.

Tourism destinations

Tourist services and facilities are usually found in regions that offer certain attractions.

Curiosity Responsibility Communicating Co-operating

38.1 In pairs, copy the following table and for each region listed in the first column, give at least one example of such a region in Ireland and at least one elsewhere in the world. Many examples are discussed throughout this textbook; you may need to do further research.

Examples of tourism destinations for types of regions

Region	Example(s) in Ireland	Example(s) around the world
Coastal		
Warm sunny climate		
Natural beauty		
Distinctive landscape		
Recreational facilities		
Cities of cultural and historical interest		
Supportive of ecotourism		

The impact of tourism

The development of tourism is important for many countries. While it does offer advantages, it can also create some disadvantages. It is also very easy to see short-term gain without taking heed of long-term damage.

Table 38.1 The impact of tourism

	Advantages	Disadvantages
Economic	<ul><li>Employment is created **directly** in hotels, restaurants and bars</li><li>Employment is created **indirectly** in transport and retail</li><li>Overseas **investment** provides finance to the country</li><li>Tourism is a great earner of **foreign exchange** (balance of payments)</li><li>The government earns money from a range of **taxes**</li></ul>	<ul><li>Much of the employment is **seasonal**</li><li>Much of the employment is **low-paid**</li><li>Some people, such as farmers and fishermen, may **lose their livelihoods** because of pollution or, for example, a fishing harbour being changed to a marina</li><li>Overseas investment can mean that the money goes back to the **country of origin**</li><li>Regions may become **over-dependent** on just the one industry</li></ul>
Social and cultural	<ul><li>Local **infrastructure** (roads, water and electricity) is improved</li><li>Locals are exposed to **new cultures**</li><li>Gaining **employment locally** can reduce migration or emigration</li><li>Historical sites may be **protected** or even rebuilt to attract tourists</li><li>More emphasis on education to **increase skills** such as linguistic and hospitality</li></ul>	<ul><li>**Tensions** may arise between locals and tourists</li><li>Local people can't afford the **higher costs of living** in tourist regions</li><li>Locals may be **priced out of the housing market**</li><li>Local culture and traditions may be **diluted** or even swamped in facilitating the needs of tourists</li></ul>

Region	Advantages	Disadvantages
Environmental	▪ Income from tourism can help to **conserve the natural environment** ▪ **National parks** may be created, and areas of natural beauty protected ▪ Tourism may develop a **greater awareness of and interest in landscape, vegetation and wildlife**	▪ Hotels and apartment blocks, especially in mass tourism resorts, **spoil the appearance** ▪ Increased **traffic congestion** leads to pollution and health issues ▪ Extra **pressure is put on water supplies and sewage treatment** facilities ▪ Large-scale tourist developments can have a **negative impact on forests, sand dunes and wildlife**

Learning Activity

Curiosity Responsibility Co-operating Literacy

38.2 Identify an area or attraction close to where you live and describe how tourism impacts it.

(a) With a partner, think of one specific example of an **advantage** of tourism for this area or attraction for each of (i) economic impacts, (ii) social and cultural impacts and (iii) environmental impacts. Write these in a copy of the following table:

Impacts of tourism on ...		
	Advantages	**Disadvantages**
Economic		
Social and cultural		
Environmental		

(b) Pass your table to another pair of students and ask them to complete the 'Disadvantages' column for your chosen tourist attraction.

(c) Join with the other pair and discuss what you have written in your tables. Do you all agree on what you have filled in?

Tourism in Spain

Spain developed its tourist industry very rapidly after 1955. With year-round attractions, it received more than 80 million visitors in 2017. Most of its tourism is based on **physical factors**: sun, sand, sea, scenery and snow. Other tourism is based on **cultural aspects**.

GEO FACT

Much of the recent increase in Spanish tourist numbers – from 68 million in 2015 to over 80 million in 2017 – was driven by terrorism and political instability in other tourism destinations, including Egypt, Turkey, Tunisia and France.

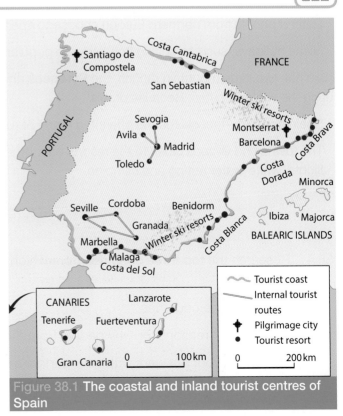

Figure 38.1 **The coastal and inland tourist centres of Spain**

Coastal tourism

Spanish coastal tourism is concentrated on three zones:

- The Mediterranean Costas

- The Balearic Islands

- The Canary Islands.

Learning
Activity

🔒 Curiosity

38.3 On your blank world map in your Activity Book (pages 6/7), mark the three areas in the bullet list above; refer to an atlas if you need to.

These regions have lots of sunshine and high temperatures for many months of the year.

Link 🔗 Mediterranean climate, chapter 21: pages 214–15

In these tourist areas:

- Hotels and apartments have been built along the coast, close to the beaches where the tourists want to be.

- Restaurants, bars and clubs are located along the seafront.

- Resorts welcome family groups as well as providing a wide variety of accommodation.

- Many resorts have marinas, attracting boating enthusiasts.

Figure 38.2 **High-rise apartments spread along the beach front at Benidorm**

Winter tourism

Coastal areas have pleasantly **mild weather** throughout the winter months. Because of this:

- Many people from northern Europe have bought apartments and holiday homes

- Retired people from northern Europe choose to spend extended time in a milder climate than home

- Niche holidays, such as golfing holidays, are popular.

Spain has two large mountain ranges, the **Pyrenees** and the **Sierra Nevada**. Both are **snow-covered** during the winter months. Because of this:

- Spain has thirty-four ski resorts offering a range of runs for both skiing and snowboarding

- The towns and villages close to the resorts offer other activities such as ice skating, hot air balloon flights, white-water rafting and climbing.

Learning
Activity

🔒 Curiosity Responsibility

38.4 Research the top three countries from which the greatest number of tourists come to Spain.

    (a) Name the countries.

    (b) Suggest reasons for why people from those countries holiday in Spain.

    (c) Check your answers with your partner's and discuss your suggested reasons for travellers from these countries.

Figure 38.3 Some of Gaudi's work at Park Güell in Barcelona. Gaudi also designed the Sagrada Família cathedral in the city

Cultural tourism

Spain has been influenced by several civilisations, European and African. As a result, Spain has one of the more distinctive cultures in all of Europe. Within the country, aspects of culture vary widely from region to region.

- Well-known aspects of Spanish culture include flamenco dancing, fiestas, bullfighting and food.

- Spain offers a wide range of museums and art galleries, as well as music and dance venues.

- Six Spanish cities, including Toledo, have been declared World Heritage cities in their entirety. Spain also has thirty-five other World Heritage sites, including the entire work of the architect Gaudi in Barcelona. Other historic cities include Madrid, Granada and Santiago de Compostela.

- Spain receives the highest number of Erasmus exchange programme students in Europe.

Tourism and transport links

Transport is a vital part of the tourism industry in any country. Transportation networks link tourists with various tourist attractions. Tourism expands more when there are better transportation systems. The networks also become a valuable resource to the local population.

Spain is now the country in Europe with:

- The most kilometres of motorways

- The most kilometres of high-speed train lines

- The highest number of international airports.

Learning Activity

Curiosity Reflecting

38.5 Think of one positive effect and one negative effect of Spain's transport network. Which category – economic, social and cultural, or environmental – does each fall into? Discuss these with your partner and share with the rest of the class.

The Spanish road network

Roads represent the main means of transport in Spain, accounting for almost 90% of the movement of people and freight.

The investment in the motorway network has meant that there has been less investment in local networks. Some of these are often choked with traffic as people choose to use them rather than pay **tolls** on the motorways.

Many tourists, especially the French, Dutch and Swiss, choose to enter Spain by road. The E15 runs along the Mediterranean coast and is also used by truck traffic to supply the needs of the tourist industry.

Figure 38.4 The Spanish motorway system radiates outwards from Madrid. The coastal routes are also well served

GEO FACT

Tourism contributes more than 5% of global greenhouse gas emissions, with transportation accounting for 90% of this.

Spanish rail

The Spanish rail system is regarded as one of the best and most modern in Europe. High-speed trains, running at up to 310 kph, operate in many parts of Spain. The electrification of more stretches of track has reduced air pollution.

As the Spanish government develops tourism in inland locations, tourists are increasingly using rail transport.

Another aim is to divert much of Spain's freight transport from road to rail, reducing both congestion and air pollution.

GEO FACT

The Spanish high-speed train system is known as the AVE. It is a play on the Spanish word **ave**, which means **bird**.

Figure 38.5 It takes less than three hours to travel from Madrid to Malaga on Spain's high-speed train network

Air travel to Spain

Spanish airports handled over 250 million passengers in 2017. Ryanair is the leading airline, transporting over 40 million people.

The steady reduction in the cost of air travel is making this a more competitive form of transport for tourists. This reduction of costs and therefore airfares is because aircraft have become larger, faster and more fuel-efficient. Air travel is, though, still a huge contributor to global warming.

Most of Spain's airports are linked to the tourist industry. Apart from Madrid, most of Spain's international airports are located close to coastal tourist resorts.

Airports are vital to the success of tourism in the Canary Islands and the Balearic Islands. Irish tourists can reach the Canary Islands on a flight that takes just over four hours.

Figure 38.6 The main tourism airports in Spain. Spain has more international airports than any European country

GEO FACT

Tourism now accounts for 60% of global air travel and is therefore responsible for an important share of air pollution.

Learning Activity

Curiosity Responsibility Communicating Co-operating

38.6 In groups of four, split into pairs.

(a) Assume you want to holiday in Barcelona, starting out from your school. Research how to travel there:

(i) Pair one: by car – which countries would you drive through, and how many kilometres would it be?

(ii) Pair two: by plane – where could you fly from and to, and what other transport would you need to use?

(b) Using an atlas, each pair explain their route to the other pair.

(c) Discuss as a group, which method of transport would be better for the environment. Do further research if you need to.

The future of Spanish tourism

Until now, the attraction of Spain for most of its tourists has rested mainly on its sandy beaches, warm waters and dependable sunny weather (*sol y playa* – sun and beach). This has led to **mass tourism** – where great numbers of tourists gather in the same resort. There are problems, however:

- The average amount that tourists are spending is down.
- The Spanish culture, especially the language, music and food, of tourist regions has been swamped by that of the tourists.
- Some popular destinations have become saturated with tourists.
- The level of anti-social behaviour by tourists has increased.

Tourist areas have taken steps to ease some of these problems. Barcelona has banned Segway tours and electric scooters from the Old City and the seafront. Majorca plans to reduce the number of beds (hotels and apartments) by 20% over the next few years.

Anti-tourism

Anti-tourism activists have been targeting popular Spanish destinations, including Barcelona, San Sebastian and Majorca. They are protesting over the negative impact of mass tourism on local life and standards of living. They argue that:

- Residents and businesses are being squeezed out of destinations by spiralling rents and property prices
- Apartments that were once let to locals are now rented to tourists through Airbnb
- Young people are denied a decent and stable living due to tourism's low-wage and long-hour employment
- Locals must put up with any anti-social behaviour from tourists.

Figure 38.7 **Locals in Barcelona protest against the impact of mass tourism**

Sustainable tourism

Sustainable tourism is travel by holidaymakers that has minimal impact on the environment and local communities and a positive effect on the economy.

GEO FACT

The United Nations declared 2017 as the **International Year of Sustainable Tourism.**

Sustainable tourism in Spain

Since 2000, Spain has been gradually developing a plan to improve the quality of the country's tourism product. The plan aims to develop tourism models that are environmentally, socially and culturally sustainable. Its aims include:

- Encouraging tourists to look beyond beach holidays
- Extending the length of the tourist season and avoiding congestion in the high season
- Promoting lesser known areas of the country, especially the interior of the country
- Developing tourism using sustainable resources
- Using the land and heritage in different ways.

Curiosity Communicating

38.7 We used the term 'tourism product' above. Consider why we call tourism a product. Discuss this with your partner and share with the rest of the class.

How tourism is sustainable in Spain

- To date, Spain has developed fifteen **national parks**. The most visited national park is the Teide National Park in the Canary Islands, which is topped by the third largest volcano in the world. Teide is the most visited national park in Europe and second most visited in the world.

- Over 10% of the land area of Spain has been declared by UNESCO as **protected reserves** where plants and animals are of unusual scientific and natural interest.

- Spain is home to world-class **museums**, such as those in Madrid and Bilbao. These contain works by artists such as Picasso and Goya.

- Spain has a wide range of **regional cuisines**, while some of the world's best restaurants are also located in Spain.

- There are many **historic cities** such as Granada and **white villages** (where the buildings are all traditionally whitewashed) such as Frigiliana.

- Some resorts are repositioning themselves in the market. For example, Majorca aims to lose its image as a young person's holiday destination, moving instead to an **upmarket holiday destination** for families and couples.

GEO FACT

Another proposal is for Spain to attract more Asian tourists, as they prefer shopping and cultural visits over sunning themselves on the beach.

Chinese tourists are the highest-spending tourists in the world.

Sustainable tourism in Ireland

Link  Chapter 8: pages 78–81

In March 2014 Fáilte Ireland launched a new coastal drive, The **Wild Atlantic Way** (WAW).

This initiative provides a signposted route along the Atlantic coast from Kinsale in West Cork to Malin Head in County Donegal.

It was planned as an opportunity to direct tourists into peripheral areas that until then had been overlooked by tourism promoters and had failed to realise any substantial benefit from the tourism industry.

It is hoped that the WAW will deliver a sustainable form of tourism as it seeks to:

- Minimise adverse impacts on the environment

- Maximise benefits for local communities and businesses

- Share an awareness of and respect for the distinctive culture and heritage in this part of Ireland.

Figure 38.8 Signage indicating the route of the Wild Atlantic Way

38.8 Read the following newspaper extract and then answer the questions following.

> ### Clare 'poorly served' by tourism industry
>
> *By* Peter O'Connell
>
> Clare is being 'poorly served' by the tourism industry, according to tourism consultant Cillian Murphy, while he believes the county should strive to attract fewer tourists but more bed nights.
>
> Mr Murphy has also suggested that the county is not benefiting sufficiently from the more than one million annual visitors to the Cliffs of Moher, with thousands of tourists arriving on a tour bus and then leaving after their visit without spending a bob.
>
> He says: 'We do not necessarily need to attract more visitors. Our problem is we are not reaping the rewards in terms of the local economic benefits in our rural and coastal economies, such as local job opportunities.
>
> 'What we need is to get more of them to stay in overnight accommodation. This is where visitor spend can be maximised. They stay, they eat, they shop and they use other local services and activities and, of course, this is where the maximum economic return can be delivered from tourism into the county and where jobs can be created,' he stated.
>
> He maintains that 'responsible tourism development is about delivering maximum benefits to host communities and minimising the negative impacts of tourism. One of the fundamental questions it asks in pursuit of this is: "is tourism using us or are we using tourism?"'
>
> *Source: Clare Champion,* 25 August 2017

Now answer these questions in your copy:

(a) Would you say Cillian Murphy is talking about responsible tourism, sustainable tourism or ecotourism for the area? Justify your answer.

(b) Identify the evidence for Mr Murphy's statement 'Clare is being "poorly served" by the tourism industry'?

(c) Explain the term 'fewer tourists but more bed nights'.

(d) Describe the ways in which staying visitors would help the economy in ways that day visitors do not.

(e) Create a table with two columns. Give them the headings 'Tourism using us' and 'Us using tourism'. Complete your table using words or phrases from the article that explain each phrase.

Learning Activity

Curiosity Responsibility Communicating

38.9 By a show of hands, state whether sustainable tourism would be important to you when planning a holiday. You might consider, for example, your carbon footprint for travelling, whether pollution at your destination will be increased by your being there, whether local heritage, landscape and wildlife is being spoiled and whether locals are benefiting from the economy.

Debate: Split into two groups: those who would find sustainable tourism an important consideration for their holiday plans, and those who would not consider it important.

In your groups, discuss your points of view. Nominate one person from each group to debate the topic in front of the whole class.

Learning Activity

Curiosity Responsibility Communicating Co-operating Creativity

38.10 (a) In pairs or small groups, use one of the following websites (and further research if you want) to plan a three-day trip for you and your partner.

https://www.wildatlanticway.com

https://www.irelandsancienteast.com

(b) Create a slide show or illustrated itinerary to describe your trip.

(c) Include at relevant points a note or icon to show whether that part of the trip is displaying responsible tourism, ecotourism and/or sustainable tourism (for the area you are visiting).

(d) Present your slide show or itinerary to the rest of the class.

Reflecting on my learning

Reflecting Communicating Literacy

Write sentences using each of the following terms from this chapter. You may use more than one of the terms in your sentence if appropriate.

anti-tourism · environmental impact · tourism · attractions · mass tourism · transport · economic impact · social and cultural impact · ecotourism · sustainable tourism

 PowerPoint summary

 Revision
Go to **www.edco.ie/geographynow** and try the interactive activities and quizzes.

39

Go to **www.edco.ie/geographynow** and try the interactive activities and quizzes.

Learning intentions

When you have completed this chapter you will be able to:

- Explain the term development assistance
- Outline the different forms of international aid
- Explain the advantages and disadvantages of international aid
- State how the Republic of Ireland provides international aid
- Describe the work of NGOs in international aid
- Explain the vital need for emergency aid in the case of a natural disaster or health crisis.

Key terms

development assistance

bilateral aid

multilateral aid

tied aid

donor country

voluntary aid

emergency aid

self-reliance

dependent mentality

corruption

Irish Aid

recipient country

sustainable solutions

NGO – non-governmental organisation

people-to-people aid

indicators of poverty

GEO FACT

Globally, governments spend thirteen times more on armies and weapons than they spend on official aid.

DEFINITION

Donor country

A country that provides aid.

What is development assistance?

Development assistance is another term for **international aid**.

For many decades, rich countries have given aid to poorer countries. Aid can take many forms:

- **Direct cash transfers** Money is given to build roads, hospitals, schools and water-filtering systems.

- **Skills** Skilled people – such as engineers, teachers and doctors – from developed countries work for a time in the South; the work might be using their skills directly to projects or training local workers. This is also known as **technical assistance**.

- **Goods** Aid is often given as goods, such as food and hospital equipment.

Figure 39.1 Emergency aid at work – a family who lost their home in the Nepali earthquake of 2015 living in a tent donated as emergency aid

Types of aid

There are different types of aid:

(a) **Bilateral aid**

(b) **Multilateral aid**

(c) **Tied aid**

(d) **Voluntary aid**

(e) **Emergency aid**.

DEFINITION

GNI

Gross National Income; a measure of a country's income, used by economists.

Curiosity

Learning Activity

39.1 Match the definitions to the different types of aid in the list on the left. The clue is in the name.

(i) Wealthy countries donate money to an agency, e.g. the United Nations (UN). This agency then distributes it to countries in need.

(ii) Aid that is provided to a region that has suffered a natural disaster, e.g. after the Nepal earthquake in 2015.

(iii) Agencies such as GOAL, Hope and Concern receive voluntary donations from the public and use them to provide aid to communities in poor countries.

(iv) One country donates to another, e.g. Ireland to Ethiopia.

(v) One country gives aid to a poorer country. But this aid comes with conditions attached that benefit the **donor country**.

Check your answers with your partner and share with the rest of the class.

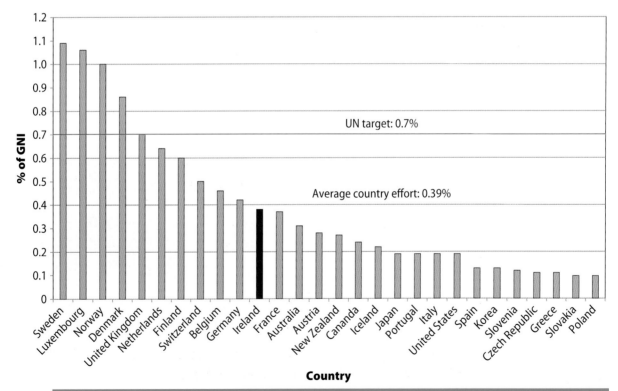

Figure 39.2 The aid donated by selected donor countries as a percentage of their GNI in 2016

Curiosity Numeracy

Learning Activity

39.2 Examine figure 39.2 and answer the following questions.

(a) How many countries donate more than the UN target?

(b) How many countries are below the average country effort?

(c) Is Ireland above the average, below the average or about on the average country effort?

(d) Does Ireland provide more or less aid as a percentage of GNI than the United States?

Does aid work?

People often ask whether the money they give to good causes helps those in need in the way they want it to. Below we look at both sides of that question.

Advantages of aid

Farmers are taught techniques such as crop rotation, fertiliser use and food storage. They can provide for their families and sell what they don't need for themselves in the market.

Refugees, fleeing from war or famine are fed, clothed and given shelter.

Emergency aid saves lives

Aid used to bore wells, to filter drinking water, or to establish blood banks, improves local people's health.

Aid can teach people **self-reliance**

Aid can contribute to people's **quality of life**

Advantages of aid

Some aid creates local **employment**

Aid that is targeted at certain groups can be very effective

Local building workers are paid by aid organisers to build schools, clinics, bridges and small dams.

Women who are trained in sewing skills can make items of clothing that they can sell in the market. This gives them **independence**.

Figure 39.3 Refugees register for food aid in the Democratic Republic of Congo, one of the world's poorest countries

Learning Activity

Curiosity Reflecting Responsibility

'Give people a fish and they eat for a day. Teach them to fish and they eat for the rest of their lives.' *Mahatma Gandhi*

39.3 Consider what this quote means, and in your copy write a short paragraph explaining it.

Disadvantages of aid

Lorries sent to parts of Ethiopia that have no roads or diesel filling stations.

Electrically powered water filtering systems that are given to remote villages with no electricity supply.

People can get used to relying on help such as food aid, and stop doing anything to help themselves.

Aid can create a **dependent mentality** among those who receive it

Dishonest people steal some aid given by donor governments. They get away with it because many countries do not have independent news media.

Some aid is not **appropriate** to local needs

Disadvantages of aid

Many developing countries are led by **corrupt politicians and officials**

A lot of aid misses its target – the poorest people

Tied aid favours the donor country

The poorest are also the weakest and the least demanding. Many of the very poor live in remote rural areas.

The donor country takes back much of what it gives in aid.

DEFINITION

Appropriate

Suited to people's needs.

Link 🔗 Chapter 32: pages 300–305

Conclusion

After sixty years of aid, there are still 795 million people going to bed hungry every night. There is plenty of food in the world. The problem is that the poor cannot afford it. Therefore, **aid has not eliminated poverty or hunger**.

Figure 39.4 Corruption among politicians and officials often reduces the amount of aid that the poor receive because some leaders steal from their own citizens

Communicating Co-operating Curiosity Reflecting

39.4 **Walking debate** Should we give aid to foreign countries?

Consider the advantages and disadvantages of aid to other countries. Consider how aid has not eliminated poverty. Do the advantages outweigh the disadvantages and should we continue to give aid – whether that is from government or by individual donations – to foreign countries?

(a) When your teacher tells you to move, go to the sign that reflects how you feel: Yes, Not sure, No.

(b) Each person should give to the class a justification for why they have chosen their position. If a student's reason makes you change your mind about your first thoughts, move to join the other group.

(c) When everyone has decided on their position on this subject, discuss as a class whether the advantages of giving aid outweigh the disadvantages.

Irish Aid programmes

Irish Aid is the official name for the support supplied by the government of the Republic of Ireland to developing countries. The Department of Foreign Affairs sends the aid to **recipient countries**. The aim of Irish Aid is 'to help developing countries to find **sustainable solutions** to the problems of poverty that confront them'. The Irish taxpayer contributes a lot of money to Ireland's bilateral aid programmes. It is important that the money is well spent.

GEO FACT

Eighty per cent of Irish Aid's budget is directed to Africa, where the need is greatest.

DEFINITION

Recipient country

A country that receives aid.

Curiosity Reflecting

39.5 **(a)** Consider the phrase 'sustainable solutions'. Discuss what this means with your partner and share with the rest of the class.

(b) Write your own definition of 'sustainable solutions' in your copy.

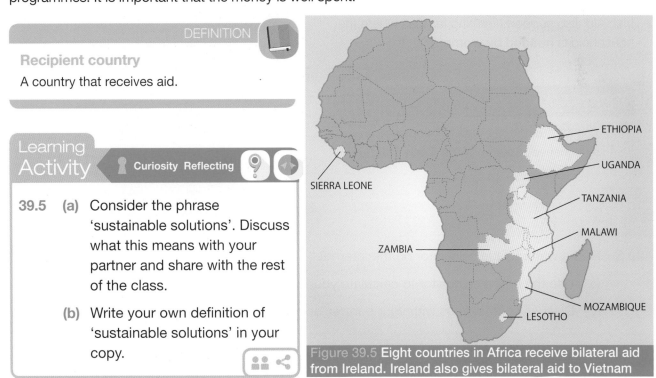

Figure 39.5 **Eight countries in Africa receive bilateral aid from Ireland. Ireland also gives bilateral aid to Vietnam**

Irish Aid's activities in Ethiopia

Ethiopia is a very poor country with a population of more than 104 million people. Its landmass is seventeen times the size of Ireland and Ethiopia suffers from **severe water shortages** because of long periods of drought. The average temperature of the country has been increasing due to climate change.

Ethiopia has been one of Ireland's partner countries for more than twenty years. Irish Aid provides **bilateral aid** to Ethiopia, working with the Ethiopian government to attain these goals:

- That poor rural households are better able to cope in times of food shortages.

- That mothers and children live healthier lives.

Link ∞ Life chances, chapter 33: pages 306–17

Figure 39.6 Ethiopian children benefit from Irish Aid funds in this rural school. How will education improve these children's life chances as they grow up?

Irish Aid works in many ways to attain these goals, including the following projects.

Water projects and food security

- Irish Aid funds the **boring of deep wells** in rural Ethiopia so that villages have a continuous water supply.

- These wells provide **water for the village**.

- Water is also used for cattle and for local **irrigation projects**. Irrigation is used to grow fruit crops, vegetables and potatoes. Irrigated land can grow three crops a year.

- Farmers can sell their **food surplus** in the towns and can afford to send their children to school. Farmers can build up some cash savings for periods of drought so that they do not have to sell their livestock to buy food.

- Irish Aid also supports farming families where the household is **headed by women**.

Figure 39.7 Cattle on good grazing land in Ethiopia. Irish Aid has helped to improve the quality of cattle there

GEO FACT

In 2015, 32% of the people of Ethiopia were undernourished. *Source:* World Bank

GEO FACT

In the world today, 2.1 billion people are obese while 795 million are hungry.

Learning Activity

 Curiosity Reflecting Responsibility

39.6 Find a water usage calculator on the internet.

    (a) Use the online calculator to calculate your daily 'water footprint'.

    (b) Discuss your findings with your partner, and share with the rest of the class.

Health projects

- The **health of mothers and children** in Ethiopia is targeted by Irish Aid. Irish Aid works with local health workers to improve the health of women and children.

- **Midwives**, who assist mothers during birth, are trained to ensure that mothers do not die in childbirth.

- **Children are vaccinated** in village clinics.

- Irish Aid helps to provide essential drugs, vaccinations and **bed nets** to prevent malaria in children.

- Mothers are educated in **children's nutrition** so that children can have a balanced diet.

- Health workers are trained to assist patients who suffer from **HIV/AIDS**.

- Irish Aid puts great effort into **training local people** in basic nutrition, hygiene and sanitation.

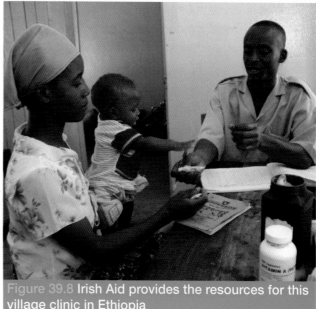

Figure 39.8 **Irish Aid provides the resources for this village clinic in Ethiopia**

> **GEO FACT**
>
> An Ethiopian woman has a 1 in 52 risk of dying in childbirth during the course of her child-bearing years. (In Denmark it is 1 in 12,000.)

The promotion of good government practices

Irish Aid works with local community organisations to identify village needs such as schools, clinics, bridges and water pipes. Communities can then demand that the Ethiopian government provide these needs. In this way people are **empowered** to put pressure on their government to provide services. This helps to make local politicians and officials more **accountable** and helps to **reduce corruption**.

By giving Ethiopians **a hand up rather than a hand out**, Irish Aid is helping villagers to help themselves. That is the purpose of Ireland's **long-term development aid** to Ethiopia.

> **Learning Activity**
>
> Communicating Co-operating Literacy
>
> **39.7** With a partner, differentiate between the phrases **hand up** and **hand out**. Use an example to explain your definitions. Share with the rest of the class.

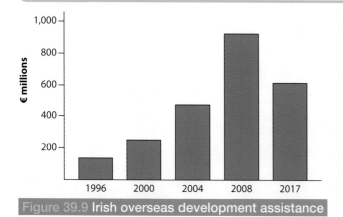

Figure 39.9 **Irish overseas development assistance**

> **DEFINITION**
>
> **Accountable**
> Having to explain and justify one's actions.
>
> **Empowered**
> Made stronger and more confident to claim their rights.

The work of Irish NGOs

Irish **NGOs** (**non-governmental organisations**) are voluntary organisations. They are independent of the Irish government. They collect money from the general public and spend it on projects in many countries in the South.

People-to-people aid

NGOs get permission from recipient governments to provide assistance to communities in poor countries. Their funds go directly into community projects. This is called people-to-people aid.

NGOs work on small-scale projects such as village clinics and women's classes in literacy, dressmaking, nutrition and household budgeting.

Learning **Activity**   🔒 Curiosity Responsibility

39.8   Research the names of three Irish NGOs working in Ethiopia. Share the names you have found with a partner, and then the rest of the class.

Figure 39.10 Niamh Sweeney, a volunteer with Nurture Africa, an Irish NGO, teaching pupils in Uganda in 2015

Education of the Irish public by NGOs

Many NGOs also **raise awareness** of development issues among the Irish public. For example, **Concern**, an Irish NGO, has conducted debates on development issues among pupils of secondary schools for many years. In this way, young people and their parents learn about issues such as poverty, debt, international trade and the arms industry.

This may help to explain why many Irish people of all ages spend time abroad on development projects.

Learning **Activity**   🔒 Curiosity Communicating Literacy Creativity

39.9   Create a poster, booklet or radio advert script to encourage Irish citizens to donate to an NGO of your choice that is working overseas. Share these with the rest of the class. (If you choose the radio advert, record it if you can.)

Emergency aid: the Ebola outbreak in West Africa

'Ebola virus disease is a severe, often fatal illness in humans. The virus is transmitted to people from wild animals and spreads in the human population through human-to-human transmission.' (World Health Organization)

The most recent outbreak of Ebola began in West Africa in 2013, mainly in Liberia, Sierra Leone and Guinea, and continued into 2015. More than 10,000 people died of Ebola in those three countries.

The three countries are **among the poorest in the world** and are poorly equipped to deal with the outbreak, as we can see from the **indicators of poverty** for Sierra Leone.

DEFINITION

Indicators of poverty

Various measurements that when combined show a country (or individual) is above or below an official line on a scale of poverty.

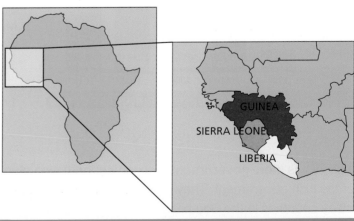

Figure 39.11 The countries of West Africa affected by the Ebola virus

Table 39.1 Sierra Leone: indicators of poverty

Population	Life expectancy	Adult literacy	Under-nourished	Access to clean water	Income per head
7.4 million	51 years	48%	35%	54%	$490 (approx. €400)

Many people were undernourished to start with, so when a life-threatening virus broke out, people were at great risk. The Ebola outbreak caused disruption of normal daily lives. Schools were closed, traffic into and out of villages that were affected ceased, and there was terrible fear. Movement to neighbouring countries was halted.

The health services of the countries affected were overwhelmed by the Ebola outbreak. **Medical aid** from abroad was urgently required. The response from abroad included the following:

- Irish **NGOs** such as **Plan Ireland** helped with funding and with aid workers.

- The **Irish government** provided direct funding of almost €17 million up to spring 2015 to organisations working on the Ebola response in Sierra Leone and Liberia.

- The Irish government dispatched 42 tonnes of practical equipment to be distributed to affected communities, including blankets, tents, mosquito nets, water cans and soap.

- In addition, Ireland's embassy in Freetown, Sierra Leone played a key role in the local **co-ordination of medical aid**.

- The French organisation **Doctors without Borders – Médecins Sans Frontières (MSF)** – was actively involved at the **front line**, working with local medical workers to contain the virus.

- Most importantly, **research in medical laboratories in the USA** led to the development of a treatment that may offer hope for the future.

Learning Activity

 Reflecting Responsibility Communicating Co-operating

39.10 'Ireland should look after its own people before giving aid to people overseas.'

(a) Do you agree with this statement?

(b) Imagine you are invited on to a TV current affairs programme that is discussing this statement. Write down the points you would like to make in such a discussion that will get your point of view across to the viewers.

(c) Conduct a class discussion on this topic.

Reflecting on my learning

  Reflecting Communicating Literacy

Write sentences using each of the following terms from this chapter. You may use more than one of the terms in your sentence if appropriate.

- bilateral aid
- corruption
- dependent mentality
- donor country
- emergency aid
- indicators of poverty
- Irish Aid
- multilateral aid
- NGO – non-governmental organisation
- people-to-people aid
- recipient country
- self-reliance
- sustainable solutions
- tied aid
- voluntary aid

 **PowerPoint summary**

 Revision
Go to **www.edco.ie/geographynow** and try the interactive activities and quizzes.

A synthesis of population, settlement and human development within the process of globalisation

40

Go to **www.edco.ie/geographynow** and try the interactive activities and quizzes.

Learning intentions

When you have completed this chapter you will be able to:

- Define globalisation
- Outline the impacts of globalisation on Ireland and India
- Synthesise aspects of population, urban settlement and human development within the process of globalisation in Ireland and India.

Learning Outcome

3.9   Synthesise
       your learning
       of population,
       settlement and
       human development
       within the process of
       globalisation

Key terms

globalisation	HDI – human development index
containerisation	gender equality
ro-ro	outsource
global communications network	medical tourism
barriers to trade	BRICS
free trade zone	start-ups
MNCs	poverty line
trade surplus	subsistence level
multilingual workforce	smart economy

Introduction

In this chapter, you will **synthesise** or draw together your knowledge of population change, settlement and human development to deepen your understanding of the process of globalisation.

Globalisation

Globalisation is the process by which the world is increasingly interconnected through trade and cultural links. These interconnections have grown rapidly in recent decades. A number of factors have brought about increasing globalisation, as discussed below.

Modern transport

The largest ships ever built, such as oil tankers and bulk ore carriers criss-cross the oceans. **Containerisation** has revolutionised transport. More than 90% of non-bulk cargo is now transported in **container ships**. The largest vessels can carry 18,000 containers.

Figure 40.1 A container ship at sea

383

Learning Activity

Curiosity Literacy Communicating

40.1 Work in pairs.

   (a) On your own, consider the terms **bulk** and **non-bulk**.

   (b) One of you create a definition for bulk, and the other create a definition for non-bulk. Use an example in your definitions.

   (c) Tell each other your definition. Do your definitions complement each other (that is, fit together)?

   (d) Together, classify the following list into bulk and non-bulk cargo:
   mobile phones, toys, grain, clothes, coal, crude oil, sofas, iron ore, biscuits.

   (e) Share your answers with the class.

Another type of transport ship is known as **ro-ro**, which means **roll on, roll off**. This describes how the cargo is loaded and unloaded. It is used for vehicles, such as cars, trucks, tractors and cranes.

GEO FACT

One 20-foot container can hold the shopping of 300 supermarket trolleys, or 1,000,000 pencils.

GEO FACT

Some ro-ro vessels can transport more than 8,500 cars in one trip.

Learning Activity

Curiosity

40.2 You may have travelled on ro-ro vessels. Recall the name that is given to ro-ro transport vessels that the public uses.

Modern communications

The increase in global trade has been made possible by a **global communications network**. The **worldwide web** and the **internet** allow orders to be placed, goods paid for and other details cleared in minutes across the world.

Learning Activity

Curiosity Responsibility

40.3 (a) Discuss with your partner how you or your family made a transaction with a company abroad.

   (b) As a class, create a list of goods and services that can be provided by foreign companies as easily as dealing with those near home.

The removal of barriers to trade

Barriers to trade are things like **import duties**, which make buying goods from abroad more expensive or more difficult. These barriers to trade have been reduced or eliminated between many countries and economic regions. The EU, for example, is a **free trade zone** among its member countries, meaning that goods can be bought and sold without the added cost of customs duties. (Taxes such as VAT are added within the country of sale.)

The role of multinational corporations

This is possibly the most important reason for the development of globalisation. There are now (in 2018) more than 103,000 MNCs in existence, **eleven times more** than in 1970.

MNCs are **global players**. MNCs invest in countries where they can make the greatest profit. They establish plants across the globe and low-skill assembly plants in countries where **labour is cheaper**. MNCs reach a worldwide market with their products. MNCs avail of low corporation tax in some countries, such as Ireland, to become established.

DEFINITION

Multinational corporation (MNC)

A company that is operating in more than one country.

GEO FACT

Very large MNCs have budgets that are greater than those of many small countries.

Learning Activity

Curiosity Responsibility Communicating Co-operating

40.4 Imagine that a company started up in your nearest town twenty years ago and now employs 700 people in its factory. It has just announced that it is becoming an MNC and will be moving its factory to Indonesia, where the labour costs are much lower than in Ireland. The bulk of the workforce will lose their jobs in the local factory. It will retain its head office that employs a mere thirty people in Ireland. Discuss as a class the effects this will have on:

(a) People working in the factory in your town, and their families.

(b) Other businesses in your town.

(c) Ireland's Department of Employment Affairs and Social Protection (welfare).

The impact of globalisation on Ireland

Ireland has a very **globalised economy**. It is a member of the EU, the largest trading bloc in the world. Ireland has an **interdependent** relationship with the rest of the world.

Learning Activity

Curiosity Reflecting

40.5 (a) On a two-ring Venn diagram, place the following imports/exports that flow into/out of Ireland:

oil, beef, cars, smartphones, computers, aircraft, dairy products, sportswear, footwear, medicinal drugs, medical devices, crafts

(b) Compare your diagram with your partner's and discuss where you have placed items.

(c) Explain why some items appear in the overlap of imports and exports, i.e. are both imported and exported.

(d) Share your diagrams with the rest of the class.

According to Enterprise Ireland, Ireland has:

9 of the top 10 global ICT companies	**8 of the top 10** gaming companies	**8 of the top 10** global pharmaceutical companies
6 of the top 7 diagnostics companies	**15 of the top 20** medical device companies	**50%** of the world's leading financial services firms

Figure 40.2 Ireland has captured a good number of global companies in several sectors

The Republic of Ireland is home to more than 1,000 MNCs including 700 from the USA. Ireland is very successful in attracting the MNCs, particularly from outside of the EU, for the following reasons:

- Very good corporation tax rates and other tax benefits

- Access to the EU market

- A skilled labour force

- An attractive quality of life for workers.

Giant companies in the IT, social media, pharmaceuticals, medical devices and financial sectors are established in Ireland. Examples are: HP, Intel, Apple, Google, Facebook, LinkedIn, Twitter, Pfizer and Boston Scientific.

Learning Activity

 Curiosity Communicating

40.6 There are many benefits to attracting MNCs to Ireland, but there are also risks. Discuss as a class what the risks are of attracting MNCs to Ireland.

The Irish export trade

Because of the presence of MNCs in Ireland, the Irish economy has very strong **exports**. In recent years, forty American companies such as Microsoft, Intel and Boston Scientific have accounted for about two-thirds of Irish exports of goods and services. Because of the exports of MNCs, Ireland has a healthy trade surplus, with exports exceeding imports.

Link Intel: **chapter 37,** pages 357–59.

GEO FACT

Ireland is the twenty-seventh largest exporter in the world, largely because of the exports of MNCs.

In addition, Ireland exports to a **worldwide market**. Several decades ago, more than half of Irish exports went to Britain. Today, that fraction is less than one-fifth. Most Irish exports today go to EU countries and the USA. That is globalisation in action.

The impact of globalisation on population and urban settlements

MNCs account for more than **210,000 jobs in Ireland**. The Irish labour force has grown, particularly in Irish cities, because of the jobs that MNCs provide. The cluster of multinational medical devices companies in Galway city provides 6,000 jobs directly. This has helped the urban settlement of Galway to grow and indeed the surrounding settlements of Athenry, Tuam and Oranmore.

Link ⧉ Chapter 35: pages 337–38.

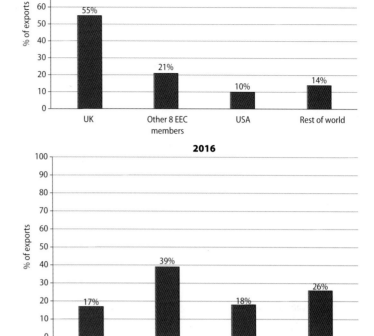

Figure 40.3 Irish export destinations 2016

The urban settlement of Leixlip has grown because of Intel's presence, as we have already seen in chapter 37.

Many of the largest MNCs are in the Dublin region. These firms require very specific skills in scientific research and in production. This has led to much **inward migration** to the Dublin region not only from the rest of the country but from abroad. Internet companies such as Google have a multilingual workforce, many of whom have migrated to Ireland from France, Germany, Switzerland and further afield.

These developments have led to strong growth of Dublin's population. With some 27% of the population of the Republic, **population density** in the Dublin region is high. Dublin has expanded outwards over the years and has much **urban sprawl** in suburban areas. The growth of population has put further pressure on Dublin's scarce housing market and partly explains the **house price inflation** of recent years.

The effect of globalisation on human development

First we will look at the Human Development Index (HDI). This is an annual report compiled by the UN for most of the countries of the world. It ranks countries in terms of life expectancy, education and gross national income (GNI) per person.

Ireland scores very highly in the HDI and was ranked eighth in the 2016 report, ahead of the UK, USA and Japan.

DEFINITION

Human development
Whether people have the means to **be** and **do**.

Index
An indicator or measure of something.

Table 40.1 The HDI scores of selected countries – UN HDI Report 2015

Country	Rank	HDI score	Life expectancy	Mean years of schooling	GNI per person
Very high human development (rankings 1–51)					
Norway	1	0.949	81.7	12.7	$67,614
Ireland	8	0.923	81.1	12.3	$43,798
High human development (rankings 52–106)					
Brazil	79	0.754	74.7	7.8	$14,145
Medium human development (rankings 107–147)					
Namibia	125	0.640	65.1	6.7	$9,770
Low human development (rankings 148–188)					
Nigeria	152	0.527	53.1	6.0	$5,443
Central African Republic	188	0.352	51.5	4.2	$587

Learning Activity

Curiosity Communicating Co-operating Numeracy

40.7 Work in groups of three.

(a) Each of you construct one of the following line graphs from the data in table 40.1:

(i) Country and Life expectancy

(ii) Country and Mean years of schooling

(iii) Country and GNI per person.

(b) Consider your three graphs. Identify and interpret a pattern of the three lines by comparing the graphs.

(c) Discuss and suggest another measure for these countries that is likely to give a similar shaped line.

(d) Share your group's findings with the rest of the class.

Keep your graphs as you will need them again for activity 40.20.

To what extent is globalisation responsible for Ireland's high HDI score? The answer is: to some extent only.

Our health services, rather than globalisation, help to account for our high life expectancy. In addition, we are a highly educated people who are aware of the impact of lifestyle on health.

High educational scores in the HDI are largely due to the priority that Irish parents and guardians place on education and to the quality of Irish schools and teachers. However, many young people enter third level courses to study STEM subjects for which there is a strong demand among MNCs.

In addition, MNCs pay taxes amounting to some €6.5 billion each year in Ireland. Well-paid MNC workers contribute several billion euros every year in income tax and in VAT on their spending. This helps to pay for education and health in the budget.

The effect of globalisation on employment

Many MNCs have left Ireland over the years and transferred their operations to Eastern Europe and to East Asia where labour costs are much cheaper. Most were labour-intensive operations such as Fruit of the Loom in Donegal, which manufactured T-shirts, and Dell in Limerick, which assembled computers. These closures led to **unemployment**, which greatly affected workers and their families.

GEO FACT

At the end of 2017, Irish unemployment was at 6%.

Learning Activity

Curiosity Responsibility Reflecting

40.8 Discuss with your partner how **employment** enhances human development. Share your thoughts with the rest of the class.

40.9 Discuss with your partner the impact on individuals and families of **unemployment**. Share your thoughts with the rest of the class.

GEO FACT

When the UK leaves the EU, Ireland will be the only English-speaking country in the European Union.

Learning Activity

Reflecting Responsibility Communicating Co-operating

40.10 (a) On a scale of 1 (not at all important) to 10 (extremely important), which score would you give in answer to the question: In a global economy, how important is it that school students learn one or more foreign languages? Share your score with the rest of the class.

(b) Discuss the question.

Whereas labour-intensive businesses have left Ireland, social media companies such as Facebook, Yahoo, LinkedIn, Twitter and Airbnb, which have their European HQs in Ireland, are likely to remain. This has partly to do with language – we share a common language with the USA. These companies are large employers and pay high salaries.

Learning Activity

Curiosity Reflecting Responsibility

40.11 State the sector that the companies listed above belong in. Agree the sector with your partner.

40.12 Is it a good thing or a bad thing that a large number of Ireland's workforce now works in the sector you named above? Justify your answer to your partner. Share your thoughts with the rest of the class.

In addition, **Irish graduates** are of high quality. Their ability to conduct research and complete the challenging manufacturing processes in pharmaceuticals and IT encourages companies in those fields to establish plants and to remain in Ireland.

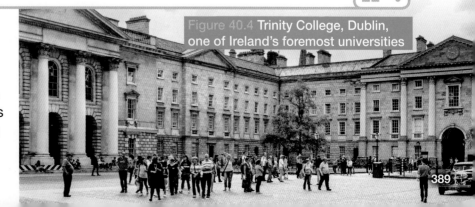

Figure 40.4 **Trinity College, Dublin, one of Ireland's foremost universities**

389

The effect of globalisation on gender equality

As late as 2016, only 14% of Irish companies in general were headed by women. This is the case even though many young women outperform men in university. **Gender equality** has more to do with the **culture** of a country than anything else. Gender equality in Ireland, as in many countries, is a work in progress.

The impact of globalisation on population, settlement and human development in developing countries

Many developing countries have embraced globalisation. We looked at China's export-led manufacturing in chapter 36.

Link 🔗 Chapter 36: page 348.

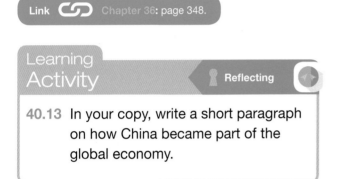

Learning Activity   Reflecting

40.13 In your copy, write a short paragraph on how China became part of the global economy.

REMINDER:

You must **synthesise** population change, settlement and human development **in one developing country** to deepen your understanding of globalisation.

We will now look at India's participation in globalisation.

India

You have already studied the life chances of young people in India. India is a vast country with more than 1.3 billion people. India embraced globalisation later than South Korea, Taiwan and China. Unlike those countries, India has focused less on export-orientated manufacturing and more on technological innovation and the **expansion of services**.

Link 🔗 Chapter 33: pages 316–17.

Services include telecommunications, software and travel services. India has many call centres in Mumbai, New Delhi and Bangalore where telephone companies, airlines, international hotel chains and others outsource their accounting, bookings and customer services.

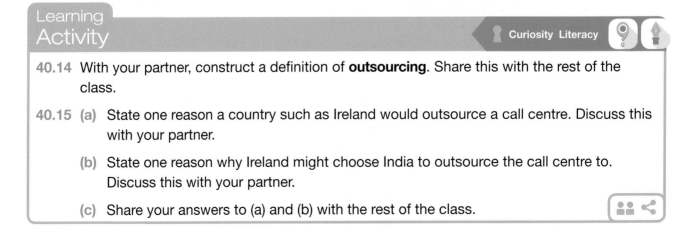

Learning Activity   Curiosity Literacy

40.14 With your partner, construct a definition of **outsourcing**. Share this with the rest of the class.

40.15 (a) State one reason a country such as Ireland would outsource a call centre. Discuss this with your partner.

(b) State one reason why Ireland might choose India to outsource the call centre to. Discuss this with your partner.

(c) Share your answers to (a) and (b) with the rest of the class.

In addition, the tourist industry has expanded especially in the **Golden Triangle** of New Delhi, Agra and Jaipur. Medical tourism has expanded sharply as people travel to Indian hospitals for cosmetic surgery.

Learning
Activity

Curiosity Communicating Co-operating Literacy

40.16 (a) With your partner, construct a definition of **medical tourism**. Share this with the rest of the class.

(b) State one reason why people travel to India for medical procedures rather than having them done in their own country.

(c) Share your answers to (a) and (b) with the rest of the class.

Learning
Activity

Curiosity Responsibility Creativity

40.17 (a) Research and state which cities comprise India's **Golden Triangle**.

(b) Explain how this area got the name Golden Triangle.

(c) Draw an outline map/diagram of India showing the cities of the Golden Triangle and how they are linked together.

(d) Add details to your map to explain the term Golden Triangle.

Learning
Activity

Communicating Reflecting

40.18 Discuss with your partner how the international tourist industry contributes to globalisation. Share your thoughts with the rest of the class.

Westerners are aware that the Indian film industry, known as **Bollywood**, is a huge employer. India also has a growing editing and printing industry where some Western publishing companies outsource magazine editing and textbook illustrations and printing to Indian companies.

India is an emerging economic power and has had annual economic growth rates of more than 7% in some recent years. However, with 17% of the global population, India has only a 7.2% share of global wealth and only 1.6% of global trade.

Learning
Activity Numeracy

40.19 Draw three pie charts in a row showing:

(a) India's percentage of the global population

(b) India's share of global wealth

(c) India's share of global trade.

Learning Activity

Curiosity Communicating Co-operating Numeracy

40.20 Work in the same group of three that you did for activity 40.7, if possible.

(a) In 2015, India's position on the HDI index was 131. Refer back to table 40.1 on page 388 and place where you think India will appear on the graphs you drew for activity 40.7.

(b) Research the HDI index and obtain the figures for the following measurements. Complete a copy of the following table in your copy.

Country	Rank	HDI score	Life expectancy	Mean years of schooling	GNI per person
India					

(c) Mark the figures from (b) on your graphs. How close were they to your predictions for their positions?

(d) State the category that India falls into.

The impact of globalisation on population

GEO FACT

India is a member of the **BRICS** group of countries.

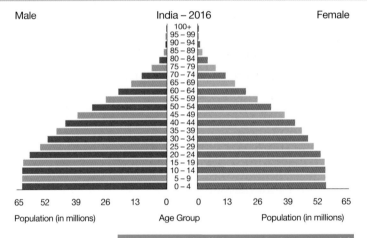

Figure 40.5 **India's population pyramid**

Learning Activity

Curiosity Reflecting Numeracy

40.21 Which country's population pyramid does India's pyramid resemble: Germany's, Ireland's or Brazil's? (See chapter 29, pages 284 and 285.) Explain your answer by describing the shape of the pyramid and what it means. Compare your answer with your partner's and then share with the rest of the class.

Learning Activity

Curiosity Responsibility

40.22 (a) Research which countries comprise the BRICS group of countries.

(b) Write a short explanation of why these countries are grouped together for economic purposes.

(c) Compare your answers with your partner's.

(d) Share your answers with the rest of the class.

Urban settlements

The majority of Indians still live in rural villages but the growing **services industry** has encouraged **migration** to the cities. More than one-third of the population now live in urban centres.

Urban settlements in India continue to grow very rapidly because of the services boom. The city of Bangalore is an example. Bangalore is the Silicon Valley of India and has doubled its population to almost 11 million people over a few decades.

Bangalore is a city of start-ups in IT, healthcare, life sciences and biotech industries. The city has a **start-up warehouse** where the government provides support to start-ups. Bangalore has thousands of well-educated middle-class Indian entrepreneurs. English is the business language of the city. Innovative products manufactured by start-ups are sold both at home and abroad.

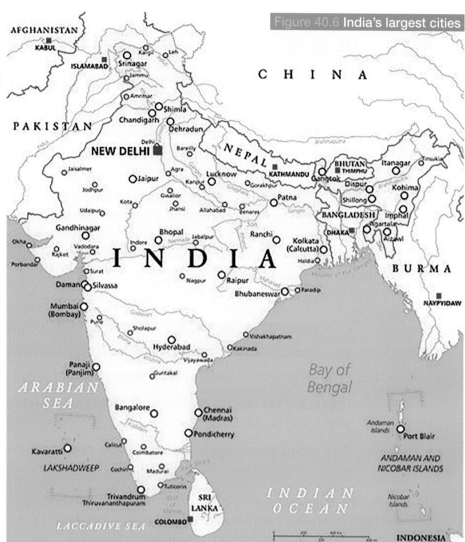

Figure 40.6 **India's largest cities**

GEO FACT

- Infosys is one of the largest Indian IT companies. It sells its services to more than 50 countries and is located in Bangalore.

- Microsoft, the US software giant, has a presence in Bangalore.

Learning Activity

Curiosity Communicating

40.23 Explain what we mean by a **start-up**. Compare your explanation with your partner's and share with the rest of the class.

The impact of globalisation on human development

As you discovered from your research for activity 40.20, India scores very poorly on the HDI ranking. Any study of India reveals extraordinary levels of poverty. Even the Indian government points out that one in five Indians lives **below the** poverty line. Average incomes are rising but only among the middle and wealthy classes; these are a small minority. Hundreds of millions of people live in the countryside in poverty or at subsistence level.

DEFINITION

Poverty line

The estimated minimum level of income needed to secure the necessities of life.

Subsistence level

The standard of living that contains only the bare necessities of life.

GEO FACT

One-third of the poorest people on Earth live in India.

GEO FACT

The Irish expression for living at subsistence level is **beo bocht**.

As we have seen, India has taken a different path towards development than China, which has chosen labour-intensive manufacturing. India has opted for mainly home-grown IT, scientific innovation and services.

Only well-educated people – a small percentage of India's 1.3 billion people – who are skilled in English can fill these jobs. Mumbai, Delhi and Bangalore are booming, but for the great mass of people who live in rural villages and especially for the **Dalits**, little has changed. Dalits are at the bottom of the Hindu caste system and still face widespread discrimination.

Learning Activity

Curiosity Responsibility Communicating Co-operating Creativity

40.24 (a) In small groups, research the caste system and Dalits.

(b) Create a short (approximately eight slides) presentation on how the caste system works and where Dalits fit into it.

(c) As a group, present your research to the rest of the class.

Therefore, for the hundreds of millions of impoverished people of India, human development remains very slow. Globalisation is passing them by. **Poor people are less likely to live long, healthy and creative lives**, which is the goal of human development. India's poor will continue to be poorly educated, become ill more frequently, will be less likely to eat a balanced diet and are more likely to die younger, than well-paid workers in the smart economy of Bangalore.

DEFINITION

Smart economy

Businesses at the forefront of the next big thing in innovation, IT, life sciences and sustainability.

Figure 40.7 Children on their way to school in Maharashtra state in India. These children have a bright future because education will greatly improve their life chances

Literacy Numeracy Creativity

40.25 Read the following extract, and then do the activity below.

So much for the smart economy: Irish lack basic digital skills

By Charlie Taylor

Ireland performs better than the EU average but it has improved at a slower rate than the EU as a whole

Businesses in Ireland are the best in Europe at using ecommerce, according to a new study. However, we are below EU standards when it comes to digital skills.

Ireland is ranked in eighth place overall in the latest European Digital Economy and Society Index (DESI), an indicator that summarises the performance of EU member states across a wide range of areas, from connectivity and digital skills to the digitisation of businesses and public services.

Denmark, Finland, Sweden and the Netherlands lead the index this year, followed by Luxembourg, Belgium, the UK, Ireland, Estonia and Austria.

The country now ranks 13th among EU countries for connectivity, up from 16th last year. It is in 10th place for human capital, compared to eighth spot previously. In addition, Ireland has moved up one spot to 14th place for use of the internet and up two places to first place for integration of digital technology. Lastly, it has fallen one spot to ninth out of 28 for digital public services.

Ireland ranks first when it comes to the integration of digital technologies by businesses, mostly because many SMEs have embraced ecommerce. However, the study says that while the Republic ranks first in the share of young people holding a science, technology, engineering or maths (STEM) degree, just 44 per cent of the population are deemed to have sufficient digital skills compared to an EU average of 55 per cent.

Fast broadband coverage in Ireland is seen to be well above the EU average.

Source: *Irish Times*, 3 March 2017

(a) From the above article, pick out the statistics that show that Ireland has a smart economy.

(b) Present these on a poster in a design of your choice.

(c) Display the posters around the room for the rest of the class to see.

Reflecting Communicating Literacy

Write sentences using each of the following terms from this chapter. You may use more than one of the terms in your sentence if appropriate.

barriers to trade	global communications network	medical tourism	ro-ro
BRICS		MNCs	smart economy
containerisation	globalisation	multilingual workforce	start-ups
free trade zone	HDI – human development index	outsource	subsistence level
gender equality		poverty line	trade surplus

PowerPoint summary

Revision
Go to **www.edco.ie/geographynow** and try the interactive activities and quizzes.

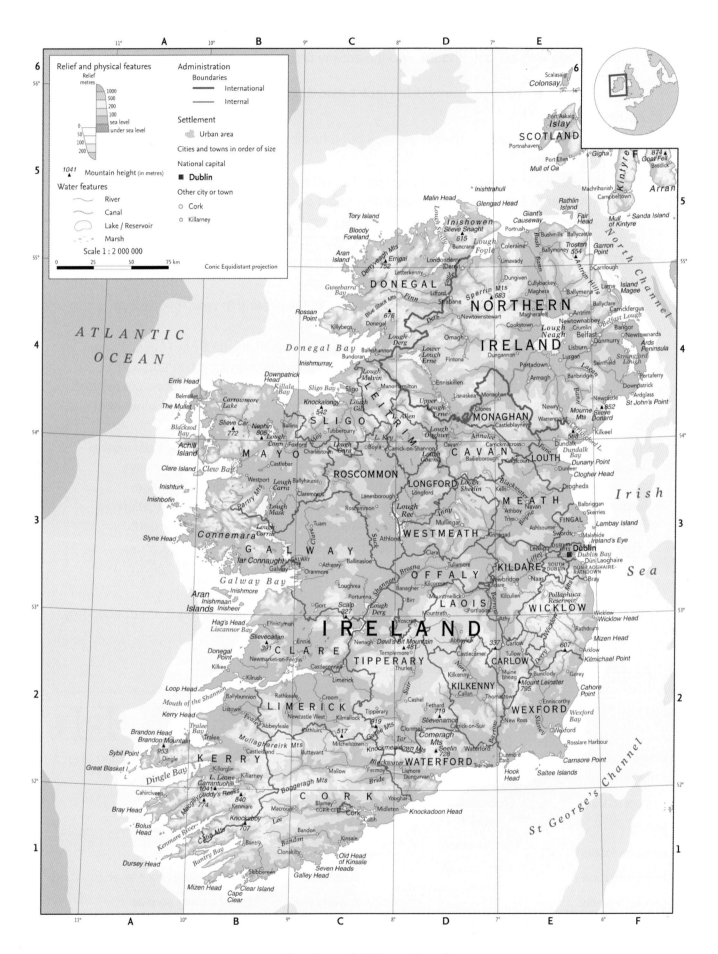

Ireland Physical

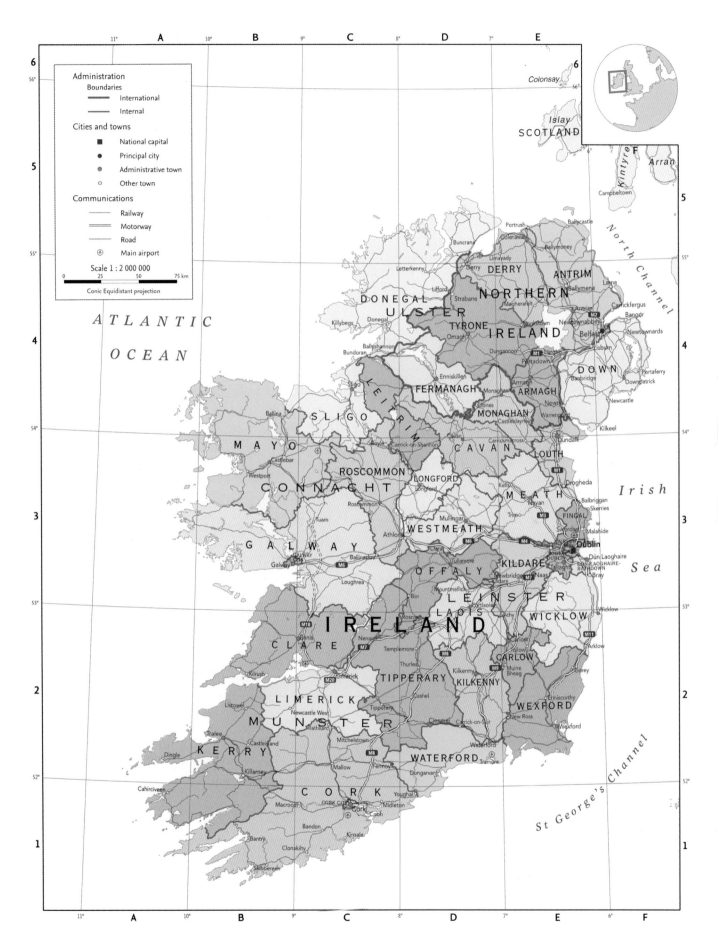

Ireland Political

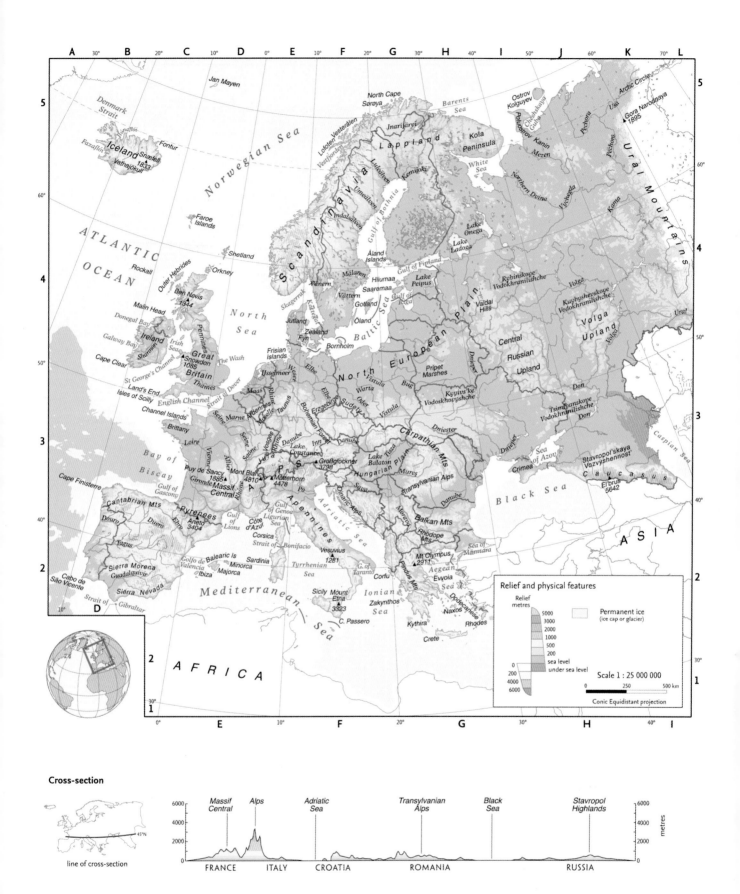

A 30° B 20° C 10° D 0° E 10° F 20° G 30° H 40° I 50° J 60° K 70° L

Jan Mayen

Denmark Strait

Snaefellsjökull
Iceland Snæfell
1833 Fontur
Faxaflói Vatnajökull

Norwegian Sea

North Cape
Søroya
Lofoten Vesterålen
Vestfjorden

Lappland

Inarijärvi

Kola Peninsula

Ostrov Kolguyev

Poluostrov Kanin

Arctic Circle

Usa
Gora Narodnaya
1895

Ural Mountains

Faroe Islands

Shetland

Luleälven
Umeälven
Indalsälven

Kemijoki

White Sea

Mezen

Northern Dvina

Pechora

ATLANTIC OCEAN

Rockall
Outer Hebrides
Orkney

North Sea

Åland Islands

Gulf of Bothnia

Lake Onega

Lake Ladoga

Rybinskoye Vodokhranilishche

Volga

Kuybyshevskoye Vodokhranilishche

Vychegda

Kama

Ural

Ben Nevis
1344
Malin Head

Donegal Bay
Ireland
Galway Bay
Shannon
Cape Clear

Irish Sea

Pennines
Great Britain
Snowdon
1085
The Wash
Thames

Vänern
Skagerrak
Kattegat
Jutland
Zealand
Fyn
Bornholm

Vättern
Gotland
Öland

Hiiumaa
Saaremaa

Gulf of Finland
Lake Peipus

Gulf of Riga

Baltic Sea

North European Plain

Valdai Hills

Central Russian Upland

Volga Upland

Volga

St George's Channel
Land's End
Isles of Scilly
English Channel
Channel Islands
Brittany

Cape Finisterre

Bay of Biscay

Cabo de São Vicente

Strait of Dover
Maas
Seine
Marne
Ardennes
Moselle
Taunus
Loire

Seine
Vienne
Puy de Sancy
1885
Gironde
Massif Central

Cantabrian Mts
Douro
Duero
Sierra Morena
Guadalquivir
Sierra Nevada

Strait of Gibraltar

IJsselmeer
Weser
Elbe
Rhine

Vosges
Jura
Allier
Mont Blanc
4810

Pyrenees
Aneto
3404

Gulf of Lions
Côte d'Azur
Corsica
Golfo de Valencia
Ibiza
Minorca
Majorca
Balearic Is

Mediterranean Sea

Elbe
Erzgebirge
Bohemian Forest

Rhône
Po

Matterhorn
4478
ALPS
Großglockner
3798
Lake Constance
Inn
Danube

Apennines
Dinaric Alps
Gulf of Genoa
Ligurian Sea
Sardinia
Strait of Bonifacio
Tyrrhenian Sea
Vesuvius
1281

Sicily
Mount Etna
3323
C. Passero

Warta
Oder
Sudety
Vistula

Danube

Lake Tisza
Hungarian Plain
Balaton
Sava
Adriatic Sea

Ionian Sea

Bug
Vistula

Pripet Marshes

Kyyivs'ke Vodoskhovyshche

Dniester

Carpathian Mts

Mureş
Transylvanian Alps
Danube
Morava
Balkan Mts
Rhodope Mts
Pindus Mts
Mt Olympus
2911
Corfu
Evvoia
Aegean Sea
Zakynthos
Naxos
Rhodes
Kythira
Crete
Dodecanese

Dnieper

Dniester

Dnieper
Don

Tsimlyanskoye Vodokhranilishche
Don

Crimea
Sea of Azov

Stavropol'skaya Vozvyshennost

Caucasus
El'brus
5642

Black Sea

Caspian Sea

Sea of Marmara

ASIA

AFRICA

Relief and physical features

Relief metres
5000
3000
2000
1000
500
200
sea level
0
under sea level
200
4000
6000

Permanent ice
(ice cap or glacier)

Scale 1 : 25 000 000

0   250   500 km

Conic Equidistant projection

Cross-section

line of cross-section

45°N

metres

Massif Central	Alps	Adriatic Sea	Transylvanian Alps	Black Sea	Stavropol Highlands	

6000
4000
2000
0

FRANCE   ITALY   CROATIA   ROMANIA   RUSSIA

6000
4000
2000
0

metres

Europe Physical

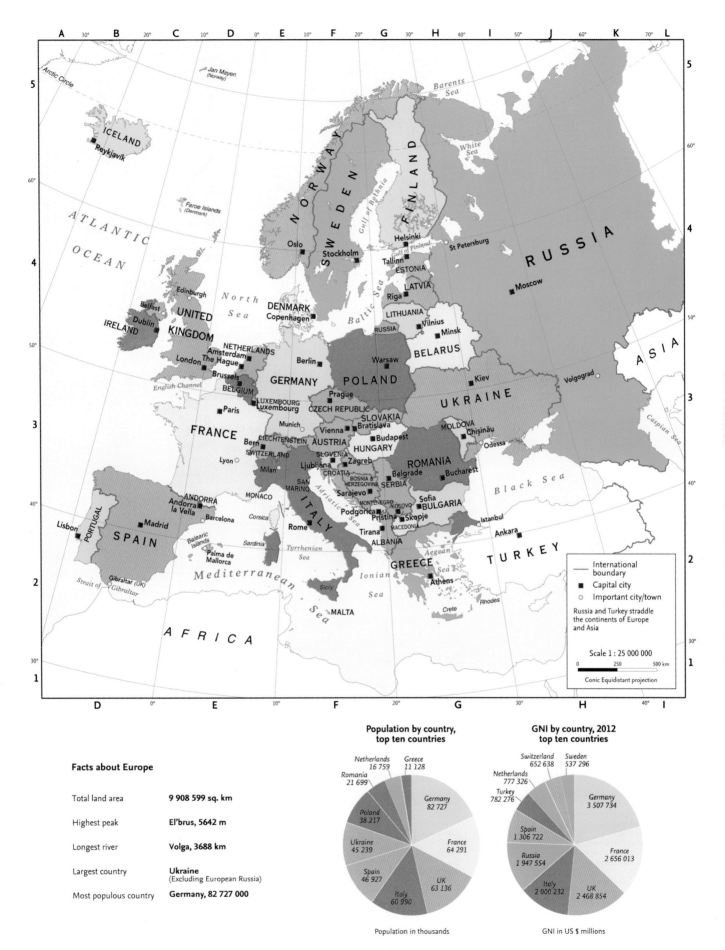

Europe Political

Facts about Europe

Total land area	**9 908 599 sq. km**
Highest peak	**El'brus, 5642 m**
Longest river	**Volga, 3688 km**
Largest country	**Ukraine** (Excluding European Russia)
Most populous country	**Germany, 82 727 000**

Population by country, top ten countries

Netherlands 16 759
Greece 11 128
Romania 21 699
Poland 38 217
Ukraine 45 239
Spain 46 927
Italy 60 990
UK 63 136
France 64 291
Germany 82 727

Population in thousands

GNI by country, 2012 top ten countries

Switzerland 652 638
Sweden 537 296
Netherlands 777 326
Turkey 782 276
Spain 1 306 722
Russia 1 947 554
Italy 2 000 232
UK 2 468 854
France 2 656 013
Germany 3 507 734

GNI in US $ millions

ARCTIC OCEAN
Greenland
Ellesmere Island
Victoria Island
Baffin
Bay
Baffin
Island
Iceland
Arctic Circle
Denali
6190
Yukon
Mt Logan
5959
Great Bear
Lake
Great Slave
Lake
Hudson
Bay
Cape
Farewell
British
Isles
Aleutian Is
Gulf of
Alaska
Coast Mts
Canadian Shield
Labrador
Newfoundland
Vancouver
Island
Missouri
NORTH
Lake
Superior
Lake
Huron
St Lawrence
Azores
Tagus
Rocky Mts
AMERICA
Great
Plains
Lake
Michigan
Ohio
Appalachian Mts
ATLANTIC
Canary Islands
S a
Mt Whitney
4418
Colorado
Mississippi
Rio Grande
Sierra Madre
Gulf of
Mexico
Bahamas
Cuba
Greater Antilles
Hispaniola
8605
Milwaukee Deep
OCEAN
Cape Verde
Islands
Hawai'ian Islands
Tropic of Cancer
Hawai'i
Yucatan
Caribbean
Sea
Fouta
Djallon
S a
Panama
Canal
Orinoco
Guiana Highlands
Line Is
PACIFIC
Galapagos
Islands
Chimborazo
6310
Amazon
SOUTH
St
Helena
Polynesia
OCEAN
Marquesas Islands
Madeira
Tocantins
AMERICA
Brazilian
Brazil Basin
Society
Is
Tuamotu
Archipelago
Andes
Paraguay
Parana
Highlands
Tonga Trench
Tropic of Capricorn
Pitcairn
Island
Peru-Chile Trench
Nevado Ojos del Salado
6908
Cerro Aconcagua
6959
Gran Chaco
Pampas
Rio de la Plata
Tristan
da Cunha
Easter
Island
Argentine
Basin
Patagonia
Equator
Falkland Islands
South
Georgia
C. Horn
Isla Grande
Tierra del Fuego
Drake Passage
Antarctic
Peninsula
Antarctic Circle
Southeast
Pacific Basin
Weddell
Sea
SOUT
A

Relief and physical features

Relief
metres

5000	
3000	
2000	
1000	
500	
200	
0	sea level
200	under sea level
4000	
6000	

Permanent ice
(ice cap or glacier)

▲ 8848 Mountain height
(in metres)

▼ 11022 Ocean depth
(in metres)

Scale 1 : 80 000 000

0   800   1600   2400 km

Mountain heights		
	metres
Mt Everest (Nepal/China)	8848
K2 (China/Pakistan)	8611
Kangchenjunga (Nepal/India)	8586
Dhaulagiri (Nepal)	8167
Annapurna (Nepal)	8091
Cerro Aconcagua (Argentina)	6959
Nevado Ojos del Salado (Arg./Chile)	6908
Chimborazo (Ecuador)	6310
Denali (USA)	6190
Mt Logan (Canada)	5959

Island areas	
	sq. km
Greenland	2 175 600
New Guinea	808 510
Borneo	745 561
Madagascar	587 040
Baffin Island	507 451
Sumatra	473 606
Honshū	227 414
Great Britain	218 476
Victoria Island	217 291
Ellesmere Island	196 236

Continents	
	sq. km
Asia	45 036 492
Africa	30 343 578
North America	24 680 331
South America	17 815 420
Antarctica	12 093 000
Europe	9 908 599
Oceania	8 923 000

World Physical

Oceans

	sq. km
Pacific Ocean	166 241 000
Atlantic Ocean	86 557 000
Indian Ocean	73 427 000
Arctic Ocean	9 485 000

Lake areas

	sq. km
Caspian Sea	371 000
Lake Superior	82 100
Lake Victoria	68 800
Lake Huron	59 600
Lake Michigan	57 800
Lake Tanganyika	32 900
Great Bear Lake	31 328
Lake Baikal	30 500
Lake Nyasa	30 044

River lengths

	km
Nile (Africa)	6695
Amazon (S. America)	6516
Chang Jiang (Asia)	6380
Mississippi-Missouri (N. America)	5969
Ob'-Irtysh (Asia)	5568
Yenisey-Angara-Selenga (Asia)	5500
Huang He (Asia)	5464
Congo (Africa)	4667
Río de la Plata-Paraná (S. America)	4500
Mekong (Asia)	4425

Eckert IV projection

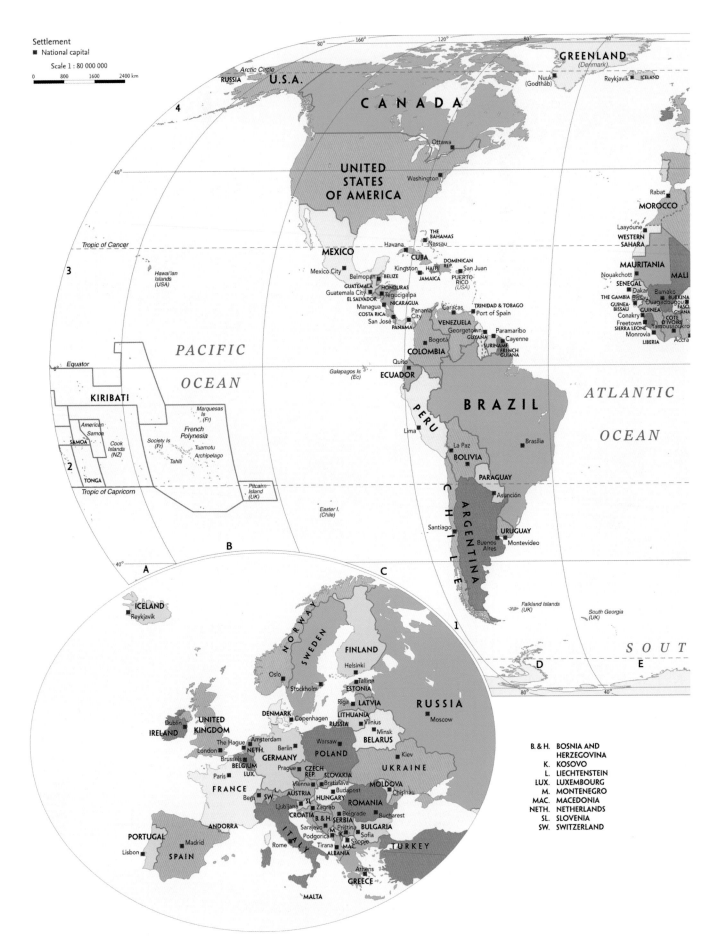

Settlement
■ National capital

Scale 1 : 80 000 000

0   800   1600   2400 km

World Political

B. & H.   BOSNIA AND
          HERZEGOVINA
K.   KOSOVO
L.   LIECHTENSTEIN
LUX.   LUXEMBOURG
M.   MONTENEGRO
MAC.   MACEDONIA
NETH.   NETHERLANDS
SL.   SLOVENIA
SW.   SWITZERLAND

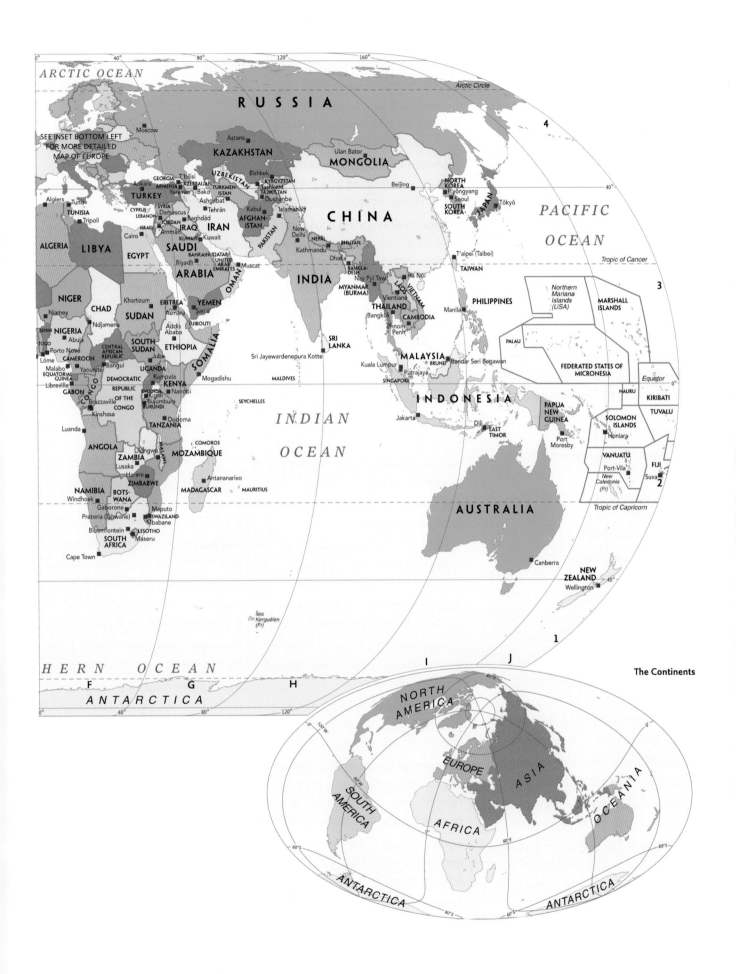

ARCTIC OCEAN

Arctic Circle

RUSSIA

4

SEE INSET BOTTOM LEFT
FOR MORE DETAILED
MAP OF EUROPE

Moscow

Astana

KAZAKHSTAN

Ulan Bator

MONGOLIA

Algiers   Tunis
TUNISIA
Tripoli

GEORGIA   T'bilisi
Ankara   ARMENIA   AZERBAIJAN
TURKEY   Yerevan   Baku
CYPRUS   SYRIA   Damascus
LEBANON   Baghdād
ISRAEL   JORDAN   Amman   IRAQ
KUWAIT   Kuwait

UZBEKISTAN
Bishkek   KYRGYZSTAN
TURKMEN-   Tashkent
ISTAN   TAJIKISTAN
Ashgabat   Dushanbe
Tehrān   Kabul
IRAN   AFGHAN-
ISTAN   Islamabad
PAKISTAN

Beijing

CHINA

NORTH
KOREA
P'yŏngyang
SOUTH   Seoul
KOREA

JAPAN   Tōkyō

PACIFIC

OCEAN

ALGERIA   LIBYA   EGYPT

Cairo

SAUDI
Riyadh   BAHRAIN   QATAR
ARABIA   UNITED
ARAB
EMIRATES   Muscat   OMAN

New
Delhi
NEPAL   BHUTAN
Kathmandu
INDIA   Dhaka   BANGLA-
DESH   Nay Pyi Taw
MYANMAR   Hà Nôi
(BURMA)   LAOS   VIETNAM
Vientiane
THAILAND
Bangkok   CAMBODIA
Phnom   Penh

T'aipei (Taibei)

TAIWAN

Tropic of Cancer

3

NIGER   CHAD
Niamey   Ndjamena
BENIN   NIGERIA   Abuja
TOGO   Porto Novo
Lomé   CAMEROON
Malabo   Yaoundé
EQUATORIAL
GUINEA
Libreville   GABON   CONGO

Khartoum

SUDAN

ERITREA
Asmara
DJIBOUTI
Addis
Ababa
ETHIOPIA

YEMEN
San'a

SOUTH
SUDAN
Juba
UGANDA
Kampala
DEMOCRATIC   RWANDA   Kigali
REPUBLIC   Bujumbura
OF THE   BURUNDI
CONGO   Kinshasa

C. Brazzaville

SRI
LANKA

Sri Jayewardenepura Kotte

MALDIVES

KENYA
Nairobi

Mogadishu

SEYCHELLES

SOMALIA

MALAYSIA
BRUNEI   Bandar Seri Begawan
Kuala Lumpur   Putrajaya
SINGAPORE

PHILIPPINES

Manila

Northern
Mariana
Islands
(USA)

MARSHALL
ISLANDS

PALAU

FEDERATED STATES OF
MICRONESIA

Equator   0°

NAURU   KIRIBATI

TUVALU

INDONESIA

Jakarta

PAPUA
NEW
GUINEA

Port
Moresby

SOLOMON
ISLANDS
Honiara

Luanda

ANGOLA

TANZANIA
Dodoma

INDIAN

OCEAN

COMOROS

MOZAMBIQUE

ZAMBIA
Lilongwe
Lusaka
MALAWI
Harare
ZIMBABWE

MADAGASCAR

Antananarivo

MAURITIUS

Dili   EAST
TIMOR

VANUATU

Port-Vila

New
Caledonia
(Fr)

FIJI

Suva

2

NAMIBIA
Windhoek   BOTS-
WANA
Gaborone   Pretoria (Tshwane)
Bloemfontein   SWAZILAND
Mbabane
SOUTH   LESOTHO
AFRICA   Maseru

Maputo

AUSTRALIA

Tropic of Capricorn

Cape Town

Canberra

NEW
ZEALAND

40°

Wellington

Îles
Kerguélen
(Fr)

1

HERN   OCEAN

I   J

F   G   H

The Continents

ANTARCTICA

NORTH
AMERICA

SOUTH
AMERICA

EUROPE

ASIA

AFRICA

OCEANIA

ANTARCTICA   ANTARCTICA

Glossary

Glossary

abrasion Erosion from the load carried by rivers, waves and ice.

acid rain Rainwater containing chemicals from the burning of fuels such as coal and oil.

aerial photograph A photograph taken from, e.g., a plane.

aid Development assistance to projects in the developing world.

air mass Large body of air that has similar temperature, pressure and moisture throughout.

alluvium Material transported and deposited by a river when it floods.

anticyclone An area of high atmospheric pressure (HP), usually associated with fine, settled weather.

anti-tourism A protest movement against the negative impact of mass tourism on local life.

aspect The direction in which a slope faces.

atmosphere The layer of gases, including nitrogen and oxygen, surrounding Earth.

attrition Erosion caused when the particles in the load carried by rivers and waves bump off one another.

backwash Water returning to the sea after a wave has broken.

barriers to migration Obstacles making it difficult for people to migrate.

bedrock Solid rock that makes up the lowest layer of a soil profile.

biodiversity The variety of plants and animal life in a habitat.

biofuels Energy sources extracted from organic matter, e.g., crops.

birth rate The number of live births per 1,000 people in one year.

boulder clay Mixture of clay and rocks deposited by a glacier.

BRICS A group of rapidly developing countries comprising Brazil, Russia, India, China and South Africa, which support each other in global economic issues.

bridging point A place where a river has been forded or bridged, at which a settlement often develops.

brown earth soil Fertile, well-drained soil that developed where deciduous forests grow.

carbonation Chemical weathering where rocks such as limestone are broken down by acid in rainwater.

carbon sink Anything (including trees, soil, oceans) that absorbs more carbon dioxide than it releases.

CBD Central business district.

chemical weathering When rocks decay or are dissolved by a chemical change.

child mortality The average number of deaths of children under five years of age per 1,000 live births.

climate The average weather conditions of a region over a long period of time. Includes temperature, rainfall and wind.

climate change Major long-term changes in climate.

cloud A visible body of very fine water droplets or ice particles suspended in the atmosphere.

colonisation One country taking political control over another country.

conservation The care, protection and careful use of resources and of the environment.

containerisation A system of freight transport metal boxes, transported in trains, trucks and ships.

convection currents Currents in the mantle that move molten magma upwards from the core towards the crust and cause the plates to move.

corporation tax The tax on company profits; MNCs pay the country in which they operate.

crust Solid outer layer of Earth.

death rate The number of deaths per 1,000 people in one year.

deforestation The destruction of forests in order to make land available for other uses.

demographic transition model A model that tells us how birth rates, death rates and natural population growth change over time.

demography The study of the structure of populations.

denudation Breaking up and removing rocks on Earth's surface by weathering, mass movement and erosion.

deposition Laying down of a load transported by rivers, waves and ice.

depression An area of low atmospheric pressure (LP), usually associated with wet, cloudy and windy weather.

desertification The gradual spread of desert conditions into surrounding areas.

developed countries Countries that are wealthy, have good services and a high standard of living (the North).

developing countries Countries that are poor, with few services and a low standard of living (the South).

development The use of resources and technology to improve people's standard of living and quality of life.

doldrums Areas of low pressure and slack winds near the equator.

drainage basin Area of land drained by a single river and its tributaries.

earthquake A sudden movement within Earth's crust, usually close to a plate boundary.

economic core A region that is the economic driver (causes a change) of a national economy.

economic migrant A person who has moved in search of work.

ecosystem A biological community of organisms that interact with each other and with their physical environment.

ecotourism Tourism that aims to reduce the impact that tourism has on the environment.

emigrant A person who leaves a country to live elsewhere.

entrepreneurial culture The can-do attitude of people who take economic risks to develop a company, product or service.

environment The living conditions in which people, animals and plants exist.

erosion The breaking down of rocks and the removal of the resulting particles by rivers, waves and ice.

exploitation Making use of and benefiting from resources.

fold mountains Mountains formed when rocks buckled and folded as two plates collided.

footloose industry An industry that has a wide choice of location.

fossil Remains of a plant or animal preserved in a layer of rock.

fossil fuels Fuels such as coal, oil and natural gas that developed from the remains of plants and animals.

freeze-thaw Mechanical weathering where rocks are broken down due to water in cracks repeatedly freezing and thawing.

front (Cold or warm) The dividing line between two air masses that have different temperatures and pressures.

gender equality Where access to all rights and opportunities are not affected by gender.

geothermal energy Heat that comes from inside Earth in the form of hot water or steam.

glacier A large, slow-moving mass of ice flowing down a valley.

globalisation The process by which the world is increasingly connected by trade and cultural links.

global warming The gradual rise in Earth's temperature caused by increased levels of greenhouse gases in the atmosphere.

greenhouse effect The process where gases in Earth's atmosphere trap solar radiation. It can be natural or human enhanced.

greenhouse gases Gases that create the greenhouse effect.

horizon A layer of a soil profile.

human development index (HDI) This index ranks countries according to life expectancy, educational levels and income per person.

hurricane A storm with continuous wind speeds over 120 kph.

hydraulic action Erosion caused by the power of moving water.

ice sheet Moving mass of ice that covers a large land area.

igneous rock Rock formed from the cooling of molten magma or lava.

immigrant A person who enters a country intending to live there.

impermeable Not allowing water to pass through.

infrastructure Networks such as road, rail, electricity, water, telephone and broadband.

Irish Aid Development assistance given by the Irish government to the developing world.

irrigation Supplying dry agricultural land with water.

karst An area of limestone with surface and underground features that result from chemical weathering.

landslide The very rapid movement of regolith down a steep slope.

latitude The angular distance north or south of the equator.

life chances Opportunities for improving one's quality of life.

life expectancy The average number of years that a person in a given country is expected to live.

longshore drift Zigzag movement of material along a coastline by waves.

magma The molten or semi-molten material that makes up Earth's mantle – the layer between Earth's crust and core.

market A place where goods are bought and sold, or a group of people who buy goods.

mass movement The movement down-slope of loose material under the influence of gravity.

mechanical weathering When rock is broken down into small pieces by freeze-thaw and plant roots.

metamorphic rock Rock changed by extremes of heat and pressure.

meteorology The study of weather.

migration The movement of people from one area to another to live and often to work.

mudflow Moving rivers of rock, soil and water.

multinational companies Those with a base in more than one country.

natural resource A material or product that is found in nature and is used by people.

NGOs Non-governmental organisations, e.g. voluntary agencies that provide assistance to projects in the developing world.

non-renewable resource A finite resource that will eventually run out or be depleted, such as oil.

North Atlantic Drift Warm ocean current that begins as the Gulf Stream and warms the waters off Ireland's coast.

ocean current Regular patterns of water flowing like giant rivers through the oceans.

Ordnance Survey Ordnance Survey Ireland (OSi) is the national mapping agency of this country.

outsource To obtain goods and services from a supplier outside the company (often abroad).

overexploitation Using a renewable resource such as fish and forestry faster than it can be replaced.

Pangaea The single land mass (supercontinent) that later broke up to form the continents.

permeable Allowing water to pass through.

petrodollars Revenues earned from the export of oil and oil products.

plate boundary Where two plates meet. Associated with volcanoes, fold mountains and earthquakes.

plate tectonics The theory that Earth's crust is divided into a number of moving plates, leading to folding, volcanic and earthquake activity.

plates The separate sections into which Earth's crust is broken.

plucking Erosion where blocks of rock are torn out by moving ice.

podzol Soil that formed in cold, wet areas that had a cover of coniferous forest.

pollution Harmful substances produced by people and machines.

population cycle The demographic transition model.

population density The average number of people living in an area, usually per km².

population distribution The spread of people over an area.

population explosion A sudden rapid increase in the population of a region.

population pyramid A bar chart displaying the population structure of an area.

population structure Composition of a country's population by age and sex.

precipitation Moisture from the atmosphere: rain, snow, hail and fog.

prevailing wind Direction from which wind blows most frequently.

primary activities Economic activities where resource materials are extracted from land or sea.

pull factors Things that attract people to live in an area.

push factors Things that make people decide to leave an area.

reafforestation Replanting trees on land that had previously been forest but had been deforested.

regolith Loose material (rocks and soil) that covers the surface of Earth.

relief Shape and height of land.

renewable resource A non-finite resource that can be used over and over again.

resource Any material or product that people find useful.

Richter scale Measurement of the strength of an earthquake.

satellite image Image of Earth taken from a satellite in space.

scree Loose pieces of rock with sharp edges at the foot of a slope, broken off by freeze-thaw.

secondary activities Economic activities where raw materials are processed into products.

sedimentary rock Formed from sediments that were laid down and compressed over millions of years.

seismometer An instrument used to measure the strength of an earthquake.

settlement The manner in which an area is settled by people.

Silicon Valley The nickname for the urban area south of San Francisco where many high-tech companies operate.

smart economy Economy with efficient public transport and energy use, cutting-edge technologies, advanced waste management and highly educated workers.

soil The thin layer of loose material on Earth's surface.

soil creep The slow, down-slope movement of soil from gravity.

soil erosion The removal of topsoil by wind, rain and running water.

soil profile A cross-section of a soil that is made up of a number of layers (horizons).

solar energy Energy from the sun, giving heat and light to Earth.

solution A mineral in rock that is dissolved in water.

special economic zones (SEZs) Specific areas in a country where investment, job growth and the export of goods are encouraged.

start-up A newly established business.

street plan A map of an urban area showing the layout and names of all the streets as well as important buildings and spaces.

suburb A mainly residential area on the edge of a city.

sustainability The use of resources in such a way that the needs of the present generation are met and the resource needs of future generations are not jeopardised.

sustainable development A way of improving standards of living and quality of life without damaging the environment or risking the wellbeing of future generations.

sustainable tourism Tourism with low impact on travel, environment and culture, while providing economic benefit for locals.

swash The movement of water up a beach after a wave breaks.

synthesis Bringing together or linking the different parts or components of a theme.

synoptic chart A map that summarises weather conditions over an area by the use of symbols.

tariffs Taxes placed on goods when they are imported.

terrain The physical features of a land area.

tertiary activities Activities that provide a service to people, such as health and tourism.

tiger economies East Asian countries that became wealthy because of export-orientated manufacturing.

trade Movement and sale of goods and services between countries.

tremors Series of shock waves after an earthquake.

tsunami A huge wave that is caused by an underwater earthquake.

urban regeneration The redevelopment or renewal of a run-down or derelict area of a city.

urban sprawl The expansion of a city into the countryside in an unplanned and uncontrolled way.

volcano A cone-shaped mountain formed by the eruption of magma from inside Earth to the surface.

water cycle The continual recycling of water as it passes between the atmosphere, oceans and land.

weather The day-to-day condition of the atmosphere – temperature, precipitation, sunshine and wind.

weathering The breakdown and decay of rocks by mechanical (freeze-thaw) and chemical (carbonation) processes.

Index

Index